Annual Perspectives in Mathematics Education

Assessment to Enhance Teaching and Learning

2015

Christine Suurtamm
Volume Editor
University of Ottawa
Ottawa, Ontario, Canada

Amy Roth McDuffie
Series Editor
Washington State University Tri-Cities
Richland, Washington

 NATIONAL COUNCIL OF
TEACHERS OF MATHEMATICS

Copyright © 2015 by
The National Council of Teachers of Mathematics, Inc.
1906 Association Drive, Reston, VA 20191-1502
(703) 620-9840; (800) 235-7566; www.nctm.org
All rights reserved

ISSN 2332-6336
ISBN 978-0-87353-923-4

The National Council of Teachers of Mathematics is the public voice of mathematics education, supporting teachers to ensure equitable mathematics learning of the highest quality for all students through vision, leadership, professional development, and research.

Printed in the United States of America

CONTENTS

Concluding Remarks

Preface

It has been twenty-two years since an annual volume from the National Council of Teachers of Mathematics (NCTM), whether in its earlier yearbook or current *Annual Perspectives in Mathematics Education* (*APME*) series, has focused on assessment. Much has changed in the assessment landscape over those years, and yet many fundamental ideas and principles still hold over time. The 1993 NCTM yearbook on assessment was "grounded in the vision of reform that is expressed in the Standards" (NCTM 1993, p. vii). It presented examples, perspectives, techniques, and issues that reflected the vision of the *Curriculum and Evaluation Standards for School Mathematics* (NCTM 1989) for assessment. In 1995, NCTM published its *Assessment Standards for School Mathematics,* which outlined the assessment standards of mathematics, learning, equity, openness, inferences, and coherence as well as provided a discussion of the different purposes of assessment. Both of these publications represented important shifts in assessment practices and called for assessment to more closely reflect a perspective of mathematics teaching and learning that values student engagement in mathematical activity. These Standards documents encouraged a move away from assessing merely through paper-and-pencil tests toward using a range of assessment strategies that provide multiple opportunities for students to show what they know and can do, given the multifaceted mathematical actions that are part of doing mathematics.

Assessment ideas have evolved from that time and are reflected in the literature of both general assessment and of mathematics education. The role and importance of formative assessment, or assessment as and for learning, has taken a central place in the assessment discussion in the past two decades. At the same time, accountability through large-scale assessment has also taken on a glaring prominence in educational discussion and enterprise. Furthermore, the original NCTM Standards have evolved, first with the publication of the *Principles and Standards for School Mathematics* in 2000, and more recently with the 2014 publication of *Principles to Actions.* Coupled with this has been the emergence of the Common Core State Standards (National Governors Association Center for Best Practices and Council of Chief State School Officers [NGA Center and CCSSO] 2010). However, the evolution of assessment research and theory, as well as the evolution of descriptions of mathematics content and practices, still rest on the basic tenets of the earlier work. This volume reflects current thinking, but it also reflects some of the issues present in the 1993 yearbook and the 1995 assessment document that we are still grappling with today. These challenges include how to describe what sound assessment looks like in classrooms, how to design assessment tasks and instruments, how to support teachers in adopting and adapting new assessment ideas, what constitutes sound evidence of student learning, and what inferences can be made from that evidence.

This *APME* volume includes chapters from a range of authors and a variety of perspectives. In our call to authors we asked for manuscripts that focused on the important role that assessment plays in informing teacher practice and encouraging student learning. We asked that the chapters reflect current research in assessment and cover topics such as classroom assessment practices to enhance student learning, professional learning with respect to assessment, attention to equity and assessment, the impact of high-stakes assessment, and assessment design. We received fifty-five chapter submissions, each of which was blind reviewed by three editorial panel reviewers. After selected chapters were revised and reviewed again by three panel members, the final selection of twenty-one manuscripts was made.

The chapters are organized into four parts: assessment in action, assessment design, professional learning to enhance classroom assessment, and assessment as evidence. Each section begins with an introduction written by one or two editorial panel members who have expertise with the topic and familiarity with the chapters in the section. These introductions provide an overview of the ideas presented in the section and also pose questions to consider while reading it. **Part I: Assessment in Action** provides concrete classroom examples of assessment to enhance student learning. While each example may be tied to a specific grade, the examples and ideas provided could be applied in a variety of grades. **Part II: Design of Assessment Tools and Strategies** presents a range of assessment strategies and tools and descriptions of their development and/or their use to enhance mathematics teaching and learning. Again, while the examples were used with specific grades, they are easily transferable to other contexts. The chapters of **Part III: Professional Learning to Enhance Classroom Assessment** provide a variety of professional learning approaches that have been shown to support teachers as they engage in assessment practices that strengthen mathematics teaching and learning. **Part IV: Assessment as Reasoning from Evidence** offers a range of perspectives and interesting examples of gathering high-quality evidence and using such evidence to make valid inferences that guide mathematics teaching and learning. The volume concludes with a chapter by Dylan Wiliam that sets the ideas presented in this volume within the full and complex assessment landscape, recognizing the interplay of beliefs, theory, and practice; teaching, learning, and assessment; and assessment purpose, evidence, and inference.

The chapters in this 2015 volume of APME represent assessment practices and issues that attend to current policies and practices but also rise above them in bringing relevance beyond a specific context. In other words, the ideas and issues presented move beyond a specific set of standards, curriculum, set of assessments, or policy. For instance, while several of the chapters deal with current contexts such as the Common Core State Standards for Mathematics (CCSSM), the ideas presented in the chapters, such as how to assess mathematical practices, have relevance beyond CCSSM. Similarly, discussions of inferences made from the National Assessment of Educational Progress (NAEP) may apply to other large-scale assessments in other jurisdictions.

The diversity and broad relevance of the ideas presented in the chapters is further evidenced by the international set of authors represented. Ideas come not only from classrooms in the United States but also from the professional learning and assessment practices of countries such as Canada, Korea, and New Zealand. These chapters help readers recognize that practices and issues related to assessment to enhance mathematics teaching and learning are not confined to the United States but are part of the global educational context, and much can be learned by sharing across countries.

In Appreciation

A comprehensive volume such as this one cannot be put together without the contributions of many people. We are grateful for the long hours, considered attention, and commitment to quality from all involved in bringing this volume to fruition. First, we would like to thank the chapter authors, as it is their work that helped to shape this volume. Their initial thought-provoking manuscripts and their responsive revisions helped to allow this volume to be published in a timely fashion.

The Editorial Panel members—Ann Arden, Melissa Boston, Sandra Crespo, Nicole Rigelman, Edward Silver, Denisse Thompson, and Dylan Wiliam—provided work that was crucial to creating a high-quality volume. Their expertise and dedication are greatly appreciated. They read many chapters multiple times, and they gave detailed comments, edits, and direction. They also helped to shape the volume into sections, and each was responsible for authoring a section introduction or concluding commentary.

We also would like to acknowledge the contributions and guidance from NCTM Headquarters staff and members. Those supporting the production of the volume included Ken Krehbiel, associate executive director for communications; Joanne Hodges, senior director of publications; Larry Shea, copy and production editor; Randy White, production manager; Kathe Richardson, meeting planner; and many others who worked behind the scenes in completing this volume. In addition, NCTM members who provided guidance and input on the volume and on the purpose of APME included Rick Hudson (Educational Materials Committee [EMC] Chair during the production of this volume), EMC committee members, as well as many other NCTM members who were willing to share their ideas.

Christine Suurtamm
Volume Editor, APME 2015
Associate Professor of Mathematics Education
University of Ottawa

Amy Roth McDuffie
Series Editor, APME 2014–2016
Professor of Mathematics Education, College of Education
Washington State University Tri-Cities

References

National Council of Teachers of Mathematics (NCTM). *Curriculum and Evaluation Standards for School Mathematics*. Reston, Va.: NCTM, 1989.

———. *Assessment in the Mathematics Classroom*. 1993 Yearbook of the National Council of Teachers of Mathematics, edited by Norman L. Webb. Reston, Va.: NCTM, 1993.

———. *Assessment Standards for School Mathematics*. Reston, Va.: NCTM, 1995.

———. *Principles and Standards for School Mathematics*. Reston, Va.: NCTM, 2000.

———. *Principles to Actions: Ensuring Mathematical Success for All*. Reston, Va.: NCTM, 2014.

National Governors Association Center for Best Practices and Council of Chief State School Officers (NGA Center and CCSSO). *Common Core State Standards for Mathematics*. Washington, D.C.: NGA Center and CCSSO, 2010.

PART I

Assessment in Action

Introduction

Ann Arden, *Ottawa Carleton District School Board, Ontario, Canada*
Melissa Boston, *Duquesne University, Pittsburgh, Pennsylvania*

In this section on Assessment in Action in the classroom, each chapter frames formative assessment as an essential classroom practice and presents specific classroom-based strategies that can be embedded into teachers' everyday instructional practices. Formative assessment involves activities undertaken by both teachers and students to modify teaching and learning activities, with a focus on learning rather than on evaluation, ranking, or judgment (Black and Wiliam 1998; Gipps 1994; Sadler 1998). A key aspect of formative assessment is that the information it generates is used by both teachers and students to improve learning.

Formative assessment strategies make students' mathematical thinking and understanding visible, thus serving as methods for "eliciting and using evidence of student thinking," as called for by the National Council of Teachers of Mathematics' (NCTM) *Principles to Actions: Ensuring Mathematical Success for All* (NCTM 2014). As an example, the chapter by Kim and Lehrer describes how "formative assessment talk" generates information to support students' progressions along learning trajectories in ways that are not possible using traditional evaluative (e.g., IRE) modes of discussion. In order to elicit and assess active thinking rather than passive recall, more diverse and complex assessment tasks and strategies are required (NCTM 1995; Shepard 2001). This point is illustrated well in the strategies for assessing and supporting children's understanding (rather than rote memorization) of number facts presented in the chapter by Bay-Williams and Kling. Similarly, the chapter by Silver and Smith makes salient the connection between cognitively challenging tasks and formative assessment. As Wiliam (2007) points out, "the task of the teacher is not necessarily to teach, but to create situations in which students learn" (p. 1087).

The chapters in this section make explicit connections between planning, instruction, and assessment. Their authors describe ways in which teachers can use formative assessment to determine next instructional steps "in-the-moment" during a lesson and in planning subsequent lessons. For example, Slavit and Nelson's chapter describes how problem-based instruction creates the need for formative assessment strategies and provides a context in which assessment and instruction become increasingly interconnected in teachers' daily practice. The chapter by Fennell, Kobett, and Wray provides a variety of formative assessment strategies and describes how such strategies can be used to "in*form*" instruction and planning. Each chapter provides a scenario or context to ground and illustrate the highlighted strategies, across grade levels (including elementary and middle grades; see chapter 15 by Marynowski in part III of this book for formative assessment in secondary classrooms), mathematical content (e.g., number facts, measures of center, and linear relationships), and in multiple contexts (e.g., problem-based learning, learning trajectories, implementing cognitively challenging tasks, and general classroom practice). The following paragraphs provide summaries of each chapter in this section, specifically highlighting how the chapter presents formative assessment in action in the mathematics classroom.

In chapter 1, **Integrating Powerful Practices: Formative Assessment and Cognitively Demanding Mathematics Tasks,** Silver and Smith describe how instructional moves that maintain students' engagement in cognitively challenging mathematical work and thinking simultaneously serve the purpose of formative assessment. The lines of research indicating the power of cognitively challenging tasks and of formative assessment techniques in supporting students' learning have previously been disconnected; here, the authors bring together these ideas and illustrate their interconnectedness in classroom practice: "engineering effective classroom discussions, questions, and learning tasks" are instructional moves essential for providing opportunities for formative assessment (e.g., Wiliam 2011) and for engaging students in cognitively challenging mathematical work and thinking (e.g., Henningsen and Stein 1997). To illustrate, the authors present the case of an eighth-grade mathematics lesson on linear relationships, set in a problem-solving context where students determine the cost of pizzas with different numbers of toppings. Prior to the lesson, the teacher selected a cognitively demanding task, anticipated students' strategies, created a monitor chart to identify these strategies during the lesson, and planned questions to ask during small-group work and the whole-group discussion. During the lesson, the teacher monitored students' work, asked questions to assess and advance students' thinking, and engaged students in a whole-group discussion. In presenting the case, Silver and Smith provide explicit connections between the five practices for orchestrating whole-group discussions (Smith and Stein 2011) and formative assessment (Suurtamm 2012).

In the chapter **Developing Fact Fluency: Turn Off Timers, Turn Up Formative Assessments,** Bay-Williams and Kling call attention to the perils of timed, frequent tests that can have potential and long-term impacts on children's mathematical confidence and view of mathematics. They contrast teaching patterns of "Memorize-Test-Continue" (M-T-C) that can neglect reasoning strategies with "Reasoning strategies, Practice, and Monitoring" (R-P-M) that can support students as they work toward mastery. The authors distinguish the R-P-M approach as shifting the learning focus from memorization to strategy development and meaningful practice, as well as shifting the assessment focus from timed tests to observations and interviews. They argue that this approach can accomplish the mastery and retention of facts that traditional approaches have failed to produce. Bay-Williams and Kling suggest five strategies to more appropriately assess fact fluency: no longer use time tests, make tests shorter to create time for students to reflect on their strategies, have students describe their strategy for solving a problem, include self-assessment, and provide teacher feedback that is more detailed than a mere score.

In chapter 3, **Using Learning Progressions to Design Instructional Trajectories,** Kim and Lehrer describe how a fifth-grade math teacher used evidence of students' learning from a Learning Progression Oriented Assessment System (LPOAS) to support students' statistical reasoning. This LPOAS involved four elements: construct maps, assessment items, scoring exemplars, and lessons. The authors argue this LPOAS supports teachers in designing an instructional path that aligns students' current understandings with a conjectured learning progression. The teacher's knowledge of mathematics is key in this approach where instructional decisions are based on the mathematical substance of students' thinking. Assessment tasks were used to determine students' current understandings along a progression of three conceptual building blocks. The teacher then asked "leveraging" questions and "engineered" formative assessment talk (FAT) based on the conjectured learning progression. The authors suggest teachers use a construct map when scoring students' responses to assessment items, identify leverage points that bridge current levels of understanding with learning performances, and design questions and supporting representations to help students move from their current understandings to those with greater disciplinary scope and precision.

In **How Changes in Instruction Support Changes in Assessment: The Case of an Inclusive STEM-Focused School,** Slavit and Nelson describe how curriculum and instructional choices influence assessment in a grades 6–12 STEM-focused school. In a problem-based learning approach, teachers at this school prioritized formative assessment in instructional design. A key component of assessment at this school was presentations to authentic audiences, such as local business professionals and professors. This required the development of rubrics where teachers had important conversations about clarifying the learning goals and criteria for success. At the end of the year, students reported positive experiences based on teacher feedback and flexibility in the way teachers viewed their learning. The project-focused learning environment changed the way teachers viewed assessment, and they felt their new formative assessment strategies made students' learning more visible.

In the final chapter of this section, **Classroom-Based Formative Assessments: Guiding Teaching and Learning,** Fennell, Kobett, and Wray argue for the value of using formative assessment as an everyday practice in mathematics classrooms. They present five classroom-based formative assessment (CBFA) techniques, validated through classroom use, that teachers can implement on a regular basis to guide and inform planning and teaching: observations, interviews, "show me," hinge questions, and exit tasks. The chapter describes each CBFA technique and provides concrete suggestions for when and how to use the technique in the mathematics classroom. The authors describe observations, interviews, and "show me" as informal techniques that could be used within any lesson to monitor students' progress and to help teachers determine the pace of the lesson, identify misconceptions, and consider potential next steps. Hinge questions and exit tasks are more formal in the sense that the question or item requires careful construction to elicit evidence of students' understandings of the main mathematical idea(s) of the lesson. Hinge questions are open-ended or specially crafted multiple-choice items that can serve as a deciding element for determining next instructional steps in planning and teaching. Exit tasks provide written documentation about each student's understandings and proficiency. In the chapter overall, Fennell and colleagues frame formative assessment techniques as in-the-moment opportunities for teachers (and students) to garner, and immediately use, evidence of learning to adapt instruction and meet students' learning needs.

Together, the five chapters in part I on Assessment in Action provide concrete suggestions for using formative assessment as an everyday classroom practice. As you read these chapters, consider the following questions:

- How do teachers connect planning, teaching, and assessment into a seamless cycle of instructional moves?

- In what ways can teachers elicit and support students' thinking?

- How are students included in the assessment process?

- In what ways does classroom assessment inform both teachers' and students' next moves?

References

Black, Paul, and Dylan Wiliam. "Assessment and Classroom Learning." *Assessment in Education: Principles, Policy & Practice* 5, no. 1 (1998): 7–74.

Gipps, Caroline V. *Beyond Testing: Towards a Theory of Educational Assessment*. London: Psychology Press, 1994.

Henningsen, Marjorie, and Mary Kay Stein. "Mathematical Tasks and Student Cognition: Classroom-Based Factors That Support and Inhibit High-Level Mathematical Thinking and Reasoning." *Journal for Research in Mathematics Education* 28, no. 5 (1997): 524–49.

National Council of Teachers of Mathematics (NCTM). *Assessment Standards for School Mathematics*. Reston, Va.: NCTM, 1995.

———. *Principles to Actions: Ensuring Mathematical Success for All*. Reston, Va.: NCTM, 2014.

Sadler, D. Royce. "Formative Assessment: Revisiting the Territory." *Assessment in Education* 5, no. 1 (1998): 77–84.

Shepard, Lorrie. "The Role of Classroom Assessment Teaching and Learning." In *Handbook of Research on Teaching*, edited by Virginia Richardson, pp. 1066–1101. Washington, D.C.: AERA, 2001.

Smith, Margaret S., and Mary Kay Stein. *5 Practices for Orchestrating Productive Mathematics Discussions*. Reston, Va.: NCTM, 2011.

Suurtamm, Christine. "Assessment Can Support Reasoning & Sense Making." *Mathematics Teacher* 106, no. 1 (2012): 28–33.

Wiliam, Dylan. "Keeping Learning on Track: Classroom Assessment and the Regulation of Learning." In *Second Handbook of Research on Mathematics Teaching and Learning*, edited by Frank K. Lester, Jr., pp. 1051–98. Charlotte, N.C.: Information Age Publishing, 2007.

———. *Embedded Formative Assessment*. Bloomington, Ind.: Solution Tree Press, 2011.

CHAPTER 1

Integrating Powerful Practices: Formative Assessment and Cognitively Demanding Mathematics Tasks

Edward A. Silver, *University of Michigan, Ann Arbor*
Margaret S. Smith, *University of Pittsburgh, Pittsburgh, Pennsylvania*

As students shuffled out of her classroom, Ms. Dyson sat at her desk and reflected on what had just occurred in her eighth-grade mathematics class. Here is a portion of her reflection:

> The Building a Pizza task worked really well today! There were a few bumps at the start, but I was able to get the confused students on track. The class was excited when they went to the Domino's website and saw that the problem was real—the price of a topping was not given! Students worked hard and generated lots of mathematics—plotting points by treating the number of toppings and corresponding cost as ordered pairs, looking for patterns in prices for medium pizzas that varied by number of toppings, and forming generalizations to express the cost for a pizza with respect to the number of toppings.
>
> Groups 1, 2, and 5 stated a generalization in words for the total price of a medium pizza, but they had trouble expressing it algebraically. Group 4 got the price per topping but had trouble writing the equation, initially confusing what was constant and what varied. Several groups had difficulty interpreting the graph produced by Group 4. Based on what I saw today, Group 3 seems ready to move on, so tomorrow I will ask them to explore how the generalization they found in part *c* would be affected if we changed the conditions by including two toppings in the base price and only charging for extra toppings. Most of the groups need more experience with the concepts in context and more practice with writing and graphing equations to express generalizations, so I will ask them to extend this investigation to small and large pizzas.

The first part of Ms. Dyson's reflection on the lesson is fairly typical of what teachers might glean from lessons that "go well," but the latter part is not at all typical. Even without knowing the details of the task, which we will present later, we can see that Ms. Dyson's comments suggest both that she learned quite a lot about her students during the lesson and that she was using that information in planning tomorrow's lesson.

How did Ms. Dyson uncover so much about her students' mathematical understandings during one lesson? How might her students benefit from the detailed insights she developed about what they know and can do, and about areas where they might need further conceptual development or skill practice? In this chapter we consider these questions in relation to some recent research on mathematics instruction.

■ Some Relevant Recent Research on Mathematics Instruction

As we elaborate below, research on effective mathematics instruction has established two distinct, robust findings. One is that students learn mathematics well in classrooms where they have regular opportunities to work on cognitively challenging tasks that promote mathematical problem solving, reasoning, and understanding, as long as their teachers support their work on the tasks in a manner that does not lower the cognitive demand as the lesson unfolds. A second robust research finding is that students learn mathematics well in classrooms where teachers employ formative assessment techniques to elicit, interpret, and use evidence about what students have learned to inform instructional decisions. These evidence-based characterizations of effective mathematics teaching have been disconnected in both the research literature and in practitioner-oriented outlets in large part because they derive from different perspectives on classroom instruction and from distinct lines of empirical inquiry. In this chapter we interweave these distinct characterizations to produce an integrated perspective that we believe can inform and support efforts to improve mathematics teaching.

Cognitively Demanding Mathematical Tasks

Mathematics classroom instruction is organized around and delivered through the mathematical tasks, activities, and problems found in curriculum materials. For example, the students in all seven countries analyzed in the TIMSS video study (National Center for Educational Statistics [NCES] 2003) spent more than 80 percent of their time in mathematics lessons working on tasks. Thus, students' opportunities to learn mathematics are determined to a great extent by the mathematical tasks they encounter in the classroom. Though mathematical tasks are a constant presence in mathematics classrooms, they also exhibit considerable variation.

Tasks vary not only with respect to mathematics content but also with respect to the cognitive processes they entail. Tasks that offer opportunities for students to sharpen their mathematical thinking and reasoning by requiring them to analyze mathematics concepts or to solve complex problems can be considered cognitively demanding or high-level tasks. In the Building a Pizza task shown in figure 1.1, for example, no solution path is explicitly suggested or implied, and students could use a variety of approaches (e.g., plot the number of toppings and cost as points on a graph to find the rate of change, build a table with the given values and interpolate, or find the difference in the number of toppings and the difference in the cost and then divide). In addition, students must determine and enact a reasonable course of action and justify the plausibility and accuracy of their solutions.

In contrast, cognitively undemanding tasks—low-level tasks that require little more than memorization and repetition—offer little or no opportunity to develop proficiency with complex, high-level cognitive processes. For example, it is likely that students would expect to solve the

Writing Equations task shown in figure 1.1 using a specific, memorized procedure (e.g., the point-slope form of a line, or a combination of the slope formula and the slope-intercept form of a line). Low-level tasks typically require neither decision-making nor justification.

Building a Pizza	Writing Equations

You and your friends are going to buy pizza from Domino's. From previous orders you know that a medium pizza with 2 toppings costs $14.00 and a medium pizza with 5 toppings costs $20.00.
 	
   a. Assuming Domino's charges the same amount for each topping added to a plain cheese pizza, determine the cost per topping.
   b. If you wanted to order a medium cheese pizza, with no additional toppings, how much would you expect to pay?
   c. Write a general rule you could use to determine the price of any medium Domino's pizza.
 	
For each part of the task, be sure to explain how you got your answer and why it makes sense.
 	
*Adapted from Mathalicious
(http://www.mathalicious.com/lessons/domino-effect)*
	For each pair of points, find the rate of change, the y-intercept, and the equation of the line that passes through the points.
	
	   a. (3,2) and (7,-4)
	   b. (2,3) and (6,4)
	   c. (1,6) and (3,2)
	   d. (0,-2) and (3,4)
	   e. 1,-4) and (-4,7)

Fig. 1.1. Mathematics tasks with different cognitive demands

Deciding to use a high-level mathematics task in a lesson is an important step, but the payoff from this decision depends on how the task is enacted in the lesson. Selecting high-level tasks for use in mathematics classrooms does not guarantee that the tasks will be used in ways that maintain the demand characteristics essential to opportunities for students to learn mathematical thinking and reasoning. Research has shown that the cognitive demands of mathematical tasks can change as tasks are introduced to students and/or as tasks are enacted during instruction (Stein, Grover, and Henningsen 1996). The mathematical tasks framework (MTF) shown in figure 1.2 models the progression of mathematical tasks from their original form, as they appear in the pages of textbooks or other curriculum materials, to the tasks that teachers actually provide to students, and then to the tasks as they are enacted by the teacher and students in classroom lessons (Stein et al. 2009).

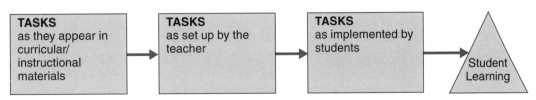

Fig. 1.2. The mathematical tasks framework

The first two arrows in the figure identify critical phases in the instructional life of tasks at which cognitive demands are susceptible to being altered. The tasks, especially as enacted, have consequences for student learning of mathematics, as is shown by the third arrow in the figure and the "Student Learning" triangle that follows it. The features of an instructional task, especially its cognitive demands, may be altered as a task passes through these phases (Stein, Grover, and Henningsen 1996; Stigler and Hiebert 2004).

Researchers who have used the MTF, and related conceptualizations, as a lens for studying mathematics classroom teaching have noted that implementing cognitively challenging tasks in ways that maintain students' opportunities to engage in high-level cognitive processes is not a trivial endeavor, especially for teachers of mathematics in the United States (e.g., Henningsen and Stein 1997; NCES 2003). Nevertheless, evidence from research conducted in a variety of U.S. classroom contexts has found that it is possible for American teachers to do this well, with clear benefits for their students.

Research has found that greater student learning occurs in classrooms where cognitively demanding mathematical tasks are used frequently and where high-level cognitive demands are maintained throughout an instructional session (Boaler and Staples 2008; Hiebert and Wearne 1993; Stein and Lane 1996; Stigler and Hiebert 2004; Tarr et al. 2008). For example, in a longitudinal comparison of three high schools over a five-year period, Boaler and Staples (2008) determined that the highest student achievement occurred in the school in which students were supported to engage in high-level thinking and reasoning. Boaler and Staples attribute students' success to the ability of the teachers to maintain high-level cognitive demands during instruction. Studies by Tarr and colleagues (2008) and Stein and Lane (1996) found that classrooms in which teachers consistently encourage students to use multiple strategies to solve problems and support students to make conjectures and explain their reasoning were associated with higher student performance on measures of thinking, reasoning, and problem solving.

Formative Assessment

Another body of research suggests that student achievement is amplified when teachers employ formative assessment techniques in classroom instruction. Black and Wiliam (1998) synthesized the results of dozens of studies of formative assessment, and they found strong evidence of greater student achievement in classrooms where teachers used such techniques. Ehrenberg and colleagues (2001) reported that the impact on student achievement of teachers using formative assessment as part of instruction was far greater than that obtained by reducing class size. Other empirical studies have demonstrated that teachers can learn to use formative assessment in the mathematics classroom with positive effects on students' learning (e.g., Wiliam et al. 2004). Although some have pointed to weaknesses and gaps in the evidence base (e.g., Bennett 2011), the preponderance of research evidence appears to support the positive influence on student learning of formative assessment in classroom instruction.

Formative assessment refers to a process of eliciting and interpreting evidence about what students have learned and then using this information to make instructional decisions (Wiliam 2011, p. 50). In contrast to summative assessment, which involves the evaluation *of* student learning, progress, or achievement to assign grades or appraise programs, formative assessment involves assessment *for* learning—gathering evidence within the stream of instruction about what students are doing, thinking, and learning and then using that evidence to inform decisions that affect teaching and learning.

Many view formative assessment as an essential aspect of effective instruction. In fact, *Principles to Actions: Ensuring Mathematical Success for All* (National Council of Teachers of Mathematics [NCTM] 2014) identifies *eliciting and using evidence of student thinking* as one of eight non-negotiable teaching practices critical for successful implementation of ambitious standards. According to Leahy and colleagues (2005, p. 19), "in a classroom that uses assessment to support learning, the divide between instruction and assessment blurs. Everything students do—such as conversing in groups, completing seatwork, answering and asking questions, working on projects, handing in homework assignments, even sitting silently and looking confused—is a potential source of information about how much they understand." Based on their analysis and synthesis of a number of studies of formative assessment in classroom instruction across a variety of school subjects, Leahy and colleagues (2005) identified several aspects of instruction that characterize effective formative assessment in classrooms, including engineering effective classroom discussions, questions, and learning tasks; promoting students' ownership of their learning; and encouraging students to be learning resources for one another.

Engineering effective classroom discussions, questions, and learning tasks involves at least three interrelated instructional practices: (1) engaging students in tasks and activities that provide insights into their thinking; (2) listening and analyzing student discussions and artifacts interpretatively, not just from an evaluative perspective; and (3) implementing instructional strategies designed to engage all students in tasks, activities, and discussions (Wiliam 2011). For this to work well, instructional tasks and activities should elicit thinking and reasoning, relate to key concepts and skills in the curriculum, and allow students to show what they understand and can do. Also, it is important that teachers and students engage in listening "interpretatively" (Davis 1997); that is, not just listening for the right answers but also listening for evidence about student thinking to inform the next instructional steps. In this way, a teacher can obtain evidence about how well students are learning important mathematical concepts and skills and detect errors or misconceptions that are prevalent in student work, especially those that may interfere with learning new concepts or solving related problems.

Effective formative assessment also means *promoting students' ownership of their learning and encouraging students to be learning resources for one another.* Providing students with challenging mathematical tasks and supporting them to develop persistence in solving such tasks helps students develop a sense of self-efficacy that also supports their motivation to tackle difficult mathematics topics. Also, teachers can engage students in self-assessment and peer-assessment, with an emphasis on listening interpretively as noted above rather than focusing only on right/wrong judgments. Classrooms in which students actively listen to their peers' presentations and explanations can be communities in which each student supports the learning of other students in a mutually enabling manner.

■ Integrating Formative Assessment with the Use of Cognitively Demanding Tasks: The Case of Ms. Dyson

We now return to the question posed earlier in this chapter: *How did Ms. Dyson uncover so much about her students' mathematical understandings during one lesson?*

We think the answer lies in the interplay between the two perspectives just reviewed, namely, cognitively demanding tasks and formative assessment. First, Ms. Dyson selected a mathematical task for her students to work on during the lesson that was—

- cognitively demanding;

- accessible to all students, whether they preferred to work with words, numbers, graphs, or equations;

- aligned with her goals for student learning (e.g., use concepts of slope and y-intercept in a problem context; write an equation to represent the relationship between a dependent and independent variable; gain facility in recognizing and expressing a linear function in a table, graph, and equation);

- motivating to students—presenting a familiar context and a question that could not be immediately answered (even if you went to the Domino's website!); and

- capable of revealing students' understanding and thinking, especially by including the requirement that students explain *how* they solved the problem and *why* their solution made sense.

Hence by selecting this particular task, Ms. Dyson took an important first step toward engineering an effective classroom discussion.

Second, she carefully planned the lesson prior to instruction—anticipating the ways in which students might approach or solve the task and generating questions she could to ask to assess what the students understood and to advance their understandings. Here is another part of her post-lesson reflection:

> I learned a lot from listening as students worked in groups on the task, using the monitoring charts I created yesterday. The charts recorded my expectations about what students were likely to do and what I could say to get them to think more deeply. I was free to watch and listen carefully and then to jot notes about what I saw and heard and to flag things that might need follow-up.

The monitoring charts (see appendices 1.A and 1.B) assisted Ms. Dyson both in preparing to teach the lesson and in allowing her to be attentive to students' thinking as they tried to solve the problem.

In each chart she listed solution strategies that she anticipated students might use, obstacles she expected they might encounter, and questions she intended to ask about their methods to highlight key mathematical issues or ways she intended to help them navigate around or through the obstacles (see the first two columns of the tables in appendices 1.A and 1.B). In so doing she illustrated the kind of lesson preparation that is crucial both to using cognitively demanding tasks effectively and to supporting a classroom discussion that clarifies and shares learning intentions and outcomes. Also, by carefully thinking in advance about likely solution methods and questions she might want to pose, Ms. Dyson was preparing herself to support students to persist in solving a challenging problem in the face of obstacles they might encounter rather than telling them explicitly how to solve the problem and thereby lowering the cognitive demand.

Next, while students worked in groups on the task, she used her monitoring chart to remind herself of the questions she wanted to ask students about their solution methods and to keep track of what students were doing (see column 3 of the tables in appendices 1.A and 1.B). Her recordings on the monitoring chart helped her decide which solutions should be presented during the discussion and in what order, key aspects of a solution she wanted to highlight, and who would be asked to present each one to the class (see column 4 of the tables in appendices 1.A and 1.B). In this way, she increased the opportunities that students would be able to learn from each other during the whole-class discussion. The monitoring chart also helped her identify concepts that students were struggling with, to reassign group members so that students have the opportunity to work with peers with different strengths, and to keep track of which students had an opportunity to present their work to the class. Hence the information on the monitoring chart would be useful to Ms. Dyson in making instructional decisions in the current lesson as well as in future lessons.

Finally, the lesson provided an opportunity for students to take ownership of their learning. Students initially visited the website and determined that this was an authentic problem. Later, by carefully selecting the solutions that would be presented and the students who would do the presenting, Ms. Dyson built the lesson upon the thinking of her students and allowed them to be authors of their own ideas. Through their discussion of varied solution methods, students compared responses to identify the strengths and weaknesses of different approaches to or explanations of a solution, rather than simply relying on the teacher to identify them as right or wrong. Students were thus held accountable for reasoning about and understanding key ideas.

Ms. Dyson's instructional practice embodies effective use of formative assessment as well as what Smith and Stein (2011) have referred to as the five practices for orchestrating a productive mathematics discussion. The practices (Anticipating, Monitoring, Selecting, Sequencing, and Connecting) are intended to help teachers maintain the cognitive demands of high-level tasks through thoughtful and thorough planning prior to a lesson, thereby limiting the amount of improvisation needed during the lesson. A lesson enacted using the five practices is similar to what Suurtamm (2012, p. 31) describes as a formative assessment approach called the "Math Forum," in which a teacher gains "a strong sense of individual students' as well as the whole class's understanding of mathematical concepts."

■ Coda

We think Ms. Dyson's lesson offers a vivid example of how formative assessment and the use of cognitively demanding mathematics tasks in instruction can be seamlessly integrated. Moreover, given recent arguments for the importance of taking a disciplinary perspective when thinking about formative assessment (e.g., Bennett 2011; Coffey et al. 2011), we see the integration of these perspectives as one way to accomplish that goal. By connecting these two lines of research in her own practice, Ms. Dyson provided her students with the opportunity to learn mathematical content and to engage in a set of practices that are the hallmark of the discipline, and she also gave herself a window into her students' thinking and a mechanism for instructional decision making and improvement.

References

Black, Paul, and Dylan Wiliam. "Assessment and Classroom Learning." *Assessment in Education: Principles, Policy & Practice* 5, no. 1 (1998): 7–74.

Bennett, Randy Elliot. "Formative Assessment: A Critical Review." *Assessment in Education: Principles, Policy & Practice* 18, no. 1 (2011): 5–25.

Boaler, Jo, and Megan Staples. "Creating Mathematical Futures through an Equitable Teaching Approach: The Case of Railside School." *Teachers College Record* 110, no. 3 (2008): 608–45.

Coffey, Janet E., David Hammer, Daniel M. Levin, and Terrance Grant. "The Missing Disciplinary Substance of Formative Assessment." *Journal of Research in Science Teaching* 48, no. 10 (2011): 1109–36.

Davis, Brent A. "Listening for Differences: An Evolving Conception of Mathematics Teaching." *Journal for Research in Mathematics Education* 28, no. 3 (1997): 355–76.

Ehrenberg, Ronald G., Dominic J. Brewer, Adam Gamoran, and J. Douglas Willms. "Class Size and Student Achievement." *Psychological Science in the Public Interest* 2, no. 1 (2001): 1–30.

Henningsen, Marjorie, and Mary Kay Stein. "Mathematical Tasks and Student Cognition: Classroom-Based Factors That Support and Inhibit High-Level Mathematical Thinking and Reasoning." *Journal for Research in Mathematics Education* 28, no. 5 (1997): 524–49.

Hiebert, James, and Diana Wearne. "Instructional Tasks, Classroom Discourse, and Students' Learning in Second-Grade Arithmetic." *American Educational Research Journal* 30, no. 2 (1993): 393–425.

Leahy, Siobhan, Christine Lyon, Marnie Thompson, and Dylan Wiliam. "Classroom Assessment: Minute by Minute, Day by Day." *Educational Leadership* 63, no. 3 (2005): 18–24.

National Center for Education Statistics (NCES). *Teaching Mathematics in Seven Countries: Results from the TIMSS Video Study.* Washington, D.C.: U.S. Department of Education, 2003.

National Council of Teachers of Mathematics (NCTM). *Principles to Actions: Ensuring Mathematical Success for All.* Reston, Va.: NCTM, 2014.

Smith, Margaret S., and Mary Kay Stein. *5 Practices for Orchestrating Productive Mathematics Discussions.* Reston, Va.: NCTM, 2011.

Stein, Mary Kay, Barbara W. Grover, and Marjorie Henningsen. "Building Student Capacity for Mathematical Thinking and Reasoning: An Analysis of Mathematical Tasks Used in Reform Classrooms." *American Educational Research Journal* 33, no. 2 (1996): 455–88.

Stein, Mary Kay, and Suzanne Lane. "Instructional Tasks and the Development of Student Capacity to Think and Reason: An Analysis of the Relationship between Teaching and Learning in a Reform Mathematics Project." *Educational Research and Evaluation* 2, no. 1 (1996): 50–80.

Stein, Mary Kay, Margaret S. Smith, Marjorie Henningsen, and Edward A. Silver. *Implementing Standards-Based Mathematics Instruction: A Casebook for Professional Development.* 2nd ed. New York: Teachers College Press, 2009.

Stigler, James W., and James Hiebert. "Improving Mathematics Teaching." *Educational Leadership* 61, no. 5 (2004): 12–16.

Suurtamm, Christine. "Assessment Can Support Reasoning." *Mathematics Teacher* 106 (2012): 28–33.

Tarr, James E., Robert E. Reys, Barbara J. Reys, Oscar Chavez, Jeffrey Shih, and Steven J. Osterlind. "The Impact of Middle-Grades Mathematics Curricula and the Classroom Learning Environment on Student Achievement." *Journal for Research in Mathematics Education* 39, no. 3 (2008): 247–80.

Wiliam, Dylan. *Embedded Formative Assessment.* Bloomington, Ind.: Solution Tree Press, 2011.

Wiliam, Dylan, Clare Lee, Christine Harrison, and Paul Black. "Teachers Developing Assessment for Learning: Impact on Student Achievement." *Assessment in Education* 11, no. 1 (2004): 49–65.

Appendix 1.A

Monitoring Chart for Parts *a* and *b* of the *Building a Pizza* Task

Strategy	Questions	Who/What	Order
Graph – Plot ordered pairs on a coordinate plane and draw a slope triangle or determine the ratio of rise to run between the two points. Connect the points with a line that includes (0,10).	• *Where is the price per topping represented on your graph?* • *What does this mean in terms of the graph?* • *What does the y-intercept mean in terms of the problem?* • *How could you use your graph to find the cost of any pizza?*	Rashard, Hala, Michael, Candace (G4) Used slope triangle; Talked about the "rate" of $6 for 3 toppings; saw equivalence to $2 for 1 topping; found y-intercept *Had trouble explaining the meaning of y-intercept* but could explain that the graph could be extended to find any cost.	Hala (G4) – 3rd Ask students how G4's solution connects with the solution that G3 had presented.
Table – Make a table that has toppings 0 through 5 (or more) and fill in the cost for 2 and 5 toppings. Then determine that since there is $6 separating the cost of 2 and 5 toppings, you must just add 2 each time. You can then use this "difference of 2" to complete the table. 0 toppings would then be $10.	• *Where is the price per topping represented in your table?* • *Where is the price of a plain pizza represented in your table?* • *What do you think the graph of your points would look like?* • *How could you use your table to find the cost of any pizza?*	No one used this approach.	Present Teacher Created Table – 2nd Ask students if the reasoning is sound and how it connects to the first solution.
Reasoning with Arithmetic – Determine that if the 5-topping pizza costs $20 and the 2-topping pizza costs $14, then the difference in cost is $6 and the difference in the number of toppings is 3. 6 ÷ 3 = 2, so each topping is $2.00. If you subtract 2 from 14 you get $12, which would be for 1 topping, so 0 toppings would be $10.	• *How did you find the cost of a plain pizza?* • *How could you find out the cost of any pizza?* • *Could you use your method to find the cost per topping given the price of any two medium pizzas?*	Chris, Ashley, Tyronne, Mirah (G1) Jennifer, Marko, Delmar, Shawna (G3) G2 and G5 later used this approach. Found the cost per topping but *initially had trouble finding the cost of a pizza with no toppings.* After getting on track, they were working on a generalization to find cost for any pizza.	Shawna (G3)- 1st
Subtract the Two Amounts – Note that one pizza cost $20 and the other cost $14, so subtract and calculate the cost per topping as 6/3 = 2.	• *How much more is a 5-topping pizza than a 2-topping pizza?* • *How many toppings were added?* • *How much do you think it would cost for a 3-topping pizza? Why?*	Aaron, Amber, Sheere, Tamika (G5) *Initially stated the cost per topping to be $6* but after I asked a few questions realized that this would be the cost for 3 toppings.	
Can't Get Started	• *What are you trying to find?* • *What is different about these two pizzas?* • *What happens to the price when you increase from 2 to 5 toppings?* • *How much do you think a 2-topping pizza would cost?*	Yolanda, Jared, Mick, Leslie (G2) Were able to answer questions about what the differences are and had some ideas on how to proceed. When I checked back in they were using a "Reasoning with Arithmetic Approach."	

Appendix 1.B

Monitoring Chart for Part c of the *Building a Pizza Task*

Strategy	Questions	Who/What	Order
Symbolic – Cost = $2t + $10 t = number of toppings	• *What does each part of equation mean in terms of the context of the problem?* • *If the cost per topping increased, what would change in your equation?* • *If the cost of a cheese pizza increased, what would change in your equation?* • *What do you think your equation will look like when graphed? Why?*	Jennifer, Marko, Delmar, Shawna (G3) Explained each part of equations in terms of context; knew what would change if different pricing. They could describe what the equation looked like when graphed. G4 got this after revising their initial work.	Hala (G4) – 2nd Ask class how G3's equation relates to what G5 described. Ask class to explain each part of equation in terms of context. Relate table, graph, equation and context. All but G3 and G4 had trouble relating the graph and the context.
Narrative – You take the number of toppings times 2 and add $10.	• *How would you figure out the cost of a pizza with 3 toppings? 10 toppings?* • *Can you write this as an equation? How could you represent the number of toppings? How are the number of toppings and cost per topping related? What happens to the $10?*	Chris, Ashley, Tyronne, Mirah (G1) Yolanda, Jared, Mick, Leslie (G2) **Had trouble using variables to express the relationship symbolically.** G5 got to this after revising their initial work.	Aaron (G5) – 1st
Algebraic – incorrect C = $10x + $2	• *How much does a 1-topping pizza cost using your rule? How much does a 2-topping pizza cost?* • *What changes and what remains the same each time?*	Rashard, Hala, Michael, Candace (G4) Once they tried their rule for specific values they found that it did not give them the same information that they found with their graph. They fixed it.	
Can't Get Started –	• *How much would a pizza cost with 1 topping?* • *How much would a pizza cost with 2 toppings?* • *What changes when you add more toppings? What remains the same no matter how many toppings you have? Can you write down what you did?*	Aaron, Amber, Sheere, Tamika (G5) Found cost per topping but were **not sure how to generalize a rule.** Ended up writing a rule in narrative form.	

CHAPTER 2

Developing Fact Fluency: Turn Off Timers, Turn Up Formative Assessments

Jennifer M. Bay-Williams, *University of Louisville, Kentucky*
Gina Kling, *Western Michigan University, Kalamazoo*

Ensuring that every child masters his or her basic facts requires instruction and assessment that can address individual needs. *Principles to Actions: Ensuring Mathematical Success for All* (National Council of Teachers of Mathematics [NCTM] 2014) states that an excellent mathematics program places assessment as an integral part of instruction, and that results from such assessment should provide useful information to students and teachers. With this assessment principle in mind, consider these two third-grade classroom excerpts:

> Brenden's class is working on their weekly multiplication timed test. The test contains 100 multiplication facts in random order, and the children are given five minutes to complete it. Once again, Brenden skips 6 × 8 because he cannot remember the product, and he knows he does not have time to figure it out.

> Meaghan's class is about to play a card game to practice their multiplication facts. Before the game begins, the teacher writes 6 × 8 on the board and asks the children to think of a related fact they could use to figure out the product. Below are three of the strategies children suggest:

> - I would start with 5 × 8 = 40 and add another group of 8, so 6 × 8 = 40 + 8 = 48.

> - I know that 6 × 4 = 24, so I can just double that to get 6 × 8. So 24 + 24 = 48.

> - I did 6 × 10 = 60, and then took away 12 to get 48.

Assuming each scenario describes typical facts practice in these two classrooms, we can reflect on how they compare with respect to (1) what data the teacher might gather about student understanding and (2) what opportunities children have to learn and to monitor their own progress.

Brenden's experience reflects what has been a common pattern of facts instruction and assessment, a pattern we will refer to as Memorize-Test-Continue (M-T-C). In this process, children memorize their facts, or a subset of facts (e.g., 3s multiplication facts), take a test, and then continue to the next set of facts. These tests are typically timed, frequent, and sometimes paired with rewards or consequences, such as stickers on a chart or staying in for recess. The ultimate consequence, however, is the potential negative and long-term impact on children's mathematical confidence and their view of what mathematics is (Boaler 2014; Ramirez et al. 2013).

Meaghan's classroom experience reflects a different pattern: Reasoning strategies, Practice, and Monitoring (R-P-M). In this process, children learn reasoning strategies (e.g., doubling) and apply them as they play games or engage in other practice while the teacher monitors how each child is progressing. When monitoring, or formative assessment, is implemented within and between lessons and units, student achievement improves (Wiliam 2007b). Implementing an R-P-M approach shifts focus from memorization to strategy development and meaningful practice activities, and from timed tests to observations and interviews. In the sections that follow, we share such activities and assessment tools.

How Children Master Basic Facts

One important distinction between Brenden's and Meaghan's classrooms is the degree to which children are gaining fluency with their facts. According to the Common Core State Standards (CCSS), procedural fluency is "skill in carrying out procedures flexibly, accurately, efficiently and appropriately" (National Governors Association Center for Best Practices and Council of Chief State School Officers [NGA Center and CCSSO] 2010, p. 6). This definition is consistent with research recommendations (e.g., Baroody 2006; National Research Council [NRC] 2001) and yet is not fully realized in an M-T-C approach that focuses on accuracy and efficiency. Teaching and assessing all four components of procedural fluency requires better and varied assessment tools.

Effective basic facts instruction begins by building on children's understanding of number. Young children are able to successfully use modeling and counting to solve problems in context, such as joining two groups of toys or sharing cookies (NRC 2001). This is phase 1 in Baroody's (2006) three-phase framework for learning basic facts (see fig. 2.1). In phase 2, children use their knowledge of number relationships to move away from counting to efficient reasoning strategies. With repeated opportunities to use these reasoning strategies, children become more and more adept at adding or multiplying and eventually come to just know the facts (phase 3). Emphasis on reasoning strategies (phase 2) is important to reaching mastery. Steinberg (1985), for example, found that the students who were consistently recalling facts (phase 3) by the end of the study were those operating at phase 2 at the beginning of the study. Going too quickly from phase 1 to phase 3 results in children memorizing facts in the short term, but falling back on counting when they are unable to recall facts in the long term (Wheatley and Reynolds 1999).

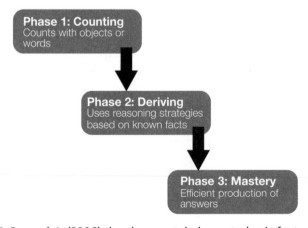

Fig. 2.1. Baroody's (2006) developmental phases to basic fact mastery

An R-P-M approach means monitoring student progress through each phase for different groups of facts. Table 2.1 suggests a progression for learning foundational facts, and a subsequent trajectory for derived facts. Importantly, children cannot *use* foundational facts if they don't know the foundational facts from memory; careful sequencing and spacing between learning groups of facts is imperative. Because space does not allow us to address assessment across the phases for both foundational and then derived facts, in our discussion of assessment related to moving from phase 1 to phase 2 we focus on foundational facts examples, and from phase 2 to phase 3 we focus on derived facts examples.

Table 2.1
Basic facts strategy development trajectories

Addition Facts Trajectory	
Foundational Facts	Derived Fact Strategies
Sums within 5 +/− 1 and +/− 2 Doubles (3 + 3, 7 + 7) Combinations of 10 (2 + 8, 4 + 6)	Near Doubles (4 + 5, 8 + 7) Making 10 (8 + 3, 9 + 5)
Multiplication Facts Trajectory	
Foundational Facts	Derived Fact Strategies
2s, 5s, 10s Multiplication Squares (4×4, 7×7) 0s, 1s	Adding a Group ($3 \times 8 = 2 \times 8 + 8 = 16 + 8 = 24$) Subtracting a Group ($9 \times 4 = 10 \times 4 - 4 = 40 - 4 = 36$) Doubling ($4 \times 9 = 2 \times 9 + 2 \times 9 = 18 + 18 = 36$) Near Squares ($7 \times 6 = 6 \times 6 + 6 = 36 + 6 = 42$) Breaking Apart ($7 \times 6 = 5 \times 6 + 2 \times 6 = 30 + 12 = 42$)

■ Assessment to Encourage Advancement from Phase 1 to Phase 2

Children begin solving basic facts through counting, whether it is "counting on" in first grade to add 8 + 2, or "skip counting" in third grade to multiply 6 × 2. Assessment strategies at phase 1 should focus on whether children are moving from counting strategies to reasoning strategies. *Observations* and *interviews* can provide such data and can be done as children engage in activities and games (rather than taking additional instructional time) (Kling and Bay-Williams 2014). For example, quick images, such as those pictured in figure 2.2, use dots or ten-frames to help children focus on decomposing and composing foundational facts. Children are shown a quick image for two to three seconds, and they then share how many they saw and how they saw it. Children do not have enough time to count, so they have to use a different strategy. (*Note:* Quick images with equal-size groups can be used for multiplication facts.)

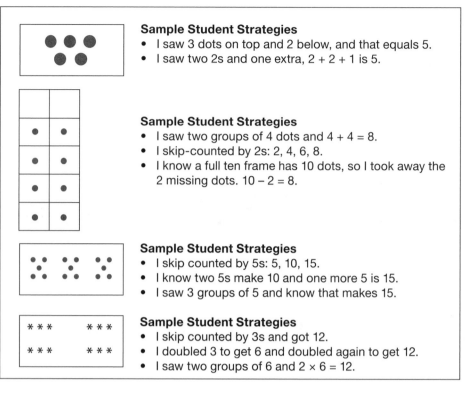

Sample Student Strategies
- I saw 3 dots on top and 2 below, and that equals 5.
- I saw two 2s and one extra, 2 + 2 + 1 is 5.

Sample Student Strategies
- I saw two groups of 4 dots and 4 + 4 = 8.
- I skip-counted by 2s: 2, 4, 6, 8.
- I know a full ten frame has 10 dots, so I took away the 2 missing dots. 10 − 2 = 8.

Sample Student Strategies
- I skip counted by 5s: 5, 10, 15.
- I know two 5s make 10 and one more 5 is 15.
- I saw 3 groups of 5 and know that makes 15.

Sample Student Strategies
- I skip counted by 3s and got 12.
- I doubled 3 to get 6 and doubled again to get 12.
- I saw two groups of 6 and 2 × 6 = 12.

Fig. 2.2. Different styles of quick images with sample student responses

Observation tools, such as those in figure 2.3, can be used to write anecdotal notes or to record where children are in learning their foundational facts. One- or two-question *interviews* can be used with individual children as they are engaged in an activity or game, which can help in gathering data. Example prompts include:

- Can you count on to solve 2 + 6?

- How did you solve 3 × 5?

Journal prompts can provide valuable data about what a child does and does not understand. For example, in multiplication:

1. *Does the child understand that multiplication involves equal groups?*
   Prompt: Write 4 × 5 as repeated addition and write or illustrate a situation that fits 4 × 5.

2. *Does the child use repeated addition efficiently and flexibly?*
   Prompt: Jacob solved 6 × 5 by thinking two 5s are 10. He then added 10 three times to get 30. Use pictures or words to critique this strategy.

Names	Multiplication Observation Notes/Checklist					
	Foundational Facts					
	2s	10s	5s	Squares	0s	1s

Fig. 2.3a. Class checklist for foundational facts: Multiplication

Basic Facts Progress Chart for: _____
[Student Name]

ADDITION	At Phase 1	Moving toward Phase 2	At Phase 2	Moving toward Phase 3	At Phase 3: Mastery
Indicators to look for:	Uses counting-based strategies	Uses some counting-based strategies and some reasoning strategies	Use reasoning strategies for facts Recognizes and applies commutative property	Is efficient and flexible in applying reasoning strategies Produces accurate solutions.	Demonstrates automaticity (solves within 3 seconds)
Sums within 5					
+/– 1					
+/– 2					
Doubles					
Combinations of 10					
Near Doubles					
Making 10					

Fig. 2.3b. Student progress chart for observation tools for foundational
facts and strategies: Addition

Finally, short, untimed *strategy quizzes,* such as the one in figure 2.4, can provide data, for example, on whether children are able to solve "+2" facts and apply the commutative property. Teachers can also incorporate self-assessment by asking children to circle the facts for which they used "counting on" and box the ones they "just knew." Post-quiz discussions might compare vertical and horizontal formats and related problems (5 + 2 and 2 + 5). This type of quiz exemplifies the NCTM vision of assessment as an integral part of instruction. Any combination of the four assessment strategies proposed here—observation tools, interviews, journal prompts, and strategy quizzes—can integrate naturally into instruction and provide critical data on a child's progress and readiness to move to phase 2.

Solve these addition problems

ROW A: 5 + 2 =   8   4 + 2 =   9 + 2 =   3
                        +2   +2

ROW B: 2 + 8 =   2 + 7 =   2   2   2 + 4 =
                                    +6   +8

Which row was easier?   A   B   Same

Explain your choice:

Fig. 2.4. Sample strategy quiz

■ Assessment to Encourage Advancement from Phase 2 to Phase 3

Children operating at phase 2 use reasoning strategies to fluently solve their basic facts, grounding these emerging strategies in foundational facts they already know. For example, they might use a combination of 10 (e.g., 7 + 3) to apply a making 10 strategy (e.g., 7 + 5 = 7 + 3 + 2). In Meaghan's classroom, children were using foundational facts or other known facts to solve the unknown multiplication fact 6×8. Repeated application of reasoning strategies as students engage in meaningful practice eventually moves them from phase 2 to phase 3 as they begin to recall these facts from memory (Steinberg 1985; Thornton 1978). Formative assessment as students are moving to phase 3 includes noticing (1) if students are selecting appropriate strategies for particular problems and (2) for which facts they are moving from strategy use to just knowing the answer. Journal prompts and observation checklists (as described in the previous section) are powerful assessment strategies for this phase of fact development.

The journal prompt responses in figure 2.5, collected midyear from a first-grade classroom, provide formative data about which strategies each child is using and the extent to which each is moving toward phase 3. The first two children are selecting and applying the near doubles strategy.

The third child suggests "counting on," indicating he is still operating mainly at phase 1, or is not able to select a reasoning strategy that fits this problem. This data helps in planning next instructional steps: the teacher can provide strategy activities and games for children such as the first two and more explicit strategy instruction for the third child (e.g., on using doubles).

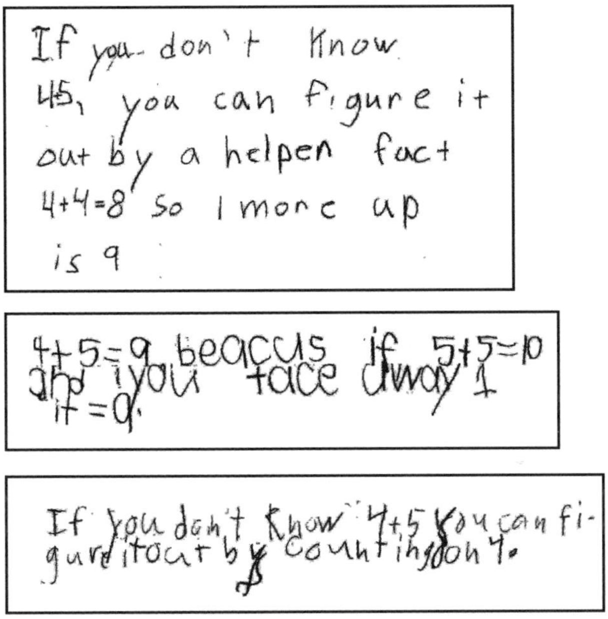

> If you don't know
> 45, you can figure it
> out by a helper fact
> 4+4=8 so 1 more up
> is 9

> 4+5=9 beaccus if 5+5=10
> and you face away 1
> it=9.

> If you don't know 4+5 you can fi-
> gure it out by counting on.

Fig. 2.5. First-grade responses to "If you don't know 4 + 5, how can you figure it out?"

Progressing from phase 2 to phase 3 requires many and differed opportunities to practice. Practice need not be tedious or stressful; in contrast, it can be engaging and enjoyable. There are many games to select from, including adaptations of well-known children's games such as Go Fish, Concentration, or War, as well as games designed specifically for learning basic facts. (See Forbringer and Fahsl 2010; Kling 2011; and Bay-Williams and Kling 2014 for ideas on using games to practice basic facts.) Games might be used to target specific facts (for example, foundational facts) or could provide general practice of all facts. Beyond the "fun factor," one critical difference between games and worksheets is the opportunity for strategy discussion. As children play, they challenge each other and elicit help, and conversations around strategy choice spontaneously arise. Therefore, games provide an excellent opportunity to formatively assess. Assessment might include observation tools, similar to those shown in figure 2.3, but adapted to include derived facts and one-question interviews. The following sample interview questions focus on phase 2:

- How did you find [3 + 8]?

- Can you say out loud how you thought about [4 × 7] in your head?

- Is there another way you could find that fact?

- Can you think of a helper fact you might have used instead?

- If someone didn't know the answer to _____, what strategy might you suggest?

A child may answer the first question saying, "I just knew it"—evidence he or she has moved to phase 3 for that fact. In observing and questioning, we can better notice if children need probing or assistance to select or apply a reasoning strategy (i.e., just entering phase 2), or if they do so effortlessly (i.e., completing phase 2, ready to enter phase 3). Different games and activities, as well as different numbers within these games, can be selected for children based on this evidence.

■ Assessing Mastery—Assessment at Phase 3

Children have "mastered" their facts when they are able to quickly generate solutions (e.g., within three seconds). This may mean they know the fact from memory or they apply a highly efficient reasoning strategy. Given the absolute necessity that children are fluent with each fact, assessment strategies must be implemented to ensure this is true for each fact for each child.

Traditional timed tests are common, but they provide limited formative assessment data, not to mention the negative impact they might have on children. Let's first consider the flawed premise of timed tests. The assumption is that if children can solve twenty problems in sixty seconds, that they are solving each of the facts within three seconds. In reality, children may be solving half of the facts in one second each, and taking ten seconds to count for some of them. In addition, timed tests provide limited insights on what a child does not know: a wrong answer could be due to miscounting, misapplication of a reasoning strategy, or a guess; a correct answer could be found by counting, using a reasoning strategy, or knowing from memory. Finally, there is mounting evidence that timed tests have damaging psychological effects, causing math anxiety from an early age in many children, regardless of ability level (Boaler 2014; Ramirez et al. 2013).

You might ask whether traditional timed assessments are needed at all. Even though timed testing is a deeply ingrained assessment practice in the United States, research suggests that the answer is no. In a study of 300 first graders, Henry and Brown (2008) found a slight negative correlation between frequency of timed testing and Basic Fact Competence (fluency). Previously, Thornton (1978) found that children in R-P-M style classrooms both in second and fourth grade greatly outperformed their counterparts in M-T-C style classrooms, even on traditional assessments. More recently, Kling (2011) conducted a three-year study with eighteen children from R-P-M style classrooms on their fact fluency and eventual automaticity (ability to answer within three seconds). The participating classrooms did not conduct any timed tests in either first or second grade. At the end of second grade, children were automatic (accurate within three seconds) 95 percent of the time and were still at 91 percent automaticity when retested the first week of third grade, prior to any facts review. These findings suggest that not only is timed testing not needed, but an R-P-M style may actually accomplish the mastery and retention of facts that traditional approaches of timed testing have long failed to produce.

Interestingly, untimed, low- or no-stakes practice tests have been found to improve student achievement, especially when feedback is provided (Dunlosky et al. 2013). Though this research is largely focused on older students and nonmathematical topics, it does support the need for lowering the stakes of practice testing and providing quality feedback. The following five strategies describe ways to use tests to more appropriately assess fact fluency:

1. **Turn off the timers!** There is no good reason to time tests, and good reasons not to.

2. **Shorten the test.** Beyond making the test more palatable and less stressful, shortening the length creates more time for students to reflect on their strategies.

3. **Focus on strategy.** Ask students to mark their answer based on their general approach: e.g., underline for "counted," box for "used a strategy," and circle for "just knew." They can pick one problem marked as "used a strategy" and write how they solved it.

4. **Include self-assessment.** Self-assessment is a practice well known to support student learning (Wiliam 2007a). After a test, have students note which facts or groups of facts they feel they have mastered and which need more work. Also, they can self-assess their use of reasoning strategies.

5. **Provide feedback.** Feedback must include more than a score. Feedback can address strategy selection as well as identify which facts children are reaching mastery with and which ones need more attention.

Whether you use tests or not, other sources of data are needed to assess fluency. Informal interview questions such as "How did you figure that one out?" will uncover which phase a child is at for that fact. A student progress chart, such as the one in figure 2.3b, can track data for individual children throughout the year. Formal interviews can be used for summative assessments. The assessment described above from Kling's (2011) study included fourteen addition facts (including primarily derived facts, such as 5 + 9 and 7 + 8) and used a protocol and coding scheme like the one in figure 2.6. One interview required four to six minutes per child and provided a specific, highly informative picture of a child's fact mastery. Thus, in a few hours of time, which can be spread out over a week, all children in a classroom could be interviewed, while others are playing strategy games or engaged in other appropriate practice. Just as with literacy assessments, support staff and/or certified classroom volunteers can assist in this work.

The observation tools described in the previous sections also apply to mastery. Furthermore, children can self-assess, sorting sets of facts into piles of "use a reasoning strategy" and "know from memory." Or, students can self-assess their automaticity pairing with a partner or working with a family member to see which facts they can answer accurately within three seconds, and which take longer. The facts that take longer can then be targeted for identifying an efficient reasoning strategy.

PROBES (For each fact selected, ask these two questions)
What is _____? (Fill in with whatever facts you wish to assess)
How did you figure it out? (Ask regardless of how quickly or accurately they solve the fact)

STRATEGY CODES
No shading reflects phase 1 or 2 (Counting or Reasoning Strategies); light shading reflects phase 3 (Knows from Memory)

Addition	Multiplication
C = Counting All or Counting On	RA/SC = Repeated Addition or Skip Counting
K5 = Knows Facts within 5	KF = Knows Foundational Facts of 0, 1, 2, 5, 10
K+/- = Knows +/- 1 and 2	KS = Knows Squares
KD = Knows Doubles	D = Doubling Strategy
KC = Knows Combinations of 10	AG = Adding a Group
ND = Near Doubles Strategy	SG = Subtracting a Group
M10 = Making 10 Strategy	NS = Near Squares
D= Other Derived Fact Strategy	B = Break Apart Strategy
K = Knows from Memory	K = Knows from Memory

MASTERY CODE

A = Automatic (within 3 seconds)

Fig. 2.6. Sample interview protocol for fact mastery

■ How Do We Ensure Basic Fact Mastery?

This question is one of the most important in mathematics teaching and learning. Without a strong command of basic facts, children cannot reasonably perform operations with larger whole numbers or solve problems involving fractions and decimals. The answer is to teach and assess fact mastery better. Teaching must move from an M-T-C approach that neglects reasoning strategies and applies high-stress timed tests to an R-P-M approach that targets and supports each child's reasoning as they work towards mastery. The M of R-P-M (monitoring) must employ assessment tools that provide data on children's fluency, including *strategy selection, efficiency, flexibility,* and *accuracy.* Observation tools, journal prompts, and interview protocols can assess these components of fluency while avoiding the potentially damaging impact of timed tests. One question remains: Can we depart from what has become ingrained educational practice and instead implement instruction and assessments that better ensures mastery of basic facts for all children? We believe the answer is yes.

References

Bay-Williams, Jennifer M., and Gina Kling. "Enriching Addition and Subtraction Fact Mastery through Games." *Teaching Children Mathematics* 21, no. 4 (2014): 238–47.

Baroody, Arthur J. "Why Children Have Difficulties Mastering the Basic Number Combinations and How to Help Them." *Teaching Children Mathematics* 13, no. 1 (2006): 22–31.

Boaler, Jo. "Research Suggests That Timed Tests Cause Math Anxiety." *Teaching Children Mathematics* 20, no. 8 (2014): 469–74.

Dunlosky, John, Katherine A. Rawson, Elizabeth J. Marsh, Mitchell J. Nathan, and Daniel T. Willingham. "Improving Students' Learning with Effective Learning Techniques: Promising Directions from Cognitive and Educational Psychology." *Psychological Science in the Public Interest* 14, no. 1 (2013): 4–58.

Forbringer, Linda, and Allison J. Fahsl. "Differentiating Practice to Help Students Master Basic Facts." In *Responding to Diversity: Grades Pre-K–5,* edited by Dorothy Y. White and Julie S. Spitzer, pp. 7–22. Reston, Va.: NCTM, 2010.

Henry, Valerie J., and Richard S. Brown. "First-Grade Basic Facts: An Investigation into Teaching and Learning of an Accelerated, High-Demand Memorization Standard." *Journal for Research in Mathematics Education* 39, no. 2 (2008): 153–83.

Kling, Gina. "Fluency with Basic Addition." *Teaching Children Mathematics* 18, no. 2 (2011): 80–88.

Kling, Gina, and Jennifer M. Bay-Williams. "Assessing Basic Fact Fluency." *Teaching Children Mathematics* 20, no. 8 (2014): 488–97.

National Council of Teachers of Mathematics (NCTM). *Principles to Actions: Ensuring Mathematical Success for All.* Reston, Va.: NCTM, 2014.

National Governors Association Center for Best Practices and Council of Chief State School Officers (NGA Center and CCSSO). *Common Core State Standards for Mathematics.* Washington, D.C.: NGA Center and CCSSO, 2010.

National Research Council (NRC). *Adding It Up: Helping Children Learn Mathematics.* Edited by Jeremy Kilpatrick, Jane Swafford, and Brad Findell. Mathematics Learning Study Committee, Center for Education, Division of Behavioral and Social Sciences and Education. Washington, D.C.: National Academies Press, 2001.

Ramirez, Gerardo, Elizabeth A. Gunderson, Susan C. Levine, and Sian L. Beilock. "Math Anxiety, Working Memory, and Math Achievement in Early Elementary School." *Journal of Cognition and Development* 14, no. 2 (2013): 187–202.

Steinberg, Ruth. "Instruction on Derived Facts Strategies in Addition and Subtraction." *Journal for Research in Mathematics Education* 16, no. 5 (1985): 337–55.

Thornton, Carol. "Emphasizing Thinking Strategies in Basic Fact Instruction." *Journal for Research in Mathematics Education* 9, no. 3 (1978): 214–27.

Wheatley, Grayson H., and Anne M. Reynolds. *Coming to Know Number: A Mathematics Activity Resource for Elementary Teachers.* Tallahassee, Fla.: Mathematical Learning, 1999.

Wiliam, Dylan. "Keeping Learning on Track: Formative Assessment and the Regulation of Learning." In *Second Handbook of Mathematics Teaching and Learning,* edited by Frank K. Lester, Jr., pp. 1051–98. Charlotte, N.C.: Information Age Publishing, 2007a.

———. "What Does Research Say the Benefits of Formative Assessment Are?" *NCTM Research Brief* (2007b). http://www.nctm.org/uploadedFiles/Research_News_and_Advocacy/Research/Clips_and_Briefs/ Research_brief_05_-_Formative_Assessment.pdf.

CHAPTER 3

Using Learning Progressions to Design Instructional Trajectories

Min-Joung Kim, *Louisiana State University, Baton Rouge*

Richard Lehrer, *Vanderbilt University, Nashville, Tennessee*

There is a consensus among researchers that formative assessment is critical for student learning (Black and Wiliam 1998b; Furtak et al. 2008). Black and Wiliam (1998a) define formative assessment as "encompassing all those activities undertaken by teachers, and/or by their students, which provide information to be used as feedback to modify teaching and learning activities in which they are engaged" (pp. 7–8). According to this definition, the key to making formative assessment effective is collecting information from student activity and then using that information to improve practice. We argue that explicit representation of students' current states of understanding along a likely trajectory of conceptual development provides teachers with a window into the mathematical horizon of current forms of student understandings, so that teaching can be oriented toward creating a bridge between current and prospective forms of learning. In this chapter, we describe how one teacher utilized evidence of student learning generated by a Learning Progression Oriented Assessment System (LPOAS) to help students make conceptual progress in the realm of statistical reasoning.

■ Formative Assessment Talk Based on Learning Progression

In traditional assessment review, typically described by an Initiate-Respond-Evaluate (IRE) model of classroom talk (Mehan 1979), there is a lack of focus on supporting the development of understanding disciplinary substance (Coffey et al. 2011). In contrast, formative assessment talk (FAT) is squarely aligned with disciplinary practices, including mathematical ideas and forms of discussing these ideas. In particular, the goal of FAT is to support students to make conceptual progress along the conjectured pathway of "successively more sophisticated ways of thinking about an idea that follow one another as students learn," which is termed "Learning Progression" (Wilson and Bertenthal 2005, p. 3).

The enactment of FAT requires the coordination of assessment and instruction: application of mathematical disciplinary perspectives in interpreting students' responses and enactment of particular forms of instructional moves in facilitating productive classroom discussions (Ball and Forzani 2011; Stein et al. 2008). For example, Ball's description of her teaching practice as an expert teacher is, essentially, a theory of learning progression oriented instruction.

> Among my aims is that of developing a practice that respects the integrity both of mathematics as a discipline and of children as mathematical thinkers . . . I seek to draw on the discipline of mathematics at its best. In so doing, I necessarily make choices about where and how to build which links and on what aspects of mathematics to rest my practice as teacher. With my ears to the ground, listening to my students, my eyes are focused on the mathematical horizon. (Ball 1993, p. 376)

She focused on leveraging current students' understanding based on her knowledge of mathematics and likely trajectories of conceptual development. Her instructional decisions on "where and how to build which links and on what aspects of mathematics" were made based on where her students were in terms of a learning progression. She emphasized that her knowledge about mathematics was a key to notice mathematical substance in students' thinking and make instructional moves to connect student ideas to mathematical content.

■ Learning Progression Oriented Assessment System

While learning progression oriented instruction, therefore, has been previously explored (Ball 1993; Simon 1995), recent research indicates that teachers may need systematic support (e.g., instructional tools and professional development) to proficiently implement learning progression oriented assessment practices (Supovitz, Ebby, and Sirinides 2013). We developed LPOAS guided by a researcher-created learning progression in the domain of statistics education (Lehrer et al. 2014). There are four elements of the assessment: (1) construct maps, (2) assessment items, (3) scoring exemplars, and (4) lessons. Briefly, *construct maps* are descriptions of the intended outcomes of learning progressions: forms of student reasoning, ordered from least to most sophisticated according to a theory of learning (Wilson 2005). *Assessment items* are designed to elicit the forms of reasoning described by the constructs. They are formative in the sense that they illuminate students' current states of mathematical understanding in relation to the constructs. *Scoring exemplars* are interpretative frameworks relating student assessment responses to the constructs. *Lessons* are written plans for instructional tasks and tools that are designed by learning researchers to provide contexts where students could engage in the invention of representations, measures, and models of data (Lehrer and Romberg 1996). Lessons and assessment items are intended to function jointly as tools for supporting the kinds of development envisioned by the learning progression, with its intended outcomes illustrated in the construct maps.

■ A Case Example

In this chapter we examine the practices of a fifth-grade math teacher, Nancy, from a southern U.S. state. Nancy received a bachelor's degree in elementary education with an emphasis in mathematics. She had been teaching fifth-grade mathematics for fifteen years. Her students were above average based on her school's tracking system.

For two years, Nancy participated in a series of professional development workshops provided by the authors. During each workshop, teachers explored mathematical concepts of data and statistics (e.g., measures of center, measures of spread, forms of statistical inference anchored to sampling distributions), read lessons with an objective of understanding how particular instructional activities were designed to support the development of student reasoning, examined the development of student reasoning illuminated by construct maps and associated video exemplars, and finally reviewed assessment items and tried to anticipate student responses. They often looked at samples of student responses and located student responses via scoring exemplars to construct maps.

■ Formative Assessment Item

The formative assessment item Caffeine in Drinks is adapted from the Connected Mathematics Project curriculum (Lappan et al. 2005); in the version shown here, the data values on the *x*-axis were hidden (fig. 3.1). The intention of the revision was to press students to reason about median and mean in relation to the distribution of data (Konold and Pollatsek 2002).

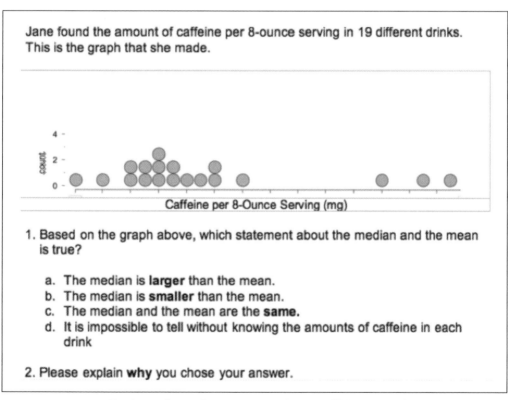

Fig. 3.1. A formative assessment item: Caffeine in Drinks

■ Landscape of Current States of Student Understanding

Caffeine in Drinks is designed to assess two significantly different ways of thinking about measures of center that are represented as levels of mathematical understanding in the Conceptions of Statistics (CoS) construct map (table 3.1).

Table 3.1

The construct map of conceptions of statistics

Level			Performances
CoS 4	Investigate and anticipate qualities of a sampling distribution.	CoS 4D	Predict and justify changes in a sampling distribution based on changes in properties of a sample.
		CoS 4C	Predict that, while the value of a statistic varies from sample to sample, its behavior in repeated sampling will be regular and predictable.
		CoS 4B	Recognize that the sample-to-sample variation in a statistic is due to chance.
		CoS 4A	Predict that a statistic's value will change from sample to sample.
CoS 3	Consider statistics as measures of qualities of a sample distribution.	CoS 3F	Choose/Evaluate statistic by considering qualities of one or more samples.
		CoS 3E	Predict the effect on a statistic of a change in the process generating the sample.
		CoS 3D	Predict how a statistic is affected by changes in its components or otherwise demonstrate knowledge of relations among components.
		CoS 3C	Generalize the use of a statistic beyond its original context of application or invention.
		CoS 3B	Invent a sharable (replicable) measurement process to quantify a quality of the sample.
		CoS 3A	Invent an idiosyncratic measurement process to quantify a quality of the sample based on tacit knowledge that others may not share.
CoS 2	Calculate statistics.	CoS 2B	Calculate statistics indicating variability.
		CoS 2A	Calculate statistics indicating central tendency.
CoS 1	Describe qualities of distribution informally.	CoS 1A	Use visual qualities of the data to summarize the distribution.

Note: A number after CoS indicates a level, and an uppercase letter after a number indicates a sublevel of performance within that level. Only a portion of the CoS construct is displayed in this classroom example. Higher levels describe students' understandings of the sampling variability of statistics.

One way to understand a statistic is as the result of a calculation. A contrasting way is to think of the statistic as a measure of central tendency of a distribution, which involves relational thinking. Note that thinking of a statistic as a measure includes calculation competence, so that in the construct map, understanding calculation only is considered less sophisticated. A student who relied on calculation would choose response D (i.e., it is impossible to tell), because she or he has no numbers to use or attempts to assign numbers to the data points to allow calculation (fig. 3.2). This way of thinking is labeled as CoS 2A in the Conceptions of Statistics construct map. Of the students in Nancy's class, twelve out of twenty-six were assessed by Nancy to be calculators. These students demonstrated how to calculate a mean with their own mock-up examples in their written responses.

Because your supposed to add up, lets say, 20 onc. of caffiene in 5 drinks and 10 in 2. So add 20x5=100, 10x2=20, 20+100=120÷7=17r1= the mean is about 17 so we must know how much caffiene in each drink.

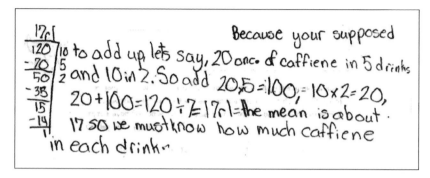

Fig. 3.2. A student's response illustrating CoS 2A

If a student were a relational thinker, she or he would integrate observation of qualities of the distribution and calculation of statistics, noting that the three outliers would increase the total of measurements and consequently increase the mean (fig. 3.3). This is labeled as CoS 3D. Only one student demonstrated relational thinking and chose the right answer.

Becuse there are outlires which makes the Mean larger and the median is in the middle of the cluster so that makes the median Smaller

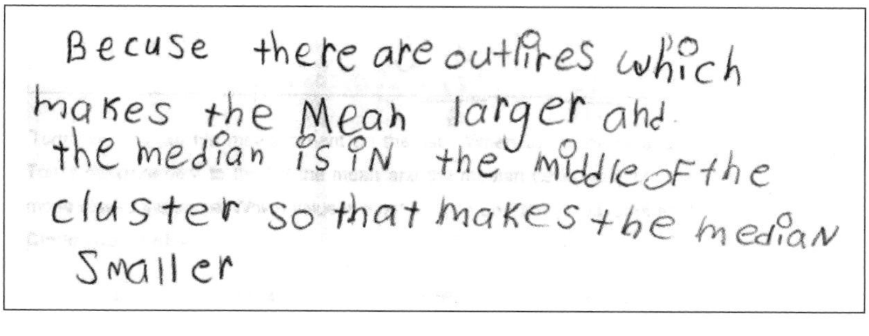

Fig. 3.3. A student's response illustrating CoS 3D

Finally, the assessment item identified students who did not read the line graph correctly, which was categorized as No Link (NL). About half of Nancy's students interpreted that each column was the amount of caffeine in each serving instead of frequencies of certain amounts of caffeine. So they figured that there were thirteen different drinks with either 1, 2, or 3 mg caffeine per 8-ounce serving (fig. 3.4). Importantly, these students demonstrated that they knew how to calculate mean and median on other assessment items.

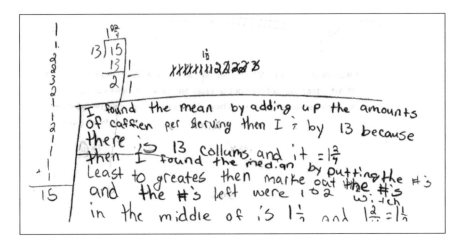

Fig. 3.4. A student's response illustrating No Link

■ A Conjectured Learning Progression

The conjectured learning progression consists of three conceptual building blocks for the highest level of performance (CoS 3D), as illustrated in figure 3.5. First, students need to notice visual qualities of the distribution such as the clump and the three outliers (CoS 1A). Second, students should know that the median is the middle of the ordered data (CoS 2A). Although there are no numbers, the data points are ordered as they are represented in the line graph. Thereby, it is possible for students to find the median. Third, students need to understand the median and the mean in relation to the distribution (CoS 3C). For example, students need to understand statistics as measures of distribution in that the mean would be located somewhere in the center clump without the three outliers because it is a measure of center, not just a number produced by formula. By connecting the three conceptual building blocks, students can reason about the effect of the three outliers on the mean and the median and compare them (CoS 3D). Although CoS 1A and CoS 3C are not target performances of the item, they are critical conceptual building blocks of the conjectured learning progression.

■ Attuning Instructional Trajectory to the Conjectured Learning Progression

Nancy scored her students' responses using the scoring exemplar and figured the distribution of her students' performance on the construct map, as illustrated by solid lined boxes in figure 3.5. Nancy summarized what she noticed about her students' performance during her interview:

> Well, there's like the top level [which] was if they could predict or know how the, the measures of center would be affected by more data and then the, down from that is if they just have to figure it out because I think a lot of the kids just think the only way to know is to actually work it out and so like by removing the numbers from that one, then it reveals you know that they're [calculators], so that's one place where they're at and then [they] just [did not interpret the display correctly].

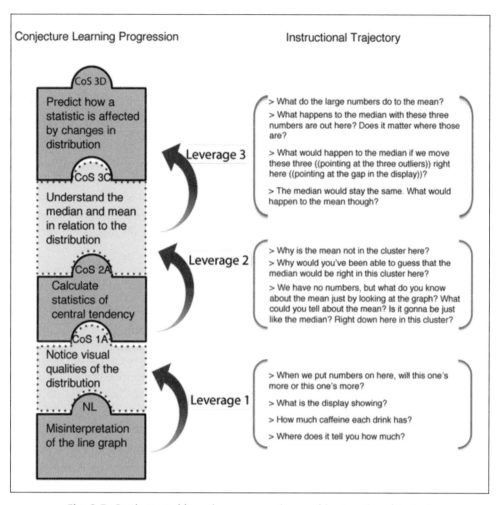

Fig. 3.5. Conjectured learning progression and instructional trajectory

The interview excerpt indicates that Nancy grasped the landscape of her students' understanding. Nancy continued to explain what she focused on during FAT:

> Mostly what I was focused on, because all of them know how to find the mean, median, and mode, they know how to do that, so I was looking at the step [on the construct map] between knowing how to do it [CoS 2A] and then knowing what's going to happen without actually working it out [CoS 3D].

The excerpt suggests that Nancy engineered FAT based on the conjectured learning progression. The right column in figure 3.5 summarizes Nancy's instructional trajectory to leverage students toward CoS 3D. Her instructional trajectory consisted of three leverages: from NL to CoS 1A, from CoS 2A to CoS 3C, and from CoS 3C to CoS 3D. In the pages that follow, we illustrate each leverage by using classroom conversation.

Leverage 1: Toward CoS 1A

As a first step to support conceptual change, Nancy began discussion by focusing on scrutinizing the elements of the line graph. Nancy asked questions like "What is the display showing?" "How much caffeine does each drink have?" "Where does it tell you how much?" and "What's it telling you on the vertical axis?"

After the class discussed the line graph, Nancy asked students, "Looking at this, without having any numbers, can you tell me if you think the median is going to be larger than the mean?" Students argued strongly that it was impossible to calculate the median "because there're no numbers that tell you." This suggests that they did not make use of the information given by the graph (i.e., ordered data). To help her students to see that data points were ordered, Nancy asked a construct-specific question: "Okay, but when we put numbers on here, will this *[pointing at a data point]*, you're saying there's no way to tell if this one's more or this one's more. Which one's more?" In this way, Nancy helped her students talk about the magnitudes of the data points without using numbers.

Leverage 2: Toward CoS 3C

Almost all students were able to calculate statistics of central tendency, but with weak connection to the distribution. Nancy employed two instructional moves in an attempt to help students link visual qualities of the distribution (CoS 1A) and calculation of statistics (CoS 2A) to a higher level of thinking (CoS 3C: seeing the statistic as a measure of a characteristic of the distribution). Nancy asked students to calculate the median, but she also connected the position of the median on the distribution to the clump. For example, Nancy asked, "Why would you've been able to guess that the median would be right in here?" as she circled the measurements on the left side of the distribution (fig. 3.1). Students noticed that the median was where most data points were.

Nancy connected the noticing of the clump to the definition of median by asking, "What is the median telling us?" The question revealed that students did not yet understand the median in relation to the distribution, as students just said, "the middle" or "the center." Nancy emphasized that not only was the median the center of the data, but moreover it was most likely located in the center clump by restating "center of most of the numbers, right?" The leverage helped students understand the meaning of the median not just as a point but as a measure of the distribution.

In talking about the mean, Nancy also related the meaning and calculation of the statistic by asking construct specific questions. She asked questions such as the following:

- "What do you know about the mean just by looking at the graph?" *[intending to draw students' attention to visual qualities of the distribution]*

- "Is it gonna be just like the median?" *[intending to build on the previous agreement that the median is in the middle of the cluster and to prompt students to infer the position of mean on the distribution]*

- "What does the mean do?" *[instigating a discussion of the definition of the mean as a balance point]*

Students were largely silent when Nancy asked these questions, suggesting that they found it difficult to reason about these ideas. In response, Nancy's instructional moves were to (1) visualize changes in the mean in a simplified distribution and (2) support students to develop relational language to talk about the mean in relation to the distribution.

The visualization of changes was mediated by Nancy's use of an interactive computer program (fig. 3.6). The computer program calculated median and mean as Nancy dragged data points on the *x*-axis, helping students to visualize changes in the statistics.

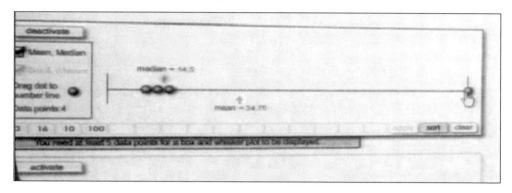

Fig. 3.6. Screenshot of the interactive computer program

First, Nancy made visible significant changes in mean and median by manipulating the computer program. She put three data points next to each other, making visible that mean and median were located in the same place as centers of measurements in this particular case. After establishing the agreement that the median and the mean were the same, she put a fourth data point on 100, resulting in a significant contrast from the previous distribution of three points: here, the median increased a little bit but was still in the cluster of the three data points. However, the mean increased so that it was no longer in the cluster of data points.

Nancy: Let's put it on 100. Okay, where's the median?

All students: 14.5.

Nancy: The median is still in this little group right here this cluster of data *[circling the three measurements next to each other]*, right? Where's the mean?

All students: 34.75.

Nancy: It's way outside the cluster.

When she asked where the median was, students had said it was on 14.5. She then highlighted its relation to the clump, saying, "The median is still in this little group right here, this cluster of data right?" When she asked where the mean is, students again read the number ("34.75"). Nancy restated it, saying, "It's way outside the cluster." The way in which Nancy used the computer program seemed to be very productive for allowing students to explore the relations between median and mean and the distribution.

Leverage 3: Toward CoS 3D

Nancy kept using the instructional program to leverage students toward CoS 3D (predict how a statistic is affected by changes in its components or otherwise demonstrate knowledge of relations among components). Nancy treated a student's response as a conjecture and engaged the class to test the conjecture by using the program.

Nancy:	Why is the mean not in the cluster here? *[showing the interactive computer program]*
Bob:	Because you've got one that's *way* at 100 points, and then, those are all. *[students talking over each other]*
Nancy:	Okay, well, let me bring this down a little bit, if that's the problem. *[moving 100 toward the three points]*
Bob:	It goes closer to it, but not quite.
Eric:	I know where mean will be. It'll be like; it'll be like on that one, near the cluster, but not in the cluster. It'll be like—
Will:	Near the cluster but close to it.
. . .	
Nancy:	Will the median change?
All students:	No.
Nancy:	Okay, let's drag it down. Okay, what happened now?

In the excerpt above, one of the students, Bob, argued that the change was caused by 100. Here she used Bob's statement to provide further opportunities for exploration. Nancy said, "Okay, well, let me bring this down a little bit, if that's the problem." Students' responses provided evidence that Nancy's instructional move was effective; students started to talk about the mean and the median in relation to the clump by using relational language (i.e., closer, near, cluster).

Then Nancy asked students to reason about the effect of change on the median. The students predicted the median would not change. Nancy operated the program to confirm their conjectures. Without being asked, Kevin said,

> The reason it doesn't matter where those three numbers are is that you're not changing how many there is—there are. It's just changing where they are. So, the median would still be the same cause you're not changing the amount of numbers that there is.

Nancy responded by revoicing what Kevin said, "Okay. Kevin's saying for the median to change, that we would have to add more, more data points. Or take away data points. Do you agree?" Kevin initially provided the NL type of reasoning, so this contribution indicated substantial conceptual progress during the course of this formative assessment conversation.

■ Conclusion

In this chapter, we have illustrated how a Learning Progression Oriented Assessment System (LPOAS) is an effective tool to improve the quality of formative assessment practices and to support student learning. An LPOAS disrupts the historically developed classification system for assessment in modern schooling (i.e., right or wrong) and eventually overwrites it with a disciplinary perspective on mathematics, by building on the disciplinary seeds evident in students' ways of thinking. The learning progression supported Nancy in assessing the landscape of the current states of her students' understanding about particular mathematical ideas.

In addition, an LPOAS supports teachers in designing an instructional trajectory that coordinates current states of student understanding with conjectured learning progression. For example, Nancy tailored leveraging questions based on where students were and where they should go next on conjectured learning progression. In leverage 1, questions allowed students to see construct-specific features from the display. Alternatively, Nancy's questions for leverage 2 pressed students to use visual qualities of the distribution (CoS 1A) to understand measures of centers (CoS 3C).

Teachers can prepare Formative Assessment Talk by taking the following steps: (1) score students' responses to an assessment item in light of a construct map (table 3.1); (2) identify leverage points that bridge current levels of student understanding with intermediate learning performances; and (3) design questions and supporting representations that support students to bridge from the mathematical ideas they currently understand to those that have greater disciplinary scope and precision. For example, Nancy used digital media to dynamically change qualities of a distribution to support student reasoning about relations between these qualities and values of statistics of center. Collectively, these steps provide classroom teachers with practical means to conduct formative assessment talk oriented toward a learning progression.

References

Ball, Deborah Loewenberg. "With an Eye on the Mathematical Horizon: Dilemmas of Teaching Elementary School Mathematics." *Elementary School Journal* 93, no. 4 (1993): 373–97.

Ball, Deborah Loewenberg, and Francesca M. Forzani. "Teaching Skillful Teaching." *Educational Leadership* 68, no. 4 (2011): 40–45.

Black, Paul, and Dylan Wiliam. "Assessment and Classroom Learning." *Assessment in Education* 5, no. 1 (1998a): 7–74.

———. "Inside the Black Box: Raising Standards through Classroom Assessment." *Phi Delta Kappan* 80, no. 2 (1998b): 139–48.

Coffey, Janet E., David Hammer, Daniel M. Levin, and Terrance Grant. "The Missing Disciplinary Substance of Formative Assessment." *Journal of Research in Science Teaching* 48, no. 10 (2011): 1109–36.

Furtak, Erin Marie, Maria Araceli Ruiz-Primo, Jonathan Shemwell, Carlos Ayala, Paul Brandon, Richard Shavelson, and Yue Yin. "On the Fidelity of Implementing Embedded Formative Assessments and Its Relation to Student Learning." *Applied Measurement in Education* 21, no. 4 (2008): 360–89.

Konold, Clifford, and Alexander Pollatsek. "Data Analysis as the Search for Signals in Noisy Processes." *Journal of Research in Mathematics Education* 33, no. 4 (2002): 259–89.

Lappan, Glenda, James T. Fey, William M. Fitzgerald, Susan N. Friel, and Elizabeth Difanis Phillips. *Connected Mathematics 2: Data about Us*. Student ed. Upper Saddle River, N.J.: Pearson Education, 2005.

Lehrer, Richard, Min-Joung Kim, Elizabeth Ayers, and Mark Wilson. "Toward Establishing a Learning Progression to Support the Development of Statistical Reasoning." In *Learning over Time: Learning Trajectories in Mathematics Education*, edited by A. Maloney, J. Confrey, and K. Nguyen. Charlotte, N.C.: Information Age Publishers, 2014.

Lehrer, Richard, and Thomas Romberg. "Exploring Children's Data Modeling." *Cognition & Instruction* 14, no. 1 (1996): 69–108.

Mehan, Hugh. "'What Time Is It, Denise?': Asking Known Information Questions in Classroom Discourse." *Theory into Practice* 18, no. 4 (1979): 285–94.

Simon, Martin A. "Reconstructing Mathematics Pedagogy from a Constructivist Perspective." *Journal for Research in Mathematical Education* 26, no. 2 (1995): 114–45.

Stein, Mary, Randi Engle, Margaret Smith, and Elizabeth Hughes. "Orchestrating Productive Mathematical Discussions: Five Practices for Helping Teachers Move beyond Show and Tell." *Mathematical Thinking and Learning* 10, no. 4 (2008): 313–40.

Supovitz, Jonathan, Caroline Ebby, and Philip Sirinides. *Teacher Analysis of Student Knowledge: A Measure of Learning Trajectory-Oriented Formative Assessment.* Consortium for Policy Research in Education, 2013.

Wilson, Mark. *Constructing Measures: An Item Response Modeling Approach.* Mahwah, N.J.: Lawrence Erlbaum Associates, 2005.

Wilson, Mark, and Meryl Bertenthal. *Systems for State Science Assessment.* Washington, D.C.: National Academies Press, 2005.

CHAPTER 4

How Changes in Instruction Support Changes in Assessment:
The Case of an Inclusive STEM-Focused School

David Slavit and Tamara Holmlund Nelson, *Washington State University Vancouver*

This chapter explores how a STEM-focused school enacted project-based learning (PBL) and the subsequent impacts this had on assessment practices. Assessment provides both evaluative and ongoing feedback regarding students' mathematical progress. In an instructional setting that highlights PBL, assessment data often comes in nontraditional forms. Therefore, teachers need to not only rethink *instruction* when shifting to a PBL approach but must also freshly examine both their evaluative and ongoing *assessment* practices (Yetkiner, Anderoglu, and Capraro 2008).

Data collected through classroom-based formative assessments can more readily focus on specific understandings students bring to an instructional setting than do more traditional measures of student learning. In this chapter, we explore the efforts of a school that developed its own PBL instructional activities as a means of engaging students in high-quality learning experiences, which allowed the teachers opportunities to formatively assess their students' progress on a variety of outcomes. We found the instruction and assessment to be intricately linked.

After a brief review of STEM-focused schools and PBL, we describe the target school and analyze the instructional approaches and practices that occurred throughout its first year, with a focus on the mathematics teachers. Connections to the formative assessment practices that occurred are highlighted throughout.

■ STEM Schools, Project-Based Learning, and Assessment

STEM (science, technology, engineering, mathematics) as an integrated topic of study is receiving increased consideration from policymakers and school administrators. Currently, a "STEM-school movement" is exponentially expanding its presence in the United States, with some reports of more than 600 such schools in operation (Tofel-Grehl 2013). One type of STEM-focused school, termed "inclusive" (National Research Council [NRC] 2011), seeks to provide experiences that are similar to those at selective STEM schools while also serving a broader population. Inclusive schools use no selective admissions criteria, with the goal of attaining student demographics that mirror those in the district at large. Ridgeview STEM Academy, the target school in this study, is an inclusive STEM-focused school. By attracting a more diverse student population, inclusive STEM-focused schools increase the opportunities for traditionally underserved students in mathematics.

STEM-focused schools have a variety of traits and structures, but a common instructional approach is the use of extended projects, often of an integrated nature, to support mathematical concept development (NRC 2011). Project-based learning is an instructional vehicle commonly used to achieve this aim. While no single definition of PBL exists, we follow the description of it as "all students engaged in a common project with unclear processes but clearly identified expected outcomes" (Yetkiner, Anderoglu, and Capraro 2008, p. 1). PBL instructional approaches typically aim to combine academic rigor with the promotion of 21st-century skills such as critical thinking, communication, and collaboration (Partnership for 21st Century Skills 2002), skills that are highly recommended by the Common Core State Standards in Mathematics (National Governors Association Center for Best Practices and Council of Chief State School Officers [NGA Center and CCSSO] 2010). Any school that takes this instructional approach seriously is in a position to rethink assessment practices both philosophically and structurally. For example, when content silos are broken down, the nature of knowledge begins to take on new forms, and issues of understanding, application, problem solving, and communication become a natural part of what is valued and considered important.

■ Ridgeview STEM Academy

Ridgeview STEM Academy (RSA) is an inclusive STEM-focused school in the northwestern United States serving students in grades 6–12. The middle school is housed in a district-owned building, and the high school is on a university campus approximately five miles away. Each student is provided a laptop that is fully integrated into the learning process, including its use as an information conduit, an assignment submission portal, and, most important, as a primary learning tool.

The school's district administrators purposely planned RSA to be an inclusive school—a school with equal access for all students. The only requirement for attending RSA is to apply and be present at one of the school's information nights. Student demographic data show that RSA has been successful at attracting student representation in line with the district as a whole. The exception to this is in gender, as RSA has a predominant male population.

The school's principal saw the focus on STEM in this way:

> We use the term we have to STEMify everything. So what we're trying to have is—because we are obligated to cover all the content areas that our state requires—finding the natural connections. So not everything will be driven by math and science, but where we can, we can fit it in.

Collaborative efforts to create multidisciplinary, project-based curriculum were a consistent part of the vision of the school. Staff met for three months prior to the school's opening to work together to plan and develop such projects. During the school year, at least one hour of weekly planning time was devoted to this ongoing process. The teachers wanted the projects to be the "main course, not dessert." Their vision was that learning would be accomplished through completion of the project, rather than regarding the project as a showcase for learning that has already occurred. Hence, formative assessment was given prominence in the instructional design. The use of essential questions (Wiggins and McTighe 2005) to guide projects focused the instruction across content areas, but it also served as a key organizational tool for creating formative and summative assessments.

■Learning and Assessment at RSA

The cross-disciplinary, project-based approach to STEM at RSA forced all teachers to rethink the core educational ideas of content and curriculum. A natural consequence was that reflections on teaching, learning, and assessment ensued. Barron and Darling-Hammond (2008) argue that assessment of cooperative and inquiry approaches to learning must involve (1) intellectually ambitious and authentic performance assessments; (2) evaluation tools, such as rubrics, that define "good work" and collaboration; and (3) formative feedback to shape instructional design. RSA teachers embedded these principles into their instructional and assessment approaches.

RSA teachers had a variety of ways of redefining their instruction and assessment practices, driven by their need to produce projects that were cross-disciplinary but with a STEM focus. Greg, a mathematics teacher, reflected on the broad impact this had on his perspectives and practices in relation to both instruction and assessment:

> I think it's been really cool to see how going outside the norm of how I used to teach—
> different order, trying to do different projects, trying to do that kind of stuff—[helps] to
> see how well I can get information about what students know. So I can make some better
> decisions about what I'm doing. It's gone really well. I haven't mastered it yet by any sense
> of the imagination, but I'm realizing what growth opportunities are there. So I think
> that's going to continue to be a good growth opportunity for me.

The incorporation of mathematics into projects at RSA generally took two forms. On some occasions, the mathematics teachers could not find ways of connecting core ideas or instructional themes into their colleague's plans, so a stand-alone mathematics project was created. For example, Greg required students to create math games that involved numeric operations and strategies, and on Pi Day (March 14) the entire school engaged in a variety of mathematics-related projects, including four different ways of approximating the value of pi.

Fig. 4.1. Student-generated math game involving number operations

On other occasions, the teachers made efforts to integrate the disciplines, with mixed success. Greg stated that the freedoms he enjoyed in regard to mathematics curriculum scope and sequence, which resulted from the school-wide PBL approach, allowed for greater opportunities to integrate content with other disciplines:

> I was kind of excited about the curriculum because I thought I'd finally get to do math how I thought it should be done. I've had a lot of freedom and not had to keep up with the scope and sequence that other schools have had to do . . . Having that freedom has allowed me to kind of go where the other teachers want. For example, the science teacher, Paul, we were able to collaborate. When he was doing radioactive decay, I could work on exponential functions. Whereas if I was under the traditional scope and sequence I would have had to work on linear functions, and it wouldn't have been able to apply in both places.

Greg's assessment approach, found on his syllabi, was mastery-based and centered entirely on student performance, including that done on projects:

> Grades will be determined using standards-based grading. This means it will be based on your specific mastery of State Learning Standards and the Common Core State Standards [for] Mathematics. Only your performance on various projects, tests, and activities will be used for grades. Multiple retake opportunities will be available for students to demonstrate mastery.

The Buck Institute (Yetkiner, Anderoglu, and Capraro 2008) recommends that project artifacts become important sources of assessment in PBL settings. The RSA teachers used artifacts in this manner, linking them to standards for mathematical learning.

Discrepancies among the teachers regarding the vision and practice of PBL at RSA led to occasional difficulties in integrating mathematics into the instructional core. Greg felt that the school curriculum should be "STEM driven," but perceived that "the humanities people are the ones that are driving the projects." Contrasting visions among the teachers between the source of a project's core—STEM topics (e.g., linearity, minerals) or general themes (e.g., immigration, sustainability)—made collaborations difficult in some cases. Greg stated:

> I thought that it would also be something where the curriculum would all be math and science, technology driven. STEM driven. Where we'd take a STEM idea and then make a project around it and that has fallen really far short, I think. Which is unfortunate. My vision of it is to start with whatever the STEM idea is, whether it's exponential decay, whether it's constant rate of change, whether it's fossils, and build a project around it. And what we've been doing this year seems like it's been a lot of, "Here's the project, how can we fit everything into this project?" . . . We're still trying to create these projects and the question that gets asked is, "What is this going to be in English? What is this going to be in history? What is this going to be in math? What is this going to be in science?" And that still is just separating it out to me.

The teachers attempted to create rubrics to assess many of the projects. Figure 4.2 shows the general rubric used by Greg and by Joan, the middle grades mathematics teacher. Greg helped generate the rubric as a member of a state-wide assessment team, and both mathematics teachers used it on the various mathematics projects in their courses. The influence of the NCTM process standards is evident in the first four categories, and many of the descriptors relate to the 21st-century skills required in PBL experiences. However, a presentation standard was also added to support their PBL instructional approach. Presentations to authentic audiences (local STEM business professionals, university STEM professors, parents, etc.) were a common project requirement, and this was given explicit value in the rubric. The rubric allowed the teachers to clarify their learning goals and criteria for success (Black and Wiliam 2009) and was helpful to students as they prepared, often for the first time, presentations of this nature. The focus on presentation was not part of the original rubric Joan used early in the year, indicating that her use of PBL affected the criteria for learning that she most valued seeing in her students.

Score Levels	Math Concepts	Problem Solving & Reasoning	Conventions	Communication	Presentation
4	Evidence shows: ■ Accurate conceptual understanding ■ Accurate use of mathematical procedures ■ Project is well thought out and supports the solution to the challenge or question ■ Clear goal that is related to the topic ■ Effective application of multiple concepts and/or procedures	Evidence shows: ■ Effective use of problem solving strategies and reasoning skills to clarify and/or solve problems ■ Effective use of mathematical reasoning to analyze situations, draw conclusions, and/or validate results ■ Effective application of critical thinking	Evidence shows: ■ Correct use of mathematical notation ■ High-level use of math vocabulary ■ Appropriate graphs and tables are clear and add to the understanding of the concept ■ No spelling, grammatical, or punctuation errors in written descriptions	Evidence shows: ■ Information is clearly focused in an organized and thoughtful manner ■ Information is constructed in a logical pattern to support the solution in appropriate and labeled forms ■ Effective planning and extraction of mathematical information ■ Effective use of different representations of mathematical information	■ Multimedia is used to clarify and illustrate the main points ■ Format enhances the content ■ Presentation captures audience attention with a variety of formats or techniques ■ Presentation is effectively organized, well laid out, and practiced ■ Team collaboration is evident
3	Evidence shows: ■ Mostly accurate conceptual understanding ■ Mostly accurate use of mathematical procedures ■ Project is thought out and generally supports the solution to the challenge or question ■ Goal that is related to the topic ■ Adequate application of multiple concepts and/or procedures	Evidence shows: ■ Adequate use of problem solving strategies and reasoning skills to clarify and/or solve problems ■ Adequate use of mathematical reasoning to analyze situations, draw conclusions, and/or validate results ■ Adequate application of critical thinking	Evidence shows: ■ Adequate/mostly correct use of mathematical notation ■ Adequate use of math vocabulary ■ Appropriate graphs and tables are clear but may have minor errors or misrepresentations of accurate information ■ Minor spelling, grammatical, or punctuation errors in written descriptions	Evidence shows: ■ Information is adequately focused in an organized and thoughtful manner ■ Information is adequately constructed in a logical pattern to support the solution ■ Adequate planning and extraction of mathematical information ■ Adequate use of different representations of mathematical information	■ Multimedia is used to illustrate the main points. ■ Format is appropriate for the content. ■ Presentation captures audience attention. ■ Presentation is adequately organized ■ Team collaboration is mostly evident

Fig. 4.2. General project rubric

Score Levels	Math Concepts	Problem Solving & Reasoning	Conventions	Communication	Presentation
2	Evidence shows: • Partially accurate conceptual understanding • Partially accurate use of mathematical procedures • Project is partially thought out and supports the solution to the challenge or question at times • Goal is partially related to the topic • Partial application of multiple concepts and/or procedures	Evidence shows: • Partial use of problem solving strategies and reasoning skills to clarify and/or solve problems • Partial use of mathematical reasoning to analyze situations, draw conclusions, and/or validate results • Partial application of critical thinking	Evidence shows: • Partial use of mathematical notation • Partial use of math vocabulary • Graphs and tables are not clear but can be followed with difficulty • Spelling, grammatical, or punctuation errors make reading difficult	Evidence shows: • Information is partially focused or partially appropriate • Information is partially constructed in a logical pattern or only partially supports a solution • Partial planning and extraction of mathematical information • Partially accurate use of different representations of mathematical information	• Multimedia is used with partial focus on main points • Format is only partially appropriate or • Presentation partially captures audience attention. • Presentation is partially organized • Team collaboration is partially evident
1	Evidence shows: • Little or no accurate conceptual understanding • Little or no accurate use of mathematical procedures • Project is not thought out and does not support the solution to the challenge or question • Goal is not related to the topic • Little or no application of multiple concepts and/or procedures	Evidence shows: • Little or no use of problem solving strategies and reasoning skills to clarify and/or solve problems • Little or no use of mathematical reasoning to analyze situations, draw conclusions, and/or validate results • Little or no application of critical thinking	Evidence shows: • Little or no use of mathematical notation • Little or no use of math vocabulary • Graphs and tables are not appropriate and/or are not clear • Spelling, grammatical, or punctuation errors make reading impossible	Evidence shows: • Information has little or no focus • Information is not constructed in a logical pattern or does not support a solution • Little or no planning and extraction of mathematical information • Little or no accurate use of different representations of mathematical information	• Presentation appears sloppy and/or unfinished. • Multimedia is overused or underused. • Format does not enhance content. • Presentation has little or no organization • Team collaboration is not evident

Fig. 4.2. *Continued*

The teachers also targeted the rubric to the mathematical aspects of the cross-disciplinary projects that emerged throughout the year. For example, nearly all of the teachers at RSA participated in a project that required students to build a simple machine, with various requirements depending on grade level. Here is how Joan and all of the RSA teachers presented the project to their middle school students:

Rube Goldberg (1883–1970) was a Pulitzer Prize–winning cartoonist, sculptor, and author. Best known for his "inventions," Rube's early years as an engineer informed his most acclaimed work. A Rube Goldberg contraption—an elaborate set of arms, wheels, gears, handles, cups and rods, put in motion by balls, canary cages, pails, boots, bathtubs, paddles and live animals—takes a simple task and makes it extraordinarily complicated. For examples of his work go to www.rubegoldberg.com.

Your task will be to create a Rube Goldberg contraption that has at least six (6) separate steps. You can create it life-size (in which case you will submit a video of it working), use miniature items (so you can bring it into school), or submit a drawing (like Goldberg's).

Students presented their final products to parents and local invited guests, including STEM-related business and university professionals. The students were required to discuss the scientific, mathematical, and engineering aspects of their designs and to provide discussion of their failed attempts prior to their final product. Despite the above challenges, presenting these kinds of cross-disciplinary, STEM-based projects to authentic audiences continues to be the most prominent means of assessment at RSA.

The students interviewed at the end of year 1 spoke passionately and positively about the PBL experiences they encountered. Some of this resulted from the difference in the instructional approach at RSA from others they had encountered, or perceived to exist, at other schools. Students eventually spoke of PBL as being "business-as-usual"; for example, one student stated that, in the past, if a teacher assigned a project due in a week he "would have freaked out," but "now we've done so many projects it's not even really a big deal anymore just to get up in front of people and start talking." Students also stated that the projects "apply a lot more to the real world and college and workplace than just right-or-wrong answer worksheets." Another explained that the teachers' use of framing essential questions allowed students "to explore in the direction that we want to go instead of just having to do research on one topic to find the one right answer." Students recognized that "there's not as much structure in the way that you have to do things" and seemed to consider this a benefit to the learning experience. In this instructional environment, the teachers also felt that student learning was more visible and that the projects changed the way they viewed assessment.

■ Mathematically Assessing a PBL Learning Experience

RSA teachers developed a "Futurama Project" at the end of year 2 that used the World's Fair as an integrative theme. This allowed for interdisciplinary projects related to topics such as economics, technology, and culture. At this time, Joan was considering all of the Common Core mathematical standards that she wished to address during the remainder of the school year. She decided to infuse mathematics into the Futurama Project by providing writing opportunities on up to eight standards that would be connected to the various aspects of the project produced by the students (see fig. 4.3). This offered student choice and a way of meeting course goals, as well as a means of supporting the interdisciplinary approach to the project. Joan stated:

> As we were creating the school-wide project, I found that the standards we were about to cover for the remaining year, there were small bits and pieces that fit in with small areas in each group project, and saw this as an opportunity for students to write about math.

Futurama – Math Application

When you buy a car, follow a recipe, or decorate your home, you're using math principles. People have been using these same principles for thousands of years, across countries and continents. Whether you're sailing a boat off the coast of Japan or building a house in Peru, you're using math to get things done. Math can help us to shop wisely, buy the right insurance, remodel a home within a budget, understand population growth, or even bet on the horse with the best chance of winning the race.[1]

Explanation of Project:

You will be writing a multi-paragraph explanation (with an introduction and conclusion) of how certain standards can be applied to your Futurama project, as well as other real-life applications. For example: if one of our standards was about area, you could describe how to find the acreage of land you will need to fit all your structures.

This may be written in an expository essay form or as a presentation. You will need to have a complete paragraph for each of the standards you choose to explain. Listed below are the standards we have and will cover over the next several weeks, and it is up to you to decide what standards you would like to expand upon.

Standard:	Brief Explanation (select standard link for full explanation, or go to www.corestandards.org):
7.EE.A.1	Apply Properties of Operations to expand linear expressions.
7.EE.A.2	Rewriting Expressions
7.EE.B.4	Use Variables to represent quantities
7.EE.B.4a	From $px + q = r$ to $p(x+q) = r$
7.EE.B.4b	From $px + q > r$ to $px + q < r$
7.G.A.2	Draw geometric shapes
7.G.A.3	Cross Sections
7.G.B.5	Angle Relationships

Grading:

Explain and apply 1-2 standard for a maximum score of a D.*
Explain and apply 3-4 standards for a maximum score of a C.*
Explain and apply 5 -6 standards for a maximum score of a B. *
Explain and apply 6 -8 standards for a maximum score of an A. *
*These are not guaranteed final scores, these are maximum scores.

Due Date (When you arrive to class)
June 12, 2014
There is **1 week left after this due date, which means there **will NOT** be a lot of wiggle room to get this assignment turned in late. Please plan accordingly!**

[1] "Math in Daily Life." Math in Daily Life. Annenberg Foundation, n.d. Web. 21 Apr. 2014.

Fig. 4.3. Futurama math application

Joan used this assessment as "another way to communicate understanding rather than just a test" (a final exam was also given, and the students were allowed to choose the higher of the two scores). She found this particular assessment helpful in various ways, both in terms of instruction and assessment:

> This was a worthwhile assessment. It allowed students who are not normally vocal in class to make comparisons about math and the real world that I didn't necessarily see them making, and also showed me that while they might understand the "steps" to solve some problems, they don't understand the actual application of them.

Joan's assessment of the Futurama Project provided specific, usable information about her students' mathematical understandings. In PBL, assessment is conceptualized more along the lines of Stiggins' (2005) notion of "assessment for learning" than as a summative assessment of learning. When using a PBL approach, the learning comes through the doing of the project; as such, students need to understand their own progress toward the learning goals (and gaps) prior to presenting the final product. Joan speaks of student work around the standard related to systems of linear equations:

> From this project, I learned that students have a brushing understanding of what systems of equations are, but not one that goes beyond surface value. Most students understand that it is the intersection between two lines, but they don't understand that it could be more than two lines. Some students' descriptions of how to use this in a real-life situation was just talking about literally graphing two lines, and didn't describe that these two lines could be comparing two different amounts.

The nuanced levels of understanding viewed by Joan, including the degree to which the students were able to understand the applicability of the mathematical standards, are clear. Further, while the project served as a summative assessment, Joan also saw its use in formative ways in regard to the long-term development of her students:

> As this was an end-of-year assignment, it didn't allow me time to adjust my instruction for this year. However, the way that RSA is set up, I am the students' math teacher next year, so I will know where to fill in the gaps. For my Math 3 students who are moving into Algebra next year, I was able see that they are beginning to recognize the foundations of Algebra (slope, y-intercept, coordinates), but not enough to go beyond graphing . . . In Math 2, I was able to see that students are really understanding solving one-step equations, and that they are ready to move on to the multi-step equations.

As a first-year teacher, Joan's assessment practices changed considerably over the course of the school year, in part because of her move toward PBL instruction. Joan was able to better articulate her learning goals and find performance-based ways of assessing student progress as the school year unfolded. Reflecting on the beginning of the school year, Joan stated:

> I didn't clearly state to the students what I expected and I didn't clearly state to myself what I expected. And so it . . . became a big hassle. I was doing activity-based, not project-based . . . Because it was an activity and not a project, they weren't really able to apply it, and so I'd have to test it. So it was always an activity and a summative assessment.

Joan's summative assessment items were rather traditional at this time. For example, her early assessments included many "rote problems, like find the rate of something." A specific assessment task early in the year was, "If someone's going 366 miles in six hours, how many hours would it take them to go 427 miles?" Joan acknowledged that such tasks "didn't require much thought other than, 'This is rate. Let's solve this rate problem.'" The use of projects allowed for more dynamic and targeted assessment practices towards the end of the year:

> I started off by showing them the rubric, "This is how I'm going to be assessing." And I liked meeting with them, and I had them do checkpoints throughout where they took a scan of the [current version of the] project and turned it in. So I could grade it critically by myself.

The nature of PBL forced reflection by Joan that led to changes in assessment more related to student thinking, and that also allowed a more targeted and personal approach to monitoring student learning.

■ Conclusions

Evidence is emerging that PBL instruction increases students' mathematical learning over more traditional approaches (Boaler 1998; Barron and Darling-Hammond 2008). Project-based learning provides teachers and schools with unique opportunities to rethink teaching and learning, as well as assessment. PBL requires students to take active and highly visible roles in the learning process, and it supports the presence of highly recommended mathematical practices (NGA Center and CCSSO 2010). However, such changes can require rethinking companion assessment practices in a way that supports the instruction by monitoring student progress throughout the project. Teachers who "get information about what students know," like Greg, can then use this to support students' growth as well as to make changes to instructional approaches and practices.

Cross-disciplinary projects are difficult and time-consuming to construct and deliver. They require enormous efforts on the part of teachers to find common ground in regard to content and instructional approach, development, and delivery. Tensions between the use of content or theme as a unifying vehicle presented significant challenges for the RSA staff. Such tensions should be explicitly explored when developing a school-wide vision for STEM-based PBL instruction, particularly given that "assessment in PBL should take into account both the organization of the knowledge base and the students' problem-solving skills" (Gijbels et al. 2005, p. 32). Assessment of mathematical practices embedded in the projects calls for departures from traditional assessment practices; tests and quizzes are replaced by authentic presentations, and observations and rubrics are employed to support the nuanced looks at student learning that projects demand.

RSA provides an example of an inclusive, STEM-focused school that found success shifting instructional and assessment practices away from traditional methods toward practices that were project-based and required nuanced views of student learning. While such shifts take enormous time and effort, the benefits to students seem clear.

References

Barron, Brigid, and Linda Darling-Hammond. *Teaching for Meaningful Learning*. San Francisco, Calif.: Jossey-Bass, 2008.

Black, Paul, and Dylan Wiliam. "Developing the Theory of Formative Assessment." *Educational Assessment, Evaluation and Accountability* 21 (2009): 5–31.

Boaler, Jo. "Open and Closed Mathematics: Student Experiences and Understandings." *Journal for Research in Mathematics Education* 29 (1998): 41–62.

Gijbels, David, Filip Dochy, Piet Van den Bossche, and Mien Segers. "Effects of Problem-Based Learning: A Meta-Analysis from the Angle of Assessment." *Review of Educational Research* 75 (2005): 27–61.

National Governors Association Center for Best Practices and Council of Chief State School Officers (NGA Center and CCSSO). *Common Core State Standards for Mathematics.* Washington, D.C.: NGA Center and CCSSO, 2010.

National Research Council (NRC). *Successful K–12 STEM Education.* Washington, D.C.: National Academies Press, 2011.

Partnership for 21st Century Skills. *Learning for the 21st Century: A Report and Mile Guide for 21st Century Skills.* Tucson, Ariz.: Partnership for 21st Century Skills, 2002.

Stiggins, Rick. "From Formative Assessment to Assessment FOR Learning: A Path to Success in Standards-Based Schools." *Phi Delta Kappan,* 87 (2005): 324–28.

Tofel-Grehl, Colby. "Specialized STEM High School Programs." Paper presented at the Annual Meeting of the American Educational Research Association, San Francisco, April 27–May 1, 2013.

Wiggins, Grant, and Jay McTighe. *Understanding by Design.* Expanded 2nd ed. Upper Saddle River, N.J./Alexandria, Va.: Pearson Education/Association for Supervision & Curriculum Development, 2005.

Yetkiner, Zeynep E., Hamza Anderoglu, and Robert M. Capraro. "Research Summary: Project-Based Learning in Middle Grades Mathematics." National Middle School Association, 2008. Accessed February 2, 2014. http://www.nmsa.org/Research/ResearchSummaries/ProjectBasedLearninginMath/tabid/1570/Default.aspx.

CHAPTER 5

Classroom-Based Formative Assessments:
Guiding Teaching and Learning

Francis (Skip) Fennell, *McDaniel College, Westminster, Maryland*
Beth Kobett, *Stevenson University, Stevenson, Maryland*
Jonathan A. Wray, *Howard County Public Schools, Ellicott City, Maryland*

Cam has 5/6 of a mile left to go on his trail walk. Mia has 3/4 of a mile left to go, and Cooper has 7/8 of a mile to go. If they all walk at the same pace, who will finish first? Second? Third?

Think about how a classroom teacher might use formative assessment to determine the extent to which her students are successful in solving the problem above and the instructional "next steps" that might be considered based on student responses to the problem. How can formative assessment be everyday connected to teaching and learning, and how can we ensure that all teachers not only recognize the importance of such assessments but are also comfortably competent in their use?

■Planning, Teaching, and Assessing to Inform Learning

Making connections among the planning process, teaching, and assessment in each lesson provides the foundation necessary to truly support teaching and learning. Planning a lesson must consider not only key mathematics content standards but also how, for instance, the Standards for Mathematical Practice (National Governors Association Center for Best Practices and Council of Chief State School Officers [NGA Center and CCSSO] 2010) will be integrally involved within a lesson. Linking assessment to planning and instruction is thus used to in*form* teaching and learning. (*Note:* We italicize *form* within in*form* here to bring attention to the central role of classroom-based formative assessment—in*form*ing teaching and learning.)

While we know quite a bit about the potential of formative assessment and its importance (Black and Wiliam 2010; National Council of Teachers of Mathematics [NCTM] 2014; National Mathematics Advisory Panel [NMAP] 2008), evidence suggests that the actual day-to-day use of formative assessment is not as prevalent in classrooms as one might expect (Popham 2013). As noted in *Principles to Actions: Ensuring Mathematical Success for All*

(NCTM 2014), we must find a way to leverage assessment opportunities to improve teaching and learning at the classroom and school levels.

Wiliam (2007) suggests that the effective use of assessment for learning consists of five key strategies:

(*a*) Clarifying and sharing learning intentions and criteria for success;

(*b*) **Engineering effective classroom discussions, questions, and learning tasks that elicit evidence of learning;**

(*c*) **Providing feedback that moves learners forward;**

(*d*) Activating students as instructional resources for one another; and

(*e*) Activating students as the owners of their own learning.

The approach to classroom-based formative assessment (CBFA) presented and discussed in this chapter, while recognizing the importance of all of the key strategies, particularly emphasizes and promotes the two strategies bolded above. The use and the related responses to the formative assessment techniques presented here are intended to guide and in*form* the intent and direction of planning and instruction.

■ Classroom-Based Formative Assessments: What We Have Done

In our work with teachers and school-based mathematics leaders we recognized a need for both developing and enhancing prerequisite knowledge regarding the use of classroom-based formative assessment. We also recognized an overload of publications, published assessments, and services advertised as the formative assessment fix for the classroom or school level. In far too many cases, such programs and services do not reflect the research nor the instructional intent related to formative assessment (Shepard 2007).

Our efforts have been centered on recognizing the importance of classroom-based formative assessment generally, and in distilling and validating, through classroom use, a small set of classroom-based formative assessment techniques that teachers can use on a regular basis. We consider the techniques as a palette of five "colors" that teachers can use, sometimes mixing the colors to find the best way to formatively assess and guide teaching and learning on a daily basis. In the sections that follow, we will discuss the five CBFA techniques—*observations, interviews, "show me," hinge questions,* and *exit tasks.* For each technique, we will define the technique, suggest when and how to use it, point out things to consider in its use, and provide concrete suggestions for employing it in classrooms.

■ Observations

The use of observations as a formative assessment technique is perhaps the most informal classroom-based formative assessment (CBFA), but its use is critical. Mathematics educators have known for some time that observation has the potential to guide teaching and learning. Freudenthal (1973) noted that "we know it is more informative to observe a student during a mathematical activity than to grade his papers" (p. 84).

Critical questions for teachers as they plan and teach include:

1. What would you hope to observe?

2. How would you know "it" if you saw it?

3. How might you record/note the observation?

4. What misconceptions might you observe?

Our work to date with the CBFA techniques has indicated that teachers seem somewhat comfortable when considering what they expect to observe, and in recognizing that observing students and their responses is an effective way to monitor learning at the lesson level. Many teachers indicate that observing is something they have always done, but perhaps they have not seen it as a formative assessment technique, or they needed support to use observations to explicitly guide and in*form* their instructional decisions.

Continuing investigations with the CBFA techniques has led us to create tools to help support, encourage, and develop understandings related to the use of particular techniques. The *planning and implementation tool for observations* (fig. 5.1) has become helpful in supporting the consistent, everyday use of observations as a formative assessment technique directly related to planning and monitoring instruction within a lesson.

Intent of the Observation	Brief Description/Comments	Observed?		
		Yes	Partially	No
Mathematics Content				
Mathematical Practice(s)				
Student Engagement				
General Comment: Feedback to Students:				

Fig. 5.1. Planning and implementation tool for observations

Guiding Teaching and Learning: Using Observations

When: Conduct observations daily to inform instruction and guide teaching and learning.

How: Observations may range from an informal observation of a student, small group, or class to a more focused, deliberate observation. As teachers consider what they might observe when they actually plan lessons, such observations will become a natural, seamless way in which they guide and monitor student and class progress.

Considerations

- Focus on observing content understandings and student engagement with particular mathematical practices, rather than being distracted by other student behaviors.

- Remember the intent of the observation. The observation should be intentionally connected to the actual planning and implementation of the lesson.

- Document, document, document. Keeping a running record and analysis of what is observed will more directly inform decisions—either during the lesson's implementation, or to advise short-term and long-term planning.

- Anticipate what might be observed. Connecting observations to the planning process allows teachers to monitor instruction, to anticipate or imagine what will happen in a lesson, and to adapt accordingly.

In your classroom

As you plan, consider what you will look for as you observe students engaging in mathematics learning. Keep a record of observations (use fig. 5.1), as observations can provide a pattern of student performance that might be useful for assessments of student progress, providing feedback to students, or guiding conferences with parents. A record of observations can also influence the pace of lessons, decision making within a lesson, and additional planning and instruction.

Interviews

Use of the interview as a formative assessment tool has a long history and includes connections to the related fields of mathematics and special education (Weaver 1955; Ginsburg 1997; Fennell 1998). Our motivation for including the interview technique as one of the CBFAs is that it provides the obvious follow-up to an observation a teacher might make when implementing a lesson. An interview allows the teacher to spend a few valuable minutes "digging deeper" with an individual student or perhaps a small group of students. In our continuing work with these CBFA techniques we have found it important to communicate that the use of an interview is not based on a deficit model. The interview may occur because of a particularly creative or advanced response just as easily as it may be a response to a misconception. In essence, the goal of the interview is to get a glimpse of what the child is thinking. We have used the questions below to help guide the use of an interview.

1. What would make you decide to work with a student one-on-one or with a small group of students?

2. What questions might you ask? How might the questions be different for particular students?

3. What will you anticipate from students? (Consider understandings *and* possible misconceptions.)

4. What follow-up questions might you ask?

Responses to the questions above might relate to examining a student's understanding of a mathematical concept, learning more about a strategy being used, extending student thinking, or assessing comprehension of a task to be solved. Depending on the student response, follow-up questions can center on a variety of learner-related needs, such as the confidence level of the student in extending a response or in taking it another direction (e.g., "Is your response reasonable?"). The interview prompt (fig. 5.2) was developed to help organize and guide the types of questions and responses that emerge with the use of this CBFA technique.

Assessing	Student Response	Feedback to Student(s)	Teacher Comments/ Observations
Conceptual Understanding			
Procedural Fluency			
Strategies Used			
Student Prerequisites and Misconceptions			
Disposition			
General Comment:			

Fig. 5.2. Interview prompt (Adapted from Larson 2012)

Guiding Teaching and Learning: Using Interviews

When: Like classroom observations, the interview can be used to guide and monitor teaching and learning on a daily basis. As with the observation, consider the use of an interview during the planning of a lesson.

How: An interview may be a one-on-one opportunity when the teacher decides to assess particular understandings as a student is being observed. It may also be conducted with a small group of students.

Considerations

- Carefully consider the specific purpose of the interview. What would the interviewer expect to learn by using this technique?

- Provide an appropriate mathematical task or a related question *and* allow the necessary time for the student(s) to process and respond, without teacher intervention. Such well-intended "assistance" sometimes results in the teacher, rather than the student, doing the mathematics.

- Consider regular use of a prompt (see fig. 5.2) to help guide the interview and provide a record of student responses. (*Note:* A Livescribe™ Smartpen or a screen capture tool may be helpful for establishing such records.)

In your classroom

In planning lessons, highlight the need and opportunities for differentiation within the lesson. Think about particular lesson "hot spots" that may prompt a one-on-one or small group interview. Regular consideration and use of an interview should help in recognizing the need not only to consider differentiation but also to recognize potential mathematical misconceptions, explore areas of advanced understandings, evaluate concerns related to student disposition, and provide a record of feedback. You can use fig. 5.2 for these purposes.

■ Show Me

We consider *show me* as a performance-based response to what a teacher observes, one that to an extent combines elements of the observation and the interview. Years ago, Sueltz, Boynton, and Sauble (1946) recognized that "observation, discussion, and interviews serve better than paper-pencil tests in evaluating a pupil's ability to understand the principles used" (p. 145). This is a "stop and drop" activity where a student, pair of students, small group, or perhaps the entire class might be asked to show how something works, how a problem was solved, how a particular manipulative material or related representation was used, etc. Teachers and mathematics leaders using the *show me* CBFA technique indicated that it validated information gathered from the observation and/or interview and that it provided a heads-up for redirecting student responses.

Guiding Teaching and Learning: Using Show Me

When: As teachers plan a lesson, thought should be given to particular "lesson bumps" where a *show me* may be helpful. While the *show me* could be paired regularly with student or class observations, and it could serve as prerequisite to an interview, the actual use of the *show me* will be related to the content focus of a lesson.

How: During planning, anticipate particular elements of the lesson where students can demonstrate what they are doing and why they are doing it. Perhaps the *show me* focuses on individual students responding to the use of particular representations (e.g., using double number lines to compare fractions).

Considerations

- The *show me* technique is frequently considered to be a way to show how particular procedures or representation tools are used. However, this technique is also useful for having students describe and demonstrate how they solved a problem. Considering the intent and products of what's to be *shown* is important.

- Consider whether to include different *show me*'s, in the same lesson, for particular students.

- Be open to considering a *show me* based on what is observed within a particular lesson. This is not to contradict thinking about planning for use of a *show me*; it is rather to recognize how the *show me* can be spontaneously implemented based on observing what is happening in the moment.

- Be prepared with regard to student response to the *show me*. Our experience has occasionally included students who could not or would not respond to the *show me* or who copied the responses of others.

In your classroom

As you plan your lesson, consider the aspects where you would want students to *show* what they are doing and/or what they have done. Such performance-based opportunities provide documentation of student thinking. Use of the *show me* will often involve strategic use of tools and representations or models. What you might observe may warrant an interview and might include a *show me* response, as all three of these formative assessment techniques are closely aligned. An example of a *show me* using the task that introduced this chapter would be to *show* and discuss, using a number line, who will finish first, second, and third on the trail walk. Responses provided from *show me* opportunities are useful to guide the pace of a lesson and, once again, provide you with responses not only to gauge student understandings but also to identify areas of instructional concern in the future.

■ Hinge Questions

Hinge questions (Wiliam 2011) provide a check for understanding/proficiency at a "hinge point" in a lesson. Stated differently, the success of the lesson hinges on responses to such questions, as they provide an indication of whether the teacher can move from one important idea/concept/skill to another. Such responses directly in*form* both planning and instruction.

At issue in creating and posing hinge-point questions, referenced here as hinge questions, is making sure that the question serves as an "on the ground" assessor of what students should know/understand/be able to do. Ideally students respond within one minute and teachers analyze and interpret responses within fifteen seconds, noting that if much more time is taken, the risk of students getting off task is increased (Wiliam 2011).

Use of the hinge question goes back to the planning of the lesson and deciding what is important, both mathematically and pedagogically. Our sense is that the hinge question is the "deal breaker" query that helps the teacher determine the next steps in planning and instruction. The hinge question planning tool (fig. 5.3) has been used to help teachers frame the development of a hinge question as they plan a lesson. We have also found it helpful to actually try out hinge questions with colleagues within a grade-level professional learning community. Trial opportunities also provide teachers with occasions to consider varied hinge question formats. For example, consider the two related questions below:

1. Can you name a fraction that is greater than $3/4$?

2. Which of the fractions below is $> 3/4$?

    A. $1/4$

    B. $1/2$

    C. $4/4$

    D. $3/5$

Note that question 1 provides for a whole-group response with a full range of possible responses, whereas question 2 is a specially developed multiple-choice item, where students raise their hands if they select choices A–D as a response to the question. A quick review of hands raised (or responses on an EPR [every pupil response] device), with particular misconceptions carefully selected as item distracters, provides the teacher with more specific possibilities for instruction based on the student responses, which could include a *show me* activity as a follow-up to the response.

Hinge Question:		
	Yes	No
Will the hinge question assess important mathematical understandings of the day?		
Will students understand the question?		
Will students be able to respond in about a minute?		
Will expected responses be such that they can be analyzed and interpreted quickly?		

General consideration:
Will responses assist in shaping planning for tomorrow's lesson?
    (circle one) YES   NO (if no, revise hinge question)

HOW?

Fig. 5.3. Hinge question planning tool

Guiding Teaching and Learning: Using Hinge Questions

When: The hinge question is an important element of every lesson. Responses to the hinge question and their analysis essentially identify the "starting line" for planning the next day's lesson.

How: Creating hinge questions and determining the amount of time dedicated to pose and assess hinge question responses expeditiously is part of the planning process. Such questions must truly capture the importance of the lesson.

Considerations

- As with all of the CBFAs, time must be spent during lesson preparation not only to create the hinge question but also to anticipate student responses.

- Teacher content and pedagogical knowledge will influence the framing and analysis of responses to hinge questions. This is particularly true for multiple-choice hinge questions.

- Regularly monitoring student responses to the hinge question is critical, as is the preparedness to adjust the question as needed.

In your classroom

As noted above, the drafting of hinge questions occurs during the planning of a lesson. Creating and implementing the hinge question will help you in identifying the most important aspect(s) of the mathematics lesson. As the mathematics lesson proceeds, your observations may suggest that the hinge question be revised. Such "on the spot" thinking and revision is important. Figure 5.3 can serve as a guide in planning these important questions, as the responses provide a profile of class understandings regarding the major mathematics emphasis of a particular lesson. It will also be useful to keep a record of hinge questions used and brief notes regarding their success as an aide for future planning.

■ Exit Tasks

"Effective formative assessment involves using tasks that elicit evidence of students' learning, then using that evidence to inform subsequent instruction" (NCTM 2014, p. 95). Exit tasks are end-of-the-lesson formative assessments. Deliberately defined here as tasks used to close a lesson, they vary from the more commonly referenced exit ticket/slip. The intent of the entry (or exit) ticket (or slip) strategy (Fisher and Frey 2004) is to help students summarize and reflect on their learning. The exit task is designed to provide a capstone problem or task that captures the major focus of the mathematics lesson for that day or perhaps the past several days. As with the hinge question, student responses to the exit task help in identifying needs and in the planning for the next day's lesson, including considerations related to grouping and differentiation. The exit task provides a product of actual work samples for teachers to review and keep on hand to assist in planning future lessons. As with the hinge question, this CBFA technique is enhanced when school or grade-level teacher learning communities work together in the creation, use, analysis, and revision of the exit tasks.

Guiding Teaching and Learning: Using Exit Tasks

When: Creating and/or locating, implementing, and analyzing an exit task is demanding and as such this technique may be more realistically used one to three times a week rather than every day.

How: Time is needed to consider how exit tasks will be implemented as well as the length and depth of the task. This is an excellent grade-level professional learning community opportunity. As with the other CBFA techniques presented in this chapter, anticipating student responses is part of the planning-teaching-assessment process. The time needed for responses will depend on the mathematics being assessed and the length and depth of the exit task. Meaningful exit tasks are not trivial, as they serve as a barometer of the students' understandings.

Considerations

- Organize planning time to interpret student responses/solutions to exit tasks, and use responses to provide feedback to students, consider student groupings, and, of course, in*form* planning for the next day.

- Recognize that written responses from the exit task provide documentation to support differentiation needs and challenges. The exit task responses can be used to provide justification for classroom groupings, which will affect planning for the next day's lesson.

In your classroom

As noted, the exit task provides end-of-lesson documentation of understandings and related mathematical proficiencies. It can assess important mathematical concepts and skills, and it will most likely be focused on problem solving and reasoning. Consider providing class time for completing the exit task and for discussing the solution strategies used. Reviewing how your students do with the exit task provides you with clear direction for the next instructional steps. Monitoring the success of your exit tasks can provide you with a collection of important problems and tasks for future years. As with the documentation of several of the classroom-based formative assessment techniques presented in this chapter, responses to the exit tasks will help define student achievement profiles that may be communicated during parent-teacher conferences.

■ Classroom-Based Formative Assessments: When and How Much?

Our continuing work with the CBFA techniques presented here has indicated that teachers should be able to dynamically engage the observation, interview, and *show me* techniques within any lesson. These more informal techniques serve as lesson guides. They monitor the progress of the lesson and their use helps to define pace, misconceptions, and potential next steps.

One of our teacher leader reviewers defined the hinge question as the "temperature gauge" for a lesson. Others recognize that the response to the hinge question, whether the question is open-ended or a specially crafted multiple-choice item, is the deciding element for the next steps taken regarding planning and teaching. A hinge question is an important element in the planning, and, of course, in the assessment, of every lesson. The exit task, while providing an individual response for each student, and thus written documentation about understandings and proficiency, takes more time (creating, editing, using, review of student responses) with optimum use being one to three days a week for most classrooms.

■ Conclusion: The Critical Importance of Classroom-Based Formative Assessment

Wiliam and Thompson (2007) suggest very poignantly that formative assessment involves students and teachers using evidence of learning to adapt teaching and learning to meet immediate learning needs, and that this is done minute-to-minute and day-to-day. The potential of formative assessment to guide teaching and learning coupled with the teacher background needs relative to implementing such assessments helped to initiate and shape the CBFAs as an understandable, usable, and valuable everyday palette of assessment techniques designed to guide mathematics teaching and learning.

(*Note:* The authors acknowledge and appreciate the comments and suggestions of our ems&tl Project elementary mathematics specialist colleagues and graduate students within McDaniel College's Elementary Mathematics Instructional Leader [EMIL] program on earlier versions of this chapter.)

References

Black, Paul, and Dylan Wiliam. "Inside the Black Box: Raising Standards through Classroom Assessment." *Phi Delta Kappan* 92, vol. 1 (September 2010): 81–90.

Fennell, Francis (Skip). "A Through the Lens Look at Moments in Classroom Assessment." In *Classroom Assessment in Mathematics,* edited by George W. Bright and Jeane M. Joyner. Lanham, Md.: United Press of America, 1998.

Fisher, Douglas, and Nancy Frey. *Improving Adolescent Literacy: Strategies at Work.* Upper Saddle River, N.J.: Pearson Prentice Hall, 2004.

Freudenthal, Hans. *Mathematics as an Educational Task.* New York: Springer Publishing, 1973.

Ginsburg, Herbert P. *Entering the Child's Mind: The Clinical Interview in Psychological Research and Practice.* New York: Cambridge University Press, 1997.

Larson, Matthew R., Francis (Skip) Fennell, Thomasenia Lott Adams, Juli K. Dixon, Beth McCord Kobett, and Jonathan A. Wray. *Common Core Mathematics in a PLC at Work™: Grades 3–5.* Bloomington, Ind.: Solution Tree Press, 2012

National Council of Teachers of Mathematics (NCTM). *Principles to Actions: Ensuring Mathematical Success for All.* Reston, Va: NCTM, 2014.

National Governors Association Center for Best Practices and Council of Chief State School Officers (NGA Center and CCSSO). *Common Core State Standards for Mathematics.* Washington, D.C.: NGA Center and CCSSO, 2010.

National Mathematics Advisory Panel (NMAP). *Foundations for Success: The Final Report of the National Mathematics Advisory Panel.* Washington, D.C.: U.S. Department of Education, 2008.

Popham, James. "Formative Assessment's Advocatable Moment." *Education Week* 32, no. 15 (2013): 29.

Shepard, Lorrie A. "Will Commercialism Enable or Destroy Formative Assessment?" In *The Future of Assessment: Shaping Teaching and Learning,* edited by Carol A. Dwyer. Mahwah, N.J.: Lawrence Erlbaum Associates, 2007.

Sueltz, Ben A., Holmes Boynton, and Irene Sauble. "The Measurement of Understandings in Elementary School Mathematics." In *Measurement of Understanding: 45th Yearbook of the National Society for the Study of Education, Part I.* Chicago: University of Chicago Press, 1946.

Weaver, J. Fred. "Big Dividends from Little Interviews." *Arithmetic Teacher* 2 (April 1955) 40–47.

Wiliam, Dylan. "Keeping Learning on Track: Classroom Assessment and the Regulation of Learning." In *Second Handbook of Research on Mathematics Teaching and Learning,* edited by Frank K. Lester, Jr., pp. 1051–98. Charlotte, N.C.: Information Age Publishing, 2007.

———. *Embedded Formative Assessment.* Bloomington, Ind.: Solution Tree Press, 2011.

Wiliam, Dylan, and Marnie Thompson. "Integrating Assessment with Instruction: What Will It Take to Make It Work?" In *The Future of Assessment: Shaping Teaching and Learning,* edited by Carol Anne Dwyer. Mahwah, N.J.: Lawrence Erlbaum Associates, 2007.

PART II

Design of Assessment Tools and Strategies

Introduction

Denisse R. Thompson, *University of South Florida, Tampa*

Assessment is "an important tool for understanding the knowledge that students are constructing, the meanings they are assigning to mathematical ideas, and the progress that they are making toward achieving mathematical power" (Webb 1993, p. 2). Since the introduction of the *Curriculum and Evaluation Standards* in 1989 and the subsequent *Assessment Standards for School Mathematics* in 1995, both from the National Council of Teachers of Mathematics (NCTM 1989, 1995), many educators have attempted to broaden their assessment practices to collect evidence of learning from instruments other than paper-and-pencil tests. Issues have naturally arisen about how to develop alternative instruments, how to evaluate the evidence obtained from such instruments, and what potential benefits might arise from using them. The five chapters in this section provide insight into these issues and illustrate how evidence from assessment is used "(1) to examine the effects of the tasks, discourse, and learning environment on students' mathematical knowledge, skills, and dispositions; (2) to make instruction more responsive to students' needs; and (3) to ensure that every student is gaining mathematical power" (NCTM 1995, p. 45).

In the first chapter in this section, **Using Task-Based Interviews to Assess Early Understanding of Number,** Young-Loveridge and Bicknell focus on the value of interviews to assess students' depth of mathematical knowledge. Although focused at the primary level, this chapter highlights the value of interviews when students may have limited literacy skills, particularly the written literacy skills needed for paper-and-pencil tests. As such, it suggests the potential of interviews for use with English language learners who may be overly quiet or shy; interviews provide an opportunity for students to interact with the teacher in one-on-one situations and demonstrate their knowledge. In addition, the authors discuss the value of using cultural contexts in interviews as well as strategies for minimizing power dynamics between teacher and student that might intimidate a student, thereby hindering their ability to share what they know.

Are Standards for Mathematical Practice Overlooked in Geometry Textbooks' Chapter Tests? describes the design and use of a rubric for analyzing the written chapter tests included within the textbooks that students regularly use. Although the other chapters in this section focus on rubrics used with individuals to assess their understanding, mathematical habits, or engagement with discourse, in this chapter Sears and colleagues demonstrate that a rubric can also be a powerful tool to assess potential opportunities for learning provided in the resources used within the instructional context. As educators focus more on the mathematical practices of the Common Core (National Governors Association Center for Best Practices and Council of Chief State School Officers [NGA Center and CCSSO] 2010) or the mathematical processes of the NCTM *Principles and Standards* (2000), they need means to determine whether their instruction and related assessments are aligned with that focus. This chapter provides one means to make such determinations, and it illustrates how to make appropriate modifications when such practices are not evident.

Using an Observational Rubric to Facilitate Change in Undergraduate Classroom Norms focuses on challenges when changing classroom practice to engage students in discourse around rich problems. In particular, Elrod and Strayer focus on dilemmas they faced in validating the importance of discourse but still assessing with required written tests. As they developed a rubric to include discourse as part of test grades, new challenges arose. The refinements and iterations in rubric development are useful reminders of the continual need to reflect and revise assessment tools to ensure they function as intended. By sharing implementation strategies relative to the revised rubric, the authors provide useful information about how to engage students with the rubric in ways that enhance their mathematical growth and ability to self-assess their own learning as well as that of their peers. Although set in an undergraduate college algebra course, the issues, challenges, and implementations are applicable across the educational spectrum and illustrate the use of assessment *for* learning.

Communal Development and Evolution of a Course Rubric for Proof Writing addresses an important mathematical process/practice, namely, reasoning and proof. Bleiler and colleagues discuss the development of their proof-writing rubric with students pursuing mathematics as a major or minor or planning to become a secondary mathematics teacher. However, the process of rubric development could just as easily have been used in K–12 classrooms in which justification and reasoning are expected and valued. By having course participants develop a rubric for what constitutes a valid proof, students had ownership of the rubric and were encouraged to view it as a work in progress that was refined over the duration of the course. The use of the rubric, with appropriate feedback by the instructors when assessing proofs both formatively and summatively, provided further validation of students' work. As the authors note, the rubric provides an illustration of assessment *as* learning, because the tool became a means for students to learn proof.

In the final chapter in part II, **Secondary Teachers' Mathematical Habits of Mind: A Paper-and-Pencil Assessment,** Sword and colleagues tackle a difficult but important area to assess: the habits of mind that influence how individuals approach mathematical tasks and the extent to which those ways are similar to approaches used by mathematicians. Although the rubric was developed for research purposes and not evaluative purposes, the authors give insight into how such a rubric might be used to focus professional development activities to strengthen such programs, as well as to determine the impact they have on how secondary teachers think about mathematics. Readers might consider how the principles embodied within the development of the rubric might be used within secondary classrooms to help students think about mathematics in a variety of ways.

As you read the chapters in this section, consider the following questions:

- How might you use the principles in the development of the rubrics within these chapters to create rubrics for practices that you want to encourage within your own classroom?

- What issues and challenges in the development and implementation of the rubrics within this section resonated with your own experiences in using rubrics? What lessons from these chapters are particularly applicable to your situation?

- What might teachers gain from having students participate in the development of a class rubric for use throughout the year? How might teachers encourage students to use such rubrics to monitor their own learning and to support the learning of their peers?

- What do these chapters suggest for your own further learning on issues related to the design of assessment tools?

References

National Council of Teachers of Mathematics (NCTM). *Curriculum and Evaluation Standards for School Mathematics*. Reston, Va.: NCTM, 1989.

————. *Assessment Standards for School Mathematics*. Reston, Va.: NCTM, 1995.

————. *Principles and Standards for School Mathematics*. Reston, Va.: NCTM, 2000.

National Governors Association Center for Best Practices and Council of Chief State School Officers (NGA Center and CCSSO). *Common Core State Standards for Mathematics*. Washington, D.C.: NGA Center and CCSSO, 2010.

Webb, Norman L. "Assessment for the Mathematics Classroom." In *Assessment in the Mathematics Classroom*, edited by Norman L. Webb and Arthur F. Coxford, pp. 1–6. Reston, Va.: NCTM, 1993.

CHAPTER 6

Using Task-Based Interviews to Assess Early Understanding of Number

Jenny Young-Loveridge and Brenda Bicknell, *University of Waikato, Hamilton, New Zealand*

In this chapter, we describe the design and implementation of a structured task-based interview that was used to assess the mathematics understanding of a diverse group of five- and six-year-old children. We focus on tasks that employ multiplication and division contexts, as well as on the use of familiar materials and cultural artifacts, language, attitudes, the role of the interviewer and power relationships, and the value of the interview as a formative assessment tool. The interviews were part of a design study that aimed to provide children with learning opportunities and challenges within the context of multiplication and division, with the goal of developing greater understanding of part-whole relationships in mathematics.

Research has demonstrated that many young children arrive at elementary school with considerable knowledge and understanding of number, although there are substantial differences among children in levels of proficiency. Frameworks have been developed to explain these differences and to describe progressions in mathematical thinking (Bobis et al. 2005; Department for Education [England], 2013; Ministry of Education [New Zealand] 2008; National Governors Association Center for Best Practices and Council of Chief State School Officers [NGA Center and CCSSO] 2010). Assessment tools have been developed alongside these frameworks to provide insights into children's knowledge and understanding that can be aligned with particular stages.

Traditionally in mathematics, pencil-and-paper tests are used to assess students' mathematical proficiency. Written tests require students to have sufficient literacy skills to read the question and either write a response or make a choice among several possible alternatives. Young children's literacy skills are not necessarily sufficient to do this. It is difficult, if not impossible, to ascertain the strategies used by young children to solve a problem using the written test as an assessment tool (Kiplinger, Haug, and Abedi 2000). Therefore, interviews are a more appropriate way to gain insights into the mathematical thinking of young children (Ginsburg 1997, 2009).

A carefully constructed task-based interview can provide rich, detailed information about students' underlying cognitive competence (Clarke, Clarke, and Roche 2011). This data can be used to inform teachers' instructional decision making for the development of student knowledge and understanding. Interviews can also be used to explore student attitude and motivation. Another advantage of the individual diagnostic interview is that "quiet achievers" are given the opportunity to converse with their teacher and show what they know and can do (Clarke, Clarke, and Roche 2011).

Interview Design

The purpose of the interview described here was to provide baseline assessment data for an exploratory study aimed at supporting the development of part-whole understanding through the use of multiplication and division contexts. Part-whole understanding is evident when students break apart (partition) and recombine numbers to find solutions, instead of using counting strategies. The tasks were carefully chosen to include key knowledge and strategies underpinning the domain of multiplication and division. For example, knowledge included counting by ones, twos, fives, and tens; recall of known facts; subitizing of stylized number patterns to identify knowledge of quantities without counting; and place-value understanding. Children's use of strategies was assessed using contextualized problems involving addition, subtraction, multiplication, and division.

The tasks were ordered, beginning with easy items so that all children experienced success, and then became progressively harder to cater to a range of abilities and to counteract possible ceiling effects for gifted and talented learners (Assouline and Lupkowski-Shoplik 2011). The interviewer stopped a particular task once it was clear that the child had reached the limits of his or her knowledge and understanding in that particular domain. The tasks were constructed so that connections could be revealed between the knowledge and strategies for solving problems involving the four operations. Some tasks involved several items at varying levels of difficulty. For example, assessment of known facts included single-digit doubles (e.g., 1 + 1, 5 + 5) and ended with division by ten with remainder (e.g., 104 ÷ 10).

Selected Tasks

The specific tasks described in this section have been extracted from the diagnostic interview and focus on multiplication, division, and place-value understanding. The following three tasks (groups of 2, 5, and 10) were used to assess a child's understanding of multiplication. In the first task (6 × 2), the researcher placed six small kete (miniature woven flax baskets), each containing two shells, on the table in front of the child (fig. 6.1). The child was told, "Each kete has two shells inside it." The first kete was upended and the shells tipped out for the child to see the two shells associated with the one kete. The shells were then put back and the kete returned to the row. The interviewer then asked, "How many shells are there altogether?" as she made a circular gesture with her hand above the row of six kete. The kete task was particularly interesting because unlike the other multiplication tasks, the children could not see the shells inside the kete and had to visualize them in order to find the total. The five- and six-year-old children in our study used a range of strategies to solve the kete task. Some children counted by ones and pointed to each kete twice. Others counted by twos to work out the answer, and a few used known facts to derive their answers (e.g., 6 + 6 = 12 or 6 × 2 = 12).

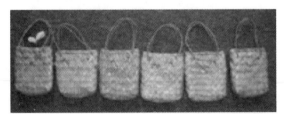

Fig. 6.1. A photograph of the kete used for the 6 × 2 task.
(*Note:* Each kete has two shells inside, as shown above the first kete.)

The second task, Monkeys and Bananas (4 × 5), showed a picture of four monkeys each with a group of five bananas and children were asked, "How many bananas are there altogether?" (fig. 6.2). Some children counted the bananas by ones, while others counted by fives. A few children used knowledge of doubles facts for five, combining two bunches of five to make ten, then two groups of ten to make twenty.

Fig. 6.2. A picture shown for the Monkey and Bananas task

In the third task, Cupcakes (3 × 10), three rows of ten cupcakes were presented, and the interviewer asked, "How many cupcakes are there altogether?" (fig. 6.3). As with the previous tasks, children used a range of strategies, including counting by ones, fives, and tens, as well as recall of number facts (3 × 10).

Fig. 6.3. The picture shown for the Cupcakes tasks (3 × 10 and 30 ÷ 5)

The tasks that were designed to assess children's understanding of division included both partitive (sharing) and quotitive (measurement) division. The first division task focused on halving collections of beans and included groups of 4 and 8 beans (concrete materials), and progressed to 20 and 100 beans (to be imagined by the child). The second division task (quotitive) asked the child to put ten baby socks into pairs and to find the number of pairs. The next division task (quotitive) used the array of 30 cupcakes, and asked the children, "If the cupcakes were put into boxes of five, how many boxes would be needed?" This was followed by a partitive division task in which children were shown a picture of a block of chocolate divided into eight equal pieces (fig. 6.4). They were asked, "How could we share all the chocolate fairly among four children so they each get the same number of pieces?"

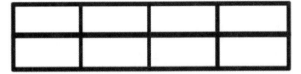

Fig. 6.4. The picture shown for the Chocolate Bar task (8 ÷ 4)

A quotitive division task was the following word problem: "There are 23 eggs. Each carton holds 10 eggs. How many full cartons are there?" If the children gave a correct answer, they were instructed to "draw what this looks like, using ten-frames." In class the children had solved problems involving quotitive division into groups of ten with remainder, using egg cartons of ten and Unifix cubes for the eggs, and they had then drawn their solutions using ten-frames. One child's drawing for this assessment task is shown in figure 6.5. This division task provided insights into children's understanding of division as measurement or repeated subtraction (quotitive division).

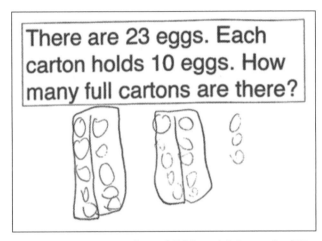

There are 23 eggs. Each carton holds 10 eggs. How many full cartons are there?

Fig. 6.5. A representation by a child (aged 6.2 years) of 23 ÷ 10

Several tasks were designed to assess children's place-value knowledge and understanding. Understanding place value requires students to understand part-whole relationships and to be able to partition numbers into "tens" and "ones." In one task, the children were given a diagram showing 2 ten-sticks and 4 single boxes. They were first asked to determine how many boxes in the picture altogether and to write this as a numeral. The interviewer then circled the "4" and asked the children to indicate "which boxes does the 4 part of 24 mean?" The interviewer circled the boxes indicated by the child and then asked, "Which boxes does the 2 part of 24 mean?" After circling the boxes indicated by the child, the interviewer asked, "So what is the 2 in 24 telling you?" One child (aged 5.9 years) made the responses shown in figure 6.6. When this child was asked about the meaning of 2 in 24, he said, "That's how many tens there are." This response contrasts with those of his peers who indicated that just two boxes should be circled to show the meaning of 2 in 24. Some children who had indicated that the 2 ten-sticks should be circled for "2" were not able to explain that the 2 in 24 meant 2 tens.

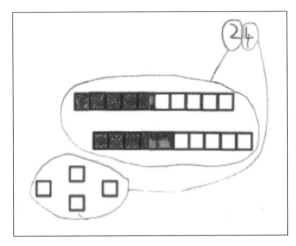

Fig. 6.6. One child's responses showing that he understood
the meaning of the digits in 24

■ Addressing the Needs of Diverse Learners

The children in our study were a group of diverse learners that included Māori (indigenous people of New Zealand) and Pasifika (immigrants from Pacific Islands nations) students, and English Language Learners (ELLs). In designing the assessment tasks, careful consideration was given to context, because context is recognized as a powerful determinant of student performance in mathematics (van den Heuval-Panhuizen 2005). The term *context* is often used to refer to real-life situations or ones that are imaginable for the child, as well as those of cultural significance (Neel 2005). If the context used in the assessment task is unfamiliar to students, then it is likely to affect students' abilities to solve the problem (Boaler 1993). We therefore presented multiplication and division tasks using representations of real-life contexts, such as monkeys with bunches of bananas, arrays of cupcakes, and chocolate bars.

We also incorporated concrete materials (manipulatives) into the design of the task-based interview, as "concrete objects may help the child to *see* what the problem is and also may external-ize the child's thinking processes" (Ginsburg 1997, p. 124). The interviewer had an opportunity to observe the children's actions on the objects, and this provided insights into key aspects of their mathematical thinking. These concrete materials included cultural artifacts (e.g., the kete and shells) as one way of acknowledging Māori and Pasifika heritage and culture. The use of cultural artifacts "enables one to teach and assess mathematics in an imaginative and creative way that both respects diversity and extends the understanding to a personal context" (Neel 2005, p. 54).

The interview did not require children to have reading or writing skills, but it required an understanding of spoken English and recognition of mathematical symbols. The ELLs faced particular challenges because they needed to understand the interviewer's questions and to com-municate their thinking and understanding. In the mathematics register, words have particular meanings. For example, the word *pair* (not *pear*) must be interpreted in the context of a mathemat-ics problem. One of the tasks required children to put ten baby socks into pairs. If children did not respond correctly to the question "How many pairs of socks are there?" it was followed by, "How many groups of two socks are there?" This alternative question took into account the linguistic challenges for ELLs of being asked about "pairs."

The interviewer also used gestures to help ELLs make sense of the questions and better understand the interviewer's intentions (Goldin-Meadow and Alibali 2013). For example, the interviewer made a circular hand movement above a group of objects when asking "How many [objects] are there altogether?" This may have helped to provide fair (and valid) opportunities for all children to demonstrate what they knew and could do, and was an attempt to minimize the English language demands of the tasks and reduce inequities (Abedi 2004).

■ Affective Dimension

In addition to assessing children's early understanding of number, we assessed their attitudes toward mathematics learning using a four-point Likert-type "face" scale (fig. 6.7). It was considered important to include both affective and cognitive dimensions of mathematics learning (Ma and Kishor 1997). Beliefs about ability, attitudes, and dispositions are associated with the willingness to take risks in mathematical problem solving (Malmivuori 2006). The interview provided an opportunity for the children to take risks in engaging with the tasks as well as to show their mathematical thinking.

The children's understanding of the scale was checked by asking them to indicate which face shows "very happy," "very sad," "a bit happy," or "a bit sad." They were then asked, "How much do you like doing mathematics at school? Point to the face that shows how much you like doing mathematics at school." The use of the "faces" enhanced the reliability of the assessment by minimizing cultural and linguistic barriers that might otherwise have influenced children's understanding. The scale used an even number of points in order to minimize "fence-sitting" choices between the positive and negative expressions (Garland 1991). The items were taken from the National Education Monitoring Project survey (Crooks, Smith, and Flockton 2010). This type of assessment task can be useful for teachers in identifying individual children's attitudes toward mathematics, as well as for gaining a sense of how positive a group (e.g., the whole class or year group) is toward mathematics learning.

Fig. 6.7. A four-point "face" scale used to assess children's attitudes toward learning mathematics

■ The Role of the Interviewer and Power Relationships

At the start of the interview, two soft toys, Dog and Rabbit, were introduced to the children to minimize any discomfort or anxiety, to motivate, and to reduce the power differential between the adult and child (Kuchah and Pinter 2012; Robinson and Kellett 2004). Children were encouraged to help Dog and Rabbit learn about numbers by explaining their thinking to the toy animals rather than the interviewer. This motivated the children to engage with the tasks in a more age-appropriate context. The children were positioned as the experts "teaching" Dog and Rabbit (two soft toys) about mathematics. For example, children were given a collection of wooden blocks, which the interviewer suggested could be imagined as "biscuits," and were then asked to give particular quantities to Dog and Rabbit. The power differential between adult and child can also be minimized by interviewing the child in a setting where they feel comfortable and at ease with the adult (Robinson and Kellert 2004).

■ Conclusion

The assessment tool described in this chapter used a variety of tasks to obtain quality information about children's mathematical knowledge, understanding, and attitudes. The interview provided an organized way of gathering deep insights into a child's mathematical thinking that could be used to guide a teacher's instructional decision making. A single task could be selected from the diagnostic interview protocol and used to make systematic observations of how a particular child engages with the task. The teacher could then observe and record how the child makes sense of the problem, uses materials to solve it, interprets language and symbols, and explains and shows his or her thinking. For example, the child may solve a multiplication problem by counting in ones or by multiples (e.g., twos or fives), use known facts (e.g., doubles), or use groups of ten. The teacher may use the information to support the child's growth toward more sophisticated strategies for solving problems.

Although the interview was designed for use with individual children, the tasks could be incorporated into the regular classroom program. In the classroom setting, the teacher could observe children working on such tasks and gain similar insights over time to inform instructional decision making. This formative assessment approach reflects current thinking and research in mathematics education that focuses on the use of assessment *for* learning.

Acknowledgment

The task-based interview was designed for a research project funded by the Teaching and Learning Research Initiative (TLRI) through the New Zealand Council for Educational Research.

References

Abedi, Jamal. "The No Child Left Behind Act and English Language Learners: Assessment and Accountability Issues." *Educational Researcher* 33, no. 1 (2004): 4–14.

Assouline, Susan G., and Ann Lupkowski-Shoplik. *Developing Math Talent: A Comprehensive Guide to Math Education for Gifted Students in Elementary and Middle School.* 2nd ed. Waco, Tex.: Prufrock Press, 2011.

Boaler, Jo. "The Role of Contexts in the Mathematics Classroom: Do They Make Mathematics More 'Real'?" *For the Learning of Mathematics* 13, no. 2 (1993): 12–17.

Bobis, Janette, Barbara Clarke, Doug Clarke, Gill Thomas, Robert Wright, Jenny Young-Loveridge, and Peter Gould. "Supporting Teachers in the Development of Young Children's Mathematical Thinking: Three Large Scale Cases." *Mathematics Education Research Journal* 16, no. 3 (2005): 27–57.

Clarke, Doug, Barbara Clarke, and Anne Roche. "Building Teachers' Expertise in Understanding, Assessing, and Developing Children's Mathematical Thinking: The Power of Task-Based, One-to-One Assessment Interviews." *ZDM Mathematics Education* 43 (2011): 901–13.

Crooks, Terry, John Smith, and Lester Flockton. *National Educational Monitoring Project: Mathematics Assessment Results 2009*. Wellington, New Zealand: Ministry of Education, 2010.

Department for Education [England]. *The National Curriculum in England: Framework Document for Consultation*. 2013. https://media.education.gov.uk/assets/files/pdf/n/national%20curriculum%20consultation%20-%20framework%20document.pdf.

Garland, Ron. "The Midpoint on a Rating Scale: Is It Desirable?" *Marketing Bulletin* 2 (1991): 66–70.

Ginsburg, Herbert P. *Entering the Child's Mind*. Cambridge, U.K.: Cambridge University Press, 1997.

———. "The Challenge of Formative Assessment in Mathematics Education: Children's Minds, Teachers' Minds." *Human Development* 52 (2009): 109–28.

Goldin-Meadow, Sara, and Martha W. Alibali. "Gesture's Role in Speaking, Learning, and Creating Language." *Annual Review of Psychology* 64 (2013): 257–83.

Kiplinger, Vonda L., Carolyn A. Haug, and Jamal Abedi. "Measuring Math—Not Reading—on a Math Assessment: A Language Accommodations Study of English Language Learners and Other Special Populations." Paper presented at the Annual Meeting of the American Educational Research Association, New Orleans, La., April 24–28, 2000. http://files.eric.ed.gov/fulltext/ED441813.pdf.

Kuchah Kuchah, Harry, and Annamaria Pinter. "'Was This an Interview?' Breaking the Power Barrier in Adult-Child Interviews in an African Context." *Issues in Educational Research* 22, no. 3 (2012): 283–97.

Ma, Xin, and Nand Kishor. "Assessing the Relationship between Attitudes towards Mathematics and Achievement in Mathematics: A Meta-Analysis." *Journal for Research in Mathematics Education* 28, no. 1 (1997): 26–47.

Malmivuori, Marja-Liisa. "Affect and Self-Regulation." *Educational Studies in Mathematics* 63, no. 2 (2006): 149–63.

Ministry of Education [New Zealand]. *Book 1: The Number Framework: Revised edition 2007*. Wellington, New Zealand: Ministry of Education, 2008. http://www.nzmaths.co.nz/sites/default/files/images/NumBook1.pdf.

National Governors Association Center for Best Practices and Council of Chief State School Officers (NGA Center and CCSSO). *Common Core State Standards for Mathematics*. Washington, D.C.: NGA Center and CCSSO, 2010.

Neel, Kanwal S. "Addressing Diversity in the Mathematics Classroom with Cultural Artifacts." *Mathematics Teaching in the Middle School* 11, no. 2 (2005): 54–61.

Robinson, Chris, and Mary Kellert. "Power." In *Doing Research with Children and Young People*, edited by Sandy Fraser, Vicki Lewis, Sharon Ding, Mary Kellert, and Chris Robinson, pp. 81–96. London: Sage, 2004.

van den Heuval-Panhuizen, Marja. "The Role of Contexts in Assessment Problems in Mathematics." *For the Learning of Mathematics* 25, no. 2 (2005): 2–9, 23.

CHAPTER 7

Are Standards for Mathematical Practice Overlooked in Geometry Textbooks' Chapter Tests?

Ruthmae Sears, *University of South Florida, Tampa*
Ilyas Karadeniz, *University of South Florida, Tampa*
Kenneth Butler, *University of South Florida, Tampa*
Dix Pettey, *University of Missouri, Columbia*

Within geometry, the Common Core State Standards for Mathematics (CCSSM) (National Governors Association Center for Best Practices and Council of Chief State School Officers [NGA Center and CCSSO] 2010) identifies six content domains that embody multiple mathematical clusters. Additionally, CCSSM documents Standards for Mathematical Practice (SMPs) that explicate processes students should exhibit when learning mathematics. The content and practice standards are designed to promote students' development of a conceptual understanding of mathematics, fluency in mathematical procedures, engagement in reasoning, and mathematical communication skills. Although CCSSM is important, it is not effective if not connected with assessment. Assessment should be a coherent process, it should reflect the mathematics deemed important, and the results of the assessment should ultimately be to further students' learning.

Teachers often use the tests and quizzes provided by the textbooks for assessment purposes. Therefore, it is critical to reflect on the extent to which the content and practice standards are emphasized on assessments within textbooks. Confrey and Krupa (2012) noted, "Since the mathematical practices are presented independent from the content standards, there is a risk that the practices will be underemphasized" (p. 13). Therefore, in preparing for assessment in the era of CCSSM, we need to examine the extent to which textbooks adequately prepare students for assessment of mathematical content as well as the SMPs.

Many textbooks include assessment components to develop students' test-taking strategies and prepare them for summative assessments. This is done without clearly indicating the extent that such assessments emphasize mathematical practices. Hunsader, Thompson, and Zorin (2013) coded elementary mathematics assessments that accompany textbooks on mathematical processes (reasoning, communication, connections, role of graphics, and translation of representations) and noted that certain processes are more evident in assessments than others. The authors concluded that the accompanying assessments for textbook curricula might not adequately integrate mathematical practices and processes, even if such attributes are evident in the textbooks. For instance, "reasoning" is identified in three of the eight SMPs; however, researchers found that within the exposition and exercise sections of secondary mathematics textbooks, there are few reasoning and proof tasks (Davis 2012; Sears and Chávez 2014; Thompson, Senk, and Johnson 2012). More particularly, within the context of geometry, Otten, Males, and Gilbertson (2013) noted that students had greater opportunities to engage in reasoning-and-proving activities in the earlier chapters of the textbook (chapters 2–7) when compared to later chapters. These research findings indicate that mathematical practices and processes, such as reasoning and proof, may not be given adequate attention across all chapters within textbooks.

In this work, we focused on chapter tests in geometry textbooks and sought to answer the following question: To what extent do chapter tests in two geometry textbooks address the SMPs? The chapter tests are practice assessments for students, and they likely mirror those used by teachers for summative purposes. Thus, gaining insight into the extent that SMPs are emphasized on the end-of-chapter tests may have implications on assessment in the era of the Common Core State Standards. We share results of our textbook analysis and discuss their implications for teachers' assessment practices.

■ Standards for Mathematical Practice within Textbooks' Chapter Tests

Three frameworks were used to carefully examine the SMPs (Davis 2012; Henningsen and Stein 1997; Hunsader, Thompson, and Zorin 2013). To examine the extent that students had to attend to the mathematical practices, persevere to solve tasks, and attend to procedural precision, we coded the mathematical practices and the cognitive demand for the tasks. The SMPs (fig. 7.1) for which the codes align and the criteria used to code tasks (table 7.1) are below.

1. Make sense of problems and persevere in solving them.

2. Reason abstractly and quantitatively.

3. Construct viable arguments and critique the reasoning of others.

4. Model with mathematics.

5. Use appropriate tools strategically.

6. Attend to precision.

7. Look for and make use of structure.

8. Look for and express regularity in repeated reasoning.

Fig. 7.1. The Common Core Standards for Mathematical Practice (NGA Center and CCSSO 2010)

Table 7.1

Description of criteria used to code tasks

Codes	Description	SMP Alignment
Identifying Patterns (IP)	Students were asked to develop or identify patterns from graphical, symbolic, numerical, or verbal representations (Davis 2012).	2, 7
Constructing and Testing Conjectures (CTC)	To complete the tasks, students developed or examined the accuracy of conjectures (Davis 2012).	3, 8
Developing Arguments (DA)	The tasks afforded students an opportunity to provide an explanation, justification, proof, etc. The arguments are accepted by the community, may be proven, and include modes of argumentation (Davis 2012).	3, 8
Mathematical Communication (MC)	The tasks require students to communicate their thinking via words, symbols, or graphics. Students may be asked to interpret mathematical vocabulary or create a representation of it (Hunsader et al. 2013).	5, 6
Connections (C)	Tasks are situated in the real world or connect multiple mathematical concepts (Hunsader et al. 2013).	2, 4, 7, 8
Representation: Role of Graphics (RG)	A graphic was provided and the graphic was integral to answering the questions. Additionally, these criteria considered whether students were asked to create a new graphic or append a graphic provided (Hunsader et al. 2013).	1, 4
Representation: Translation of Representational Form (TRF)	Students were required to translate representations (and vice versa) between verbal and symbolic, graphic and symbolic, verbal and graphical, graphical to another graphical, or embodied multiple representations (Hunsader et al. 2013).	1, 2, 4
Levels of Cognitive Demands (LCD)	Refers to the depth of thinking needed to complete the tasks. It "can range from memorization to the use of procedures and algorithms (with or without attention to concepts, understanding, or meaning) to complex thinking and reasoning strategies that would be typical of 'doing mathematics' (e.g., conjecturing, justifying, or interpreting)" (Henningsen and Stein 1997, p. 529). Thus, the levels of cognitive demands are coded as: • Memorization • Procedures without connections • Procedures with connections • Doing mathematics	1, 6

Figures 7.2 and 7.3 illustrate how tasks were coded. The task in figure 7.2 requires students to produce a graphical representation of their interpretation of parallelograms, and the TRF is between graphical and symbolic representation. Furthermore, the task is not situated in the real world and does not provide opportunities for CTC, DA, or IP. The LCD of this task was coded as *procedures with connections.*

> 7. Sketch two noncongruent parallelograms *ABCD* and *EFGH* such that $\overline{AC} = \overline{BD} = \overline{EG} = \overline{FH}$.

Fig. 7.2. Sample task: chapter 6, question 7, *Prentice Hall Mathematics: Geometry* (Bass et al. 2004, p. 342)

The task in figure 7.3 is situated in an abstract context, and the graphic is needed to understand the question. However, the task does not provide opportunities for MC or TRF. As it relates to LCD, it was also coded as *procedures without connections*.

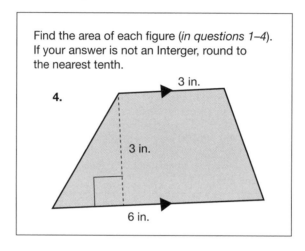

Fig. 7.3. Sample task: chapter 7, question 4, *Prentice Hall Mathematics: Geometry* (Bass et al. 2004, p. 412)

■ Our Findings

We examined the extent to which *Prentice Hall Mathematics: Geometry* (Bass et al. 2004) and *Holt McDougal Geometry* (Burger et al. 2011) textbooks' end-of-chapter assessments promoted the SMPs, rather than the alignment of the content standards addressed within the chapters. These textbooks were selected because they are large-market shareholders for publisher-developed textbooks (Tarr et al. 2010). Both textbooks have twelve chapters, and they have similar organizational structures.

We examined 334 tasks in *Prentice Hall Mathematics: Geometry* and 229 tasks in *Holt McDougal Geometry*. The results were comparable between the textbooks because they both allotted few tasks that assessed the SMPs. In both textbooks, students were seldom afforded opportunities for IP, CTC, DA, TRF, or to engage in tasks that required perseverance. For instance, 1.2 percent of the tasks in *Prentice Hall Mathematics: Geometry* and 0.9 percent of the tasks in *Holt McDougal Geometry* required students to identify patterns. Most of the tasks were situated in abstract context, and they rarely encouraged students to make connections across multiple disciplines. Furthermore, a large percentage of the geometry tasks included a graphical representation and required *procedures without connections*. Procedures with connections were coded in 4.1 percent of *Prentice Hall Mathematics: Geometry* tasks and 10 percent of *Holt McDougal Geometry* tasks. No tasks were coded as *doing mathematics*.

■ Implications for Practice

If the SMPs are important, teachers must emphasize the practices in instruction and on assessments. However, the results suggest there is a lack of attention to some of the SMPs within chapter tests in geometry textbooks, which can potentially influence teachers' instructional practices and what is assessed (Sears and Chávez 2014). A possible way for teachers to address SMPs that may be overlooked on assessment is to engage in problem analysis by modifying and extending tasks in chapter tests. According to Garcia and Davis (2014), "Problem analysis is the process of examining a given mathematics exercise to find ways in which the problem can be modified and extended to create a richer learning opportunity for students" (p. 349). Teachers engaged in problem analysis may create their own tasks, use exploration activities included in the chapter to extend practice assessments, make use of web-based resources, or consult mathematical journals that include tasks that assess geometrical content. Benchmarks can be created to evaluate students' competencies for the tasks.

The time required to complete the modified and extended tasks that are a result of engaging in problem analysis can vary. Some assessment tasks can be completed during a class period, while other tasks may need to be completed out of class. Nonetheless, the ultimate goal of the additional assessment tasks should be to address the SMPs that are remotely addressed in the chapter tests.

We engaged in problem analysis and modified tasks, among ourselves, to identify geometrical tasks that can be used to assess the SMPs. In our analysis, we sought to align the tasks with curriculum objectives, transform published tasks that required little cognitive rigor into rich mathematical tasks that engage students in higher-level cognitive demands, and considered the complexities of completing the tasks. Hence, we used four examples to illustrate how engaging in problem analysis can be used to attend to the SMPs on assessments. These example tasks address content discussed in the beginning, middle, and latter chapters of the two textbooks.

Task 1
Original task

Describe each pattern and find the next two terms of each sequence.

    2.   0, 2, 4, 6, 8

Fig. 7.4. Mathematical task: chapter 1, question 2, *Prentice Hall Mathematics: Geometry* (Bass et al. 2004, p. 64)

Modified task after engaging in problem analysis

(*a*) How many squares, of all sizes, are on an 8 × 8 chessboard? Justify your answer.

(*b*) How many rectangles, of all sizes, are on an 8 × 8 chessboard? Justify your answer.

Stating the next two even numbers in the sequence can solve the original task. To complete the modified task in its entirety, students will have to engage in reasoning and pattern recognition (IP). It extends the concepts presented in the original task such that students have to consider multiple patterns of the various squares (1×1, 2×2, 3×3, etc.) and rectangles within an 8×8 chessboard. For part *a*, students should engage in reasoning about the square patterns and then skillfully deduce that there are 204 squares of different sizes on the board. Initially, students might suggest potential estimates for the total amount of squares and seek to refine their thinking. For instance, students might suggest the chessboard has "more than 64 squares" and then begin to consider a pattern to generate a definitive solution. Part *b* of the task is an extension of the pattern observed in part *a*. For part *b*, students must reflect on the hierarchy of quadrilaterals, such that all squares are rectangles, but not all rectangles are squares. The solution for part *b* is 1,296. Similar to part *a*, students may hypothesize a minimum or a maximum number of rectangles and subsequently seek to test their conjectures. This task is available on multiple mathematical websites (such as http://illuminations.nctm.org/Lesson.aspx?id=978) and aligns with SMPs 2 and 7.

Task 2
Original task

> For Exercises 22–26, use the Law of Detachment and the Law of Syllogism to make any possible conclusion. Write not possible if you cannot make any conclusion.
>
> 22. People who live in glass houses shouldn't throw stories. Lindsay shouldn't throw stones.

Fig. 7.5. Mathematical task: chapter 2, question 22, *Prentice Hall Mathematics: Geometry* (Bass et al. 2004, p. 108)

Modified task after engaging in problem analysis

Create a realistic story using conditional statements. Use a minimum of 8 conditional statements that can employ the law of syllogism and law of detachment. Ensure that the conditional statements are preserved in the arguments presented.

To complete the modified task, students are required to communicate their thinking in writing (MC) and to engage in repeated reasoning to produce statements that are viable (DA) and connected (C). As with the original task, the modified task is situated within the real world, which allows students to make connections between everyday events and geometrical constructs. However, the modified task transcends the original task because students will have to create a logical story, rather than merely deduce superficial conclusions. This modified task engages students in logic and requires reflection on the accuracy of their statements in relation to previous claims made. These types of competencies can be productive in the development of students' reasoning and proof skills. The modified task, which is adapted from Sears (2012), is open-ended and aligns with multiple SMPs (namely, SMPs 1, 3, 6, and 8).

Task 3
Original task

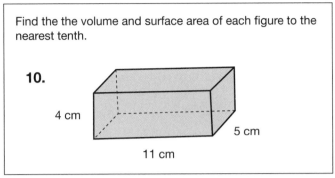

Find the the volume and surface area of each figure to the nearest tenth.

10.

4 cm

11 cm

5 cm

Fig. 7.6. Mathematical task: chapter 10, question 10, *Prentice Hall Mathematics: Geometry* (Bass et al. 2004, p. 576)

Modified task after engaging in problem analysis

A cola company would like to redesign the cylindrical can for their 330 ml carbonated drink. For the redesign, they would like to use the least amount of aluminum while maintaining the same amount of soda in the can. Hence, you are to make recommendations as to how the can could be adjusted such that it uses the least amount of aluminum. Be sure to report the calculations that support your recommendation, a comparison between the ideal and actual dimensions, and a discussion about the dimensions and what influenced your final recommendations. (*Note:* 1 cm³ = 1 ml.) (Tran and Dougherty 2014)

For this modified task, students will have to engage in reasoning, model mathematically, and translate between verbal (TRF), symbolic, and graphical representations (RG) to share their thinking. Students will have to develop mathematical arguments based on data they created, consider surface area for the aluminum to be used, and consider volume for the dimensions and possible shapes of the cans. Students may also observe potential changes in patterns and ratio, relationships between the surface area and volume, and relationships between the radius and the height. Additionally, this task can have students use properties of calculus—knowingly or unknowingly—while exploring possibilities. For a cylindrical model, students should deduce that an approximate height of 7.5 cm and radius of 3.7 cm would utilize the least amount of aluminum. Alternatively, students may propose other models such as a cube or a prism. To complete the task, technological tools can be used to help students visualize, analyze, and adjust their designs. Therefore, this task can facilitate students in demonstrating creativity as they seek to carefully make use of structure.

Admittedly, sufficient time needs to be allocated for students to persevere and solve the problem. The original task can be solved formulaically. The modified task extends the original task because it applies the formulas for surface area and volume in a real-world situation. The task was adapted from an article published in *Mathematics Teacher* (Tran and Dougherty 2014) and aligns with SMPs 1, 2, 4, 5, 6, and 7.

Task 4
Original task

---

23. Complete this coordinate proof that the diagonals of a square are congruent.

Given: Square *ABCD* with vertices
A (0, 0), B (a, 0), C (a, a), and D (0, a)

Prove: $\overline{AC} \cong \overline{BD}$

AC = **a.** _?_ , and BD = **b.** _?_ . So, **c.** _?_ = BD and $\overline{AC} \cong \overline{BD}$.

Fig. 7.7. Mathematical task: chapter 6, question 23, *Prentice Hall Mathematics: Geometry* (Bass et al. 2004, p. 342)

Modified task after engaging in problem analysis

Given the following quadrilateral:

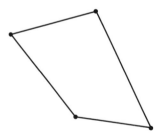

(*a*) Construct the midpoints of the four sides of the quadrilateral.

(*b*) Write a conjecture concerning what you get when you connect the midpoints of the sides of a quadrilateral.

    i.   What figure would you get?

ii. Will you always get this kind of figure when you connect the midpoints of the sides of a quadrilateral, even if the quadrilateral is concave (as is the case with the figure below)?

(*c*) Provide a proof for your conjecture.

(*d*) Explain possible relationships between the area of the figure that is constructed by connecting the midpoints of the quadrilateral, relative to the area of the quadrilateral.

In the original task, calculating lengths can complete the proof, while the modified task provides an opportunity for students to engage in constructing conjectures (CTC) and extends the notion of proving. The purpose of the modified task is for students to discover and prove Varignon's theorem: *The midpoints of the four sides of a quadrilateral are always the vertices of a parallelogram.* Additionally, students ought to explain that the area of the parallelogram is one-half the area of the quadrilateral. For this task, students can potentially explore and test their conjectures using technological software such as Geometer's Sketchpad or GeoGebra. Encouraging students to use technology can provide opportunities for students to verify the accuracy of their conjecture, explain their conjecture, discover new relationships, and communicate their thinking by writing a proof. This task is a modification of *Quadrilaterals in Quadrilaterals* Technology Activity (Bass et al. 2004, p. 319) and aligns with SMPs 1, 2, 3, 6, and 8.

■ Conclusion

In closing, if assessment is to be a coherent process, it needs to connect with both curriculum and instruction (NCTM 2000). The SMPs are described as expertise that students should develop and should be cultivated during instruction (NGA Center and CCSSO 2010). If the SMPs are emphasized during instruction and less often on assessment, there may be a weak linkage in the coherence of the assessment process. Therefore, textbook publishers and practitioners must seek to increase opportunities to attend to the SMPs on assessments.

We found that end-of-chapter assessments in geometry textbooks seldom assess the SMPs, and we suggest that teachers engage in problem analysis to address the shortcoming of textbooks. When we collaborated to examine tasks and engaged in problem analysis, we adhered to the following principles: directly address the SMPs, promote students' engagement with mathematics, and provide opportunities for students to demonstrate cognitive rigor. We did this by creating or finding tasks that were situated in real-world contexts, translated between representations, used technology, and were open-ended—while maintaining the mathematical content being assessed by the original tasks.

Teachers can engage in problem analysis to decide whether the original assessment tasks adequately assess the SMPs based on the coding scheme, or to determine the extent assessment tasks need to be modified. If the percentages of the various categories are relatively low or not evident, teachers should intentionally seek to increase the number of tasks that address the SMPs. If teachers seek to find better tasks than the tasks written in the textbooks, it is important to reflect on the objectives that need to be assessed, the amount of time required to complete the tasks, the implications of familiar or unfamiliar context, the clarity of the mathematical language used, and the possibilities for students' responses. The modified and extended tasks should seek to assess depth of understanding for topics that are assessed on a surface level. It is highly unlikely, or desired, that one question will address all of the SMPs; therefore, multiple questions should be used to ensure that all of the SMPs are adequately addressed and assessed.

The four exemplary assessment tasks addressed SMPs that were minutely assessed in chapter tests and provided opportunities to engage in higher levels of cognitive demand. Although these tasks are not exhaustive, they illustrate that it is possible to adequately assess SMPs within the context of geometry. Additionally, the modified tasks used in the examples were generally adapted from assessment tasks published in journals and online websites devoted to school mathematics. Using published resources can reduce potential challenges that may arise from creating new tasks. Nevertheless, if teachers choose to create their own tasks, they should reflect on the extent such tasks encourage students to identify patterns, investigate and make conjectures, develop arguments, communicate mathematically, make connections, utilize graphics, translate between representational forms, and demonstrate cognitive rigor. When teachers modify tasks on their own, they may choose to have students critique the validity of claims made in the arguments presented. For instance, teachers may pose potential arguments that reflect common errors that students make, and they may require students to identify the errors and consider correct approaches to solve the problem. Thus, if teachers choose to create their own tasks they may consider having students write proofs, engage in error analysis of responses to mathematical tasks, or solve tasks that are situated in the real world. Therefore, teachers can utilize published tasks or create their own tasks in an effort to assess the SMPs on chapter tests.

References

Bass, Laurie E., Randall I. Charles, Art Johnson, and Dan Kennedy. *Prentice Hall Mathematics: Geometry.* Upper Saddle River, N.J.: Pearson Education, Inc, 2004.

Burger, Edward B., David J. Chard, Paul A. Kennedy, Steven J. Leinwand, Freddie L. Renfro, Tom W. Roby, Dale G. Seymour, and Bert K. Waits. *Holt McDougal Geometry.* Boston: Houghton Mifflin Harcourt Publishing Company, 2011.

Confrey, Jere, and Erin E. Krupa. "The Arrival of the Common Core State Mathematics Standards: How Did We Get Here and What Needs to Happen Next?" In *Curriculum Issues in an Era of Common Core State Standards for Mathematics,* edited by Chris R. Hirsch, Glenda Lappan, and Barbara J. Reys, pp. 3–16. Reston, Va.: NCTM, 2012.

Davis, Jon D. "An Examination of Reasoning and Proof Opportunities in Three Differently Organized Secondary Mathematics Textbook Units." *Mathematics Education Research Journal* 24, no. 4 (2012): 467–91.

Garcia, Katie, and Alicia Davis. "Problem Analysis: Challenging All Learners." *Mathematics Teacher* 107, no. 5 (2014): 348–53.

Henningsen, Marjorie, and Mary Kay Stein. "Mathematical Tasks and Student Cognition: Classroom-Based Factors That Support and Inhibit High-Level Mathematical Thinking and Reasoning." *Journal for Research in Mathematics Education* 28, no. 5 (1997): 524–49.

Hunsader, Patricia D., Denisse R. Thompson, and Barbara Zorin. "Engaging Elementary Students with Mathematical Processes during Assessment: What Opportunities Exist in Tests Accompanying Published Curricula?" *International Journal for Mathematics Teaching & Learning* (2013): 1–25.

National Council of Teachers of Mathematics (NCTM). *Principles and Standards for School Mathematics.* Reston, Va.: NCTM, 2000.

National Governors Association Center for Best Practices and Council of Chief State School Officers (NGA Center and CCSSO). *Common Core State Standards for Mathematics.* Washington, D.C.: NGA Center and CCSSO, 2010.

NCTM Illuminations. "Counting Embedded Figures." Accessed April 13, 2014, at http://illuminations .nctm.org/Lesson.aspx?id=978.

Otten, Samuel, Lorraine M. Males, and Nicholas J. Gilbertson. "The Introduction of Proof in Secondary Geometry Textbooks." *International Journal of Educational Research* 64 (2013): 107–18.

Sears, Ruthmae. *An Examination of How Teachers Use Curriculum Materials for the Teaching of Proof in High School Geometry.* PhD dissertation, University of Missouri–Columbia, 2012.

Sears, Ruthmae, and Óscar Chávez. "Opportunities to Engage with Proof: The Nature of Proof Tasks in Two Geometry Textbooks and Its Influence on Enacted Lessons." *ZDM* 46, no. 5 (2014): 767–80.

Tarr, James E., Daniel J. Ross, Melissa D. McNaught, Óscar Chávez, Douglas A. Grouws, Robert E. Reys, Ruthmae Sears, and R. Didem Taylan. "Identification of Student-and Teacher-Level Variables in Modeling Variation of Mathematics Achievement Data." Paper presented at the Annual Meeting of the American Educational Research Association, Denver, Colo., May 2010.

Thompson, Denisse R., Sharon L. Senk, and Gwendolyn J. Johnson. "Opportunities to Learn Reasoning and Proof in High School Mathematics Textbooks." *Journal for Research in Mathematics Education* 43, no. 3 (2012): 253–95.

Tran, Dung, and Barbara J. Dougherty. "Authenticity of Mathematical Modeling." *Mathematics Teacher* 107, no. 9 (2014): 672–78.

CHAPTER 8

Using an Observational Rubric to Facilitate Change in Undergraduate Classroom Norms

Melody Jeane Elrod, *University of South Florida, Tampa*
Jeremy F. Strayer, *Middle Tennessee State University, Murfreesboro*

Inquiry-based instruction is a powerful pedagogy for learning mathematics (Hmelo-Silver, Duncan, and Chinn 2007), and students who engage in solving nonroutine problems and sharing their solution strategies with others show increases in learning (Boaler 2008; Cirillo 2013). To experience this success, however, teachers must establish new *sociomathematical norms* for the mathematical contributions students and teachers make during instruction (Kosko and Wilkins 2012; Yackel and Cobb 1996). It can be difficult for educators to establish sociomathematical norms that support inquiry-based instruction and classroom discourse, particularly when students have come to expect teacher-centered classroom norms (e.g., where the teacher does most or all of the speaking during class). In this chapter, we describe how we developed a problem-solving discourse rubric to assess and support students' engagement in mathematical discourse during inquiry-based instruction. We describe how the rubric originated to meet a particular classroom need, the effect the rubric had on the sociomathematical norms in the classroom, the factors that led to its revision, the implementation of the new rubric, and implications for future use.

■ Developing the Problem Solving Rubric

During the spring of 2013, we conducted an iterative self-study to investigate changing sociomathematical norms in an undergraduate college algebra classroom (Elrod and Strayer, under review). Melody, the first author, taught college algebra students using an inquiry-based approach. During each class session, she introduced a nonroutine problem, asked students to solve the problem in groups, and facilitated a whole-class discussion of student solutions.

Original Dilemma and Solutions

Within the first week of instruction, the authors identified a troubling dilemma. Melody expected students to struggle productively with nonroutine problems to develop understanding. Her students, however, expected Melody to explain how to complete procedural problems and to assign homework to practice those procedures.

Melody's commitment to student-centered learning clashed with students' expectations of teacher-centered mathematics instruction.

Having identified this dilemma, Melody established an open dialogue with students, acknowledging their concerns and frustrations. She facilitated this dialogue using surveys, one-on-one conversations, and talk about the study itself. Melody also maintained a firm commitment to her pedagogical strategy, beginning instruction with a cognitively demanding problem and resolutely redirecting students to construct their own mathematical knowledge while solving it.

Despite an observable improvement in students' mathematical thinking during the initial weeks of the semester, student buy-in for the sociomathematical norms necessary to support inquiry-based learning became threatened by poor performance on predominantly computational chapter tests. In her researcher journal, Melody reflected:

> Thus far, the story has gone something like this: We do problem solving in class, the students excel and feel confident asking mathematical questions and contributing to mathematical discussions. Then we take a test, they do poorly, and we have to start again at confidence ground zero. This is a very frustrating cycle for all involved. (Elrod 2013)

Because chapter tests were required by the mathematics department and students were required to take a computationally based common final exam, Melody was hesitant to change the format of chapter tests. Melody was also aware of the "implementation dip" that occurs when new instructional methods are introduced (Fullan, Cuttress, and Kilcher 2005). She remained confident that her students could eventually be successful on computationally driven chapter tests and the departmental final. For these reasons, Melody decided to augment the calculation of chapter test grades by assessing students' mathematical efforts during class. To clarify the value Melody placed upon the desired sociomathematical norms, she created a rubric that assigned numerical value to students' problem-solving behaviors. In the sections that follow we describe how we have developed this rubric into an effective tool for facilitating change in sociomathematical norms.

The Problem Solving Rubric

The Problem Solving Rubric (PSR) was initially created using six categories with a maximum score of 3 for each category (see fig. 8.1). We used the Process Standards found in *Principles and Standards for School Mathematics* (National Council of Teachers of Mathematics [NCTM] 2000) as the first five categories. These standards (*problem solving, reasoning and proof, representation, communication,* and *connections*) form the foundation for the sociomathematical norms needed for inquiry-based instruction and were a natural starting place for developing the rubric. Melody added the sixth category (*productive disposition*) from the Strands for Mathematical Proficiency (National Research Council [NRC] 2001). Productive disposition is defined in *Adding It Up* as "the inclination to see mathematics as sensible, useful, and worthwhile, coupled with a belief in diligence and one's own efficacy" (NRC 2001, p. 116). Without a productive position, students' development of the necessary discourse and problem-solving skills would be quite difficult.

Category	3	2	1	0
Problem Solving	Evidence of active problem solving: (1) restating and understanding the question, (2) discussion of solution strategies, (3) executed plan, (4) checked solution for reasonableness (not necessarily completed)	Some evidence of active problem solving, but students miss one of the initial two steps (as in the previous column)	Little evidence of active problem solving—guessing, giving up, or not focused on the problem at hand.	No attempt.
Reasoning & Proof	Student effectively uses logic to prove his/her solution method and can explain that reasoning to others.	Student uses logic to prove his/her solution, but that logic is flawed or inappropriate or the student is unable to explain that reasoning to others.	Student can follow the logic of others, but cannot explain this reasoning to others.	No attempt
Representations:	Evidence of multiple solution methods or attempts; organized flow of thought	Evidence of multiple solution methods or attempts; unorganized or inaccurate	No evidence of multiple solution methods or attempts; work disorganized and illogical	No attempt
Communication	Student is actively engaged in listening to others and contributing to the group discussion.	Student listens actively or contributes to the discussion, but does not do both.	Student copies down what others say, but is not engaged in problem solving	Student shows no evidence of involvement in the group's work.
Connections	Student actively uses prior knowledge to solve current problems in creative ways.	Student uses prior knowledge in attempts to solve problems, but may do so in an inappropriate way.	Student uses only the simplest of prior knowledge and experience to solve problems.	No attempt
Productive Disposition	Student is willing to struggle with problem solving even when the answer or solution path is not obvious.	Student is willing to struggle to a point, but allows others to do his/her work.	Student is unwilling to struggle, but re-engages when a reasonable solution path is found.	Student is unwilling to engage.

Fig. 8.1. The original Problem Solving Rubric, built on an 18-point scale

After introducing the PSR to students, Melody used it to assess students' problem solving during small-group and whole-class discussions. She also developed a data collection device that listed students according to group and listed PSR criteria by name only (see fig. 8.2). This format provided space to note specific evidence for each category. The data collection tool allowed Melody to focus on facilitating discourse during class, yet still collect data to easily score using the PSR at a later time.

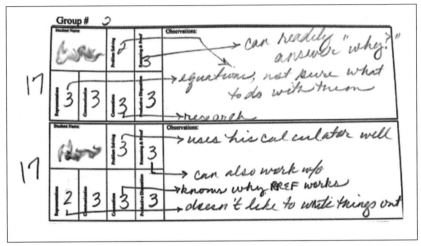

Fig. 8.2. Melody used a data collection device to make the observation and grading process more efficient.

A New Dilemma

As the semester continued, students' scores on the PSR were incorporated in their chapter exam grades, and they became less resistant to solving problems together in class. Unfortunately, this led to a new pedagogical pitfall. We had hoped the PSR would increase the value students placed on mathematically meaningful discourse. However, students focused on how that discourse translated into a PSR grade. Consequently, students showed little interest in truly improving their discourse skills.

This result exemplifies a limitation of rubrics. When rubric levels are described so specifically, they may constrain student learning and unwittingly create a teacher-centered environment as students focus solely on meeting the rubric level. Mathematical meaning making may have been in the students' hands, but the evaluation of the worth of discourse remained in the instructor's hands. While the PSR initiated a positive change in classroom norms, the progress stalled. Faced with a new version of the original dilemma (i.e., creating new sociomathematical norms that are *student*-centered), we turned to the literature to continue our progress.

■ Literature Review

Research studies investigating productive discourse, cooperative work, rubric creation, and assessment in general have produced results that illuminate the successes and failures of the PSR. In this section, we describe four themes in the literature that grounded our PSR revisions.

First, research shows that assessment should be constructed according to the goals for learning. In describing their "Backwards Design," Wiggins and McTighe (2005) urge educators to develop a clear picture of what students should know, understand, and be able to do before designing assessment or instruction. When we built the PSR from the five NCTM Process Standards we exhibited this type of design.

Second, knowledge is not isolated from the context within which it is constructed (Anderson et al. 2007; Pryor and Crossouard 2010). So for inquiry-based instruction, it is not enough to simply view students' finished work. Students' understanding may be assessed by attending to student discourse while that work is completed. These findings support our original intent to assess students' problem-solving skills during discourse, and we focused this emphasis during revision.

Next, rubric writers must be wary of allowing grading to overshadow the developmental advantages of formative assessment (Arter and McTighe 2001). For example, when Melody's students focused on grades rather than discourse, the rubric's ability to support learning goals was diminished. Furthermore, students should use assessment to inform their own improvement and come to understand that self-evaluation and peer evaluation are just as important as teacher-directed evaluation (Anderson et al. 2007; Shepard 2001; Suurtamm, Koch, and Arden 2010). Qualitative feedback, then, must be more prominent than any grades received (Wiliam 2007). Students must be challenged to move beyond minimal expectations to mastery of a higher order (Arter and McTighe 2001). Unfortunately, Melody's students were not offered narrative feedback, and the original PSR established only minimum expectations at the highest proficiency level.

Finally, when using a rubric to facilitate changes in sociomathematical norms, implementation is as important as the rubric itself. It is not enough to distribute a rubric intended to help students develop discourse skills. Instructors and students must be trained to use it. This training should be overt, either through formalized training seminars (Crotwell Timmerman et al. 2011) or by openly addressing the skills associated with discourse during class discussions (Pryor and Crossouard 2010). Although Melody distributed and presented the rubric to her students before implementation, she did not make overt references to it during classroom discourse.

■ Rubric Revision

Based on our experiences and review of the literature, we revised the PSR to better support a change in sociomathematical norms (see fig. 8.3). We began this redesign by placing less of an emphasis on the grade. We removed the overt point values and created a new structure that set proficiency levels of *Above Standard*, *At Standard*, *Below Standard*, and *Unacceptable*. Though the rubric can still be used to generate a quantitative score, its primary focus is the development of students' problem-solving and discourse skills. To reflect this change in focus, we renamed the PSR the Problem Solving Discourse Rubric (PSDR).

Problem Solving Discourse Rubric

The problem solving rubric is meant to be used during observations of students' group and whole-class discourse and can also apply to students' written work for some categories. It is generalized to cover all mathematical problem solving situations.

	Above Standard	At Standard	Below Standard	Unacceptable
Problem Solving	Student demonstrates evidence of all four problem solving steps outlined in the "At Standard" description.	Student demonstrates evidence of active problem solving by doing two or more of the following: (1) restating and understanding the question, (2) discussion of solution strategies, (3) executed plan, (4) checked solution for rationality.	Though student demonstrates some evidence of problem solving, he/she is overly dependent upon others' work to get started. Student demonstrates evidence of one or none of the list in the "At Standard" level.	Student allows others in the class/group to engage in problem solving and only writes down what others have done.
Reasoning & Proof	Student not only explains his/her own reasoning to others with clarity, completeness, and correctness, but also draws those sorts of explanations out of other students in the group.	Student provides a clear, complete and correct explanation of the mathematical work s/he has finished.	Student provides an explanation of the mathematical work s/he has finished, but the explanation is lacking in clarity, completeness, and/or correctness.	Student does not offer an explanation of the mathematical work s/he had finished.
Representation	Student demonstrates multiple meaningful representations for the same problem.	Student demonstrates written evidence that represents solution strategies in a mathematically meaningful way.	Though student demonstrates written evidence of solution strategies, the representation is not mathematically meaningful.	No attempt is made to represent the solution strategies.
Communication	Student is actively engaged in drawing out others' ideas and building upon them in small groups OR Student is actively engaged in listening to **and** sharing ideas with others in whole-class discussions.	Student is actively engaged in listening to **and** sharing ideas with others in small groups OR Student is actively engaged in listening to **or** sharing ideas with others in whole-class discussions. (Active listening includes questioning and clarifying others' ideas.)	Student either listens actively **or** contributes to the discussion in small groups, but does not do both. OR Student actively takes notes during whole-class discussions, but does not contribute vocally.	Student demonstrates no evidence of involvement in the group's work OR Student is not engaged in full class discourse (i.e., writing down final answers only, taking pictures of work, or engaged in off-task behavior).
Connections	Student not only connects multiple mathematical ideas together, s/he recognizes and encourages others' efforts to make those connections.	Student connects multiple mathematical ideas. This includes connections in his/her own thinking or connections in the thinking of others.	Student is not able to recognize connections between mathematical ideas in their own thinking or in the thinking of others.	
Productive Disposition	Student not only persists in his/her efforts to understand and solve the problem mathematically, but encourages others to do so as well.	Student persists in his/her efforts to understand and solve the problem mathematically.	Student begins to persist in his/her efforts to understand and solve the problem, but ultimately seeks out answers from others or gives up.	Student is unwilling to engage the mathematics in the problem.

Fig. 8.3. The revised Problem Solving Discourse Rubric (PSDR) is formatted to remove overt grading schemes and include a level of exemplary performance.

The PSDR contains more gradations than the original. We used the three-point level of the original PSR to inform the new *At Standard* level, representing minimum expectations for the category. The *Above Standard* level descriptions were written to challenge students to recognize others' mathematical thinking and encourage their classmates to attain high levels of mathematical discourse. Descriptions of the *Below Standard* level recognize students' efforts to meet the standard, and portrayals of the *Unacceptable* level depict students who are disengaged from the process.

After field-testing the rubric in undergraduate courses (Precalculus and Introduction to Proof) with two different professors, we made changes to three categories to clarify minimum expectations with respect to the Process Standards and the vision for productive disposition cast by *Adding It Up*. First, the Reasoning and Proof category was clarified to describe evidence of students' explanations of mathematical thinking in a clear, concise, and correct manner (Bénéteau, Bleiler, and Thompson 2014). Next, we refocused the Connections category on connections among mathematical ideas. (We left the *Unacceptable* level intentionally blank due to the inability to observe disengagement from making connections.) Last, the Productive Disposition category was revised to illustrate students' persistence in understanding and solving mathematical problems.

Because explicit scoring features have been removed from the rubric, educators are free to develop their own scoring method. For example, as formative assessment, no scoring may be required. If the rubric is used as a summative assessment (or a formalized formative assessment), a scoring method might use a baseline value, adding and deducting points for various levels of achievement (see fig. 8.4).

Scoring

25 points = All items "At Standard" and at least 2 items "Above Standard."

22 points = All items "At Standard" and 1 item "Above Standard."

20 points = All items "At Standard."

Deduct 2 points for each item "Below Standard."

Deduct 5 points for each item "Unacceptable."

Fig. 8.4. Educators are free to set their own scoring method.

■ Implementation

As recommended by the research, the PSDR is intended to be used by both educators and students, so implementation is key. All participants must agree on the descriptions of the various levels of achievement for each category. Any confusion or disagreement must be settled prior to implementation (Shepard 2001). To accomplish this goal, students might use the rubric to evaluate one another. Once agreement is reached, the criteria described in the rubric must become a natural part of class discourse. Teachers may want to post an enlarged copy of the rubric in the classroom so that it might be internalized. Posting the rubric in the classroom allows teachers to naturally address evidence of proficiency *during* discourse (Pryor and Crossouard 2010).

Another important consideration for implementation is the teacher's day-to-day data collection. It is unrealistic to expect to assess every student using the PSDR during a single class session. Indeed, even with Melody's data collection tool, assessing the entire class (twenty-seven students) took at least three class periods. To compensate, she set a goal of one full observational cycle per chapter and found that with regular use the process became more natural. It is important to note, though, that regardless of the data collection procedure, students must receive thoughtful instructor comments in order to inform future growth (Wiliam 2007).

With the above points in mind, Jeremy (the second author) used the PSDR with his students in an inquiry-based introductory statistics classroom in summer 2014. During this course students met daily in three-hour sessions for three weeks. At the beginning of the term, Jeremy hung a large poster of the PSDR in the room once agreement on each category and level description was reached. He emphasized that students would be more successful learning in groups if everyone aimed for *Above Standard* in all categories. He also noted that each student would be assessed using the rubric and that this score would count as a percentage of their exam grades.

During class investigations, Jeremy frequently referred to the PSDR to highlight student behaviors that were in line with high levels on the rubric. This teacher move encouraged students to share the sociomathematical vision cast by the PSDR. Jeremy also occasionally reminded students to remain engaged by referencing lower-level descriptions when students were not exhibiting their best work. At the end of a few class sessions, Jeremy asked students to assess themselves and their group mates using the PSDR. After a few days, Jeremy began over-hearing students referring to the PSDR when they "caught" one of their classmates performing at high levels on the rubric.

Throughout the term, Jeremy focused on making the rubric a natural, integral part of the classroom culture. With the PSDR's reduced emphasis on earning points and increased emphasis on meeting standards, students rarely (if ever) questioned how the use of the rubric might allow them to earn high marks in the course. Because of the abbreviated timeline of the course, Jeremy was not able to provide detailed authentic feedback to students using the rubric, as the literature recommends. Concerned that this could have a negative impact on the sociomathematical norms, Jeremy invited several colleagues to observe class sessions and offer additional feedback on the PSDR. During debriefing sessions, Jeremy and his collaborators agreed that students fully embraced learning in this inquiry-based classroom. Factors such as three-hour daily class sessions and stellar student atten-dance certainly contributed to the success of the course. We contend, however, that the PSDR helped the class negotiate the sociomathematical norms necessary for successful inquiry-based instruction. Also, though students did receive a summative assessment score on the PSDR that was incorporated into their final grade, the PSDR grade was not a focus for Jeremy or his students.

■ Discussion

Melody's and Jeremy's experiences demonstrate ways educators can facilitate inquiry-focused sociomathematical norms using the PSDR. It is important to note, however, that the PSDR cannot create an inquiry-based classroom. No rubric can do that. Indeed, it takes teachers fully committed to establishing necessary sociomathematical norms and carrying out inquiry-based instruction to create successful learning experiences for students in an inquiry-based environment. Unless the PSDR is implemented by teachers who possess the belief that all students are capable of contributing mathematically to their learning communities (NCTM 2014) and the expectation that they do so, the PSDR's utility may be severely limited or lost completely.

Educators and students must work together to form shared understandings of the PSDR categories and levels so that the descriptions of each level do not constrain students as they solve problems during class. Indeed, implementation must be strategic—merely posting the PSDR is not enough. Students must be free to struggle in their own way as they solve problems, and if rubric descriptions are overemphasized as the only way to interact, they may impede student learning.

The road from the original dilemma through the construction, implementation, and revision of the PSDR to support inquiry-focused sociomathematical norms has been long. We have encountered opportunities to improve the way we support and assess our students' discourse skills and to grow professionally ourselves. This project has challenged our own perceptions of mathematical thinking, problem solving, and discourse, and it serves as a model for reflective practice that all professional educators should employ (NCTM 2014).

By sharing our experience developing the PSDR, we hope to encourage educators to exercise due diligence when using rubrics for assessment. Educators who may use the PSDR should periodically reevaluate its effectiveness and make changes as necessary. Just as all educational tools should be iteratively evaluated after use, the PSDR should be subject to regular scrutiny so that it might best serve the learning goals of the educators and students who use it.

References

Anderson, Kate T., Steven J. Zuiker, Gita Taasoobshirazi, and Daniel T. Hickey. "Classroom Discourse as a Tool to Enhance Formative Assessment and Practise in Science." *International Journal of Science Education* 29, no. 14 (2007): 1721–44.

Arter, Judith, and Jay McTighe. *Scoring Rubrics in the Classroom: Using Performance Criteria for Assessing and Improving Student Performance.* Experts in Assessment series, edited by T. R. Guskey and Robert J. Marzano. Thousand Oaks, Calif.: Corwin Press, 2001.

Bénéteau, Catherine, Sarah K. Bleiler, and Denisse R. Thompson. "Promoting Mathematical Reasoning through Critiquing Student Work." In *Annual Perspectives in Mathematics Education 2014: Using Research to Improve Instruction*, edited by Karen Karp, pp. 151–60. Reston, Va.: NCTM, 2014.

Boaler, Jo. *What's Math Got to Do with It? Helping Children Learn to Love Their Most Hated Subject—and Why It's Important for America.* New York: Viking, 2008.

Cirillo, Michelle. "What Does Research Say the Benefits of Discussion in Mathematics Class Are?" Research Brief. Reston, Va.: NCTM, 2013.

Crotwell Timmerman, Briana E., Denise C. Strickland, Robert L. Johnson, and Jeremy R. Payne. "Development of a 'Universal' Rubric for Assessing Undergraduates' Scientific Reasoning Skills Using Scientific Writing." *Assessment & Evaluation in Higher Education* 36, no. 5 (2011): 509–47.

Elrod, Melody J., and Jeremy F. Strayer. "Standards-Based Mathematics Instruction and Sociomathematical Norms: Facilitating Change in an Undergraduate Classroom." *Investigations in Mathematics Learning.* Under review.

Fullan, Michael, Claudia Cuttress, and Ann Kilcher. "8 Forces for Leaders of Change." *Journal of Staff Development* 26, no. 4 (Fall 2005): 54–64.

Hmelo-Silver, Cindy E., Ravit Golan Duncan, and Clark A. Chinn. "Scaffolding and Achievement in Problem-Based and Inquiry Learning: A Response to Kirschner, Sweller, and Clark." *Educational Psychologist* 42, no. 2 (2007): 99–107.

Kosko, Karl W., and Jesse L. M. Wilkins. "Students' Quality of Mathematical Discussion and Their Self-Determination in Mathematics." *Investigations in Mathematics Learning* 4, no. 3 (2012): 15–31.

National Council of Teachers of Mathematics (NCTM). *Principles and Standards for School Mathematics.* Reston, Va.: NCTM, 2000.

————. *Principles to Actions: Ensuring Mathematical Success for All*. Reston, Va.: NCTM, 2014.

National Research Council (NRC). *Adding It Up: Helping Children Learn Mathematics*. Edited by Jeremy Kilpatrick, Jane Swafford, and Bradford Findell. Washington, D.C.: National Academies Press, 2001.

Pryor, Jeremy, and Barbara Crossouard. "Challenging Formative Assessment: Disciplinary Spaces and Identities." *Assessment & Evaluation in Higher Education* 35, no. 3 (2010): 265–76.

Shepard, Lorrie A. "The Role of Classroom Assessment in Teaching and Learning." In *Handbook of Research on Teaching*, edited by Virginia Richardson, 4th ed., pp. 1066–1101. Washington, D.C.: American Educational Research Association, 2001.

Suurtamm, Christine, Martha Koch, and Ann Arden. "Teachers' Assessment Practices in Mathematics: Classrooms in the Context of Reform." *Assessment in Education: Principles, Policy & Practice* 17, no. 4 (2010): 399–417.

Wiggins, Grant, and Jay McTighe. *Understanding by Design*. 2nd ed. Alexandria, Va.: Association for Supervision and Curriculum Development, 2005.

Wiliam, Dylan. "Keeping Learning on Track: Classroom Assessment and the Regulation of Learning." In *Second Handbook of Research on Mathematics Teaching and Learning*, edited by Frank K. Lester, Jr., pp. 1053–98. Charlotte, N.C.: Information Age Publishing, 2007.

Yackel, Erna, and Paul Cobb. "Sociomathematical Norms, Argumentation, and Autonomy in Mathematics." *Journal for Research in Mathematics Education* 27, no. 4 (1996): 458–77.

CHAPTER 9

Communal Development and Evolution of a Course Rubric for Proof Writing

Sarah K. Bleiler, *Middle Tennessee State University, Murfreesboro*
Yi-Yin (Winnie) Ko, *Indiana State University, Terre Haute*
Sean P. Yee, *University of South Carolina, Columbia*
Justin D. Boyle, *University of Alabama, Tuscaloosa*

Mathematical proof is a critical tool for communicating ideas and deepening individuals' mathematical understanding (Stylianides 2007). Furthermore, proof is used to verify claims, provide insight into mathematical statements, systematize and build upon prior work, communicate mathematics to others, and discover new results in the mathematics community (de Villiers 1990). Given the centrality of proof in mathematics, recent reforms have overwhelmingly recommended the inclusion of proof and proving within prekindergarten through grade 12 and in undergraduate mathematics courses across all content areas (Conference Board of the Mathematical Sciences [CBMS] 2012; National Council of Teachers of Mathematics [NCTM] 2000; National Governors Association Center for Best Practices and Council of Chief State School Officers [NGA Center and CCSSO] 2010).

Unfortunately, proof and proof-related reasoning are underrepresented within curricular materials (Thompson, Senk, and Johnson 2012) and have traditionally been restricted to high school geometry (e.g., Stylianou, Blanton, and Knuth 2009). Even undergraduate students and preservice teachers report limited engagement with mathematical proof in both their high school and college-level courses (Boyle et al., under review). Undergraduate students' experiences with proof are often limited to observing their instructors' model proof and being asked to mimic similar strategies on practice problems (Stylianou, Blanton, and Knuth 2009). Below is a vignette from Smith and colleagues (2009) depicting teacher-centered instruction in an introduction to proofs course:

> When asked to imagine a typical undergraduate "introduction to proof" or "transition" course, many readers would envision a university classroom with an instructor at the board lecturing about various proof techniques, such as induction or contradiction, giving a series of examples of each, and assigning proofs for the students to complete for homework. The students, mostly undergraduate mathematics majors, would dutifully take notes, ask a few questions, and then later attempt to replicate the proofs that were presented simply and logically in class. (p. 307)

The mathematical authority in such a course rests largely with the instructor. Students have little opportunity to actively construct and evaluate proofs, make sense of why a particular proof method (e.g., direct or indirect proof) is appropriate, or determine when a proof is complete.

We view learning as "increasing participation in communities of practice" (Lave and Wenger 1991, p. 49), and therefore students' increased participation in the practice of proving is a necessary component of learning mathematics. Mathematicians see proving as a social process and actively *negotiate* the validity of mathematical arguments (de Villiers 1990; Harel and Sowder 2007). Teacher-centered instruction, however, does not emphasize students' engagement in negotiation or active consideration of what counts as mathematical proof. Instead, students typically rely on their instructor as the authority and sole arbiter of their proofs (Harel and Sowder 2007).

Fortunately, alternative models of proof instruction have been successfully implemented. At the high school level, Fawcett (1938) and Healy (1993) described models of geometry instruction wherein students held primary responsibility for building their course textbook. Accounts from these classrooms depict students whose reasoning processes afford them legitimate mathematical authority. At the college level, Smith (2006) described an undergraduate transition-to-proof course employing the Modified Moore Method—a method of instruction where students hold responsibility for proving and presenting most of the course content. Students in this course worked on problems, presented their arguments to the class, and engaged in an instructor-facilitated discussion about the given problems. Blanton, Stylianou, and David (2009) described an undergraduate discrete mathematics course where the instructor presented a problem and students worked in small groups to solve the problem and construct proofs. Students explained their reasoning and challenged others' thinking throughout the course. In these classrooms, students were afforded autonomy to actively construct proofs and communicate ideas (Blanton, Stylianou, and David 2009; Smith 2006). As a result, students tended to use sense-making approaches to new problems, whereas their peers in traditional teacher-centered classrooms focused on getting the "correct" end product (Smith 2006).

The above studies show that students in reform-based classrooms gain a broader view of proof when they move beyond thinking of proof as a rigid format or structure and toward seeing proof as a means to communicate and make sense of mathematics (Healy 1993; Smith 2006). Students in these classrooms have opportunities to engage with mathematics that more closely resembles the practice of mathematicians (Fawcett 1938), and they quickly grow to see proof and mathematical reasoning as something that is both useful and accessible (Healy 1993).

To further increase students' legitimate participation in proving, it is also important to promote autonomy in their role as assessors of proof. As described by Nicol and Macfarlane-Dick (2006), "While students have been given more responsibility for learning in recent years there has been far greater reluctance to give them increased responsibility for assessment processes (even low stakes formative processes)" (p. 215). In this chapter, we describe an instructional model for assessment of proof writing that engaged undergraduates in actively and reflectively developing a rubric for writing proofs and self-regulating their learning of proof. Although this model was implemented in a transition-to-proofs course at the college level, we see it as applicable across grade levels and mathematical content domains.

■ Theoretical Framework

We frame our chapter using Earl's (2013) conceptualization of assessment *as* learning, wherein assessment is utilized as a tool for students to self-monitor and self-correct. Nicol and Macfarlane-Dick (2006) explain, "To develop systematically the learner's capacity for self-regulation, teachers need to create more structured opportunities for self-monitoring and the judging of progression to goals" (p. 207). Aligned with these perspectives, we view assessment not primarily as a metric for student performance, but rather as a means to deepen understanding of mathematical proof.

Earl (2013) contrasts assessment *as* learning with assessment *for* learning and assessment *of* learning. Assessment *for* learning informs instructional decision making (commonly termed formative assessment). Alternatively, assessment *of* learning measures student achievement at the end of a learning sequence (commonly termed summative assessment). In this chapter, we focus on assessment *as* learning, but we also describe how the class-developed rubric can be used for assessment *of* learning and assessment *for* learning.

■ Context

The instructional model described in this chapter was implemented during two semesters (fall 2013 and spring 2014) of an undergraduate-level transition-to-proofs course taught by the first author. Students were sophomores, juniors, and seniors who had completed calculus 2. The fall 2013 course enrolled four mathematics minors and twenty mathematics majors, five of whom were preservice secondary mathematics teachers (PSMTs). The spring 2014 course enrolled five mathematics minors and eleven mathematics majors, eight of whom were PSMTs. At the beginning of each semester, students wrote a reflection on their previous learning experiences with proof. The majority of students claimed to have little or no prior experience with proof. Students cited high school geometry or college-level calculus as their main experience with proof, typically through instructor presentation. Below is a representative reflection from Carla.

> For mathematical proofs during high school, they were few and far between. When we did by chance have them, they were complicated and not much sense was made . . . The only class that taught me any formal structure to proofs was Geometry, but to form my own is a new concept to me.

■ Communal Development of the Proof Rubric

For their first homework assignment, students developed a generalization and proof for two mathematical tasks: the Sticky Gum problem (Smith et al. n.d.) and the Growing S's problem (Smith, Silver, and Stein 2004). These tasks were selected because they are mathematically accessible, can be solved using a variety of strategies and representations, and elicit common misconceptions about what counts as proof. We focus here on the Growing S's problem, depicted in figure 9.1.

Question 1. Consider the pattern below. How many square tiles would there be in the eighth step of this pattern?

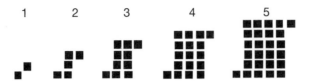

Question 2. Write an expression for the total number of square tiles in the figure at an arbitrary step *(n)* of the pattern.

Question 3. Prove that your expression is a valid representation of the number of tiles at step *n* of the pattern. You may use drawings, words, numbers, and/or symbols for your proof.

Fig. 9.1. The Growing S's problem

Students submitted their responses to the Growing S's problem through the course website two days before class. The instructor then reviewed the students' work and selected five sample arguments for students to critique during the subsequent class session, rewriting the chosen work for confidentiality. Figures 9.2, 9.3, and 9.4 illustrate three of the five sample arguments presented to students in fall 2013 (a different set was presented in spring 2014). The instructor selected sample arguments purposefully to provoke students' thinking in relation to proof writing. For example, figures 9.2–9.4 highlight differences between arguments that use particular cases as the sole justification for their generalization (fig. 9.3) and those that provide insight into why the generalization holds for all positive integers (figs. 9.2 and 9.4). Also, the instructor wished to highlight the diversity of possible representations used to develop $n^2 + 1$, but that conceptualized the pattern in different ways. More generally, the instructor anticipated the students would consider distinctions across the five arguments such as clarity, completeness, and correctness (Bénéteau, Bleiler, and Thompson 2014).

Upon receiving the five arguments, students worked individually to read each argument, decide whether or not they believed each was a proof, and provide a written rationale for their decision. After individually critiquing the five arguments, the instructor asked students to discuss their judgments and the related rationales in small groups. More specifically, the instructor asked each group to come to a consensus as to whether each of the five arguments was a proof, and to be able to justify their decision as a group. This group discussion was aimed at priming students to reflect on the criteria for what counts as proof.

Once students had come to a consensus in their small groups, the instructor asked each group to create a list of the criteria that were most important for determining if a particular argument should be considered proof. Each group recorded their criteria on chart paper and posted these around the room for other groups to consider. The instructor asked students to identify common criteria across the group posters and share their observations to develop a whole-class list.

Question 1. Consider the pattern below. How many square tiles would there be in the eighth step of this pattern?

In this pattern, the number of square tiles in the eighth step would be equal to 65.

Question 2. Write an expression for the total number of square tiles in the figure at an arbitrary step (n) of the pattern.

Let T be the total number of tiles and n be the step in the series. Then the series can be represented as:
$$T = n^2 + 1$$

Question 3. Prove that your expression is a valid representation of the number of tiles at step n of the pattern. You may use drawings, words, numbers, and/or symbols for your proof.

In each step of the equation, we are given (n+1) rows and (n+1) columns. From the first and last columns, we are missing n number of squares. From this, we get the equation:
$$T = (n+1)(n+1) - 2n$$

This means that for each step, we get a square made up of (n+1) rows and columns missing a unit squares from each side of the bigger square, which is representative of the pattern shown above. By simplifying the equation we can see
$$T = (n+1)(n+1) - 2n = n^2 + 2n + 1 - 2n \sim n^2 + 2n - 2n + 1 = n^2 + 1.$$
Therefore, as long as the pattern holds, the equation can be represented by: $T = n^2 + 1$.

Fig. 9.2. An argument that suggests why a generalization holds for all integers

---

Question 1. Consider the pattern below. How many square tiles would there be in the eighth step of this pattern?

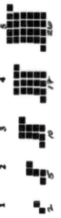

There would be 65 tiles in the 8th step.

Question 2. Write an expression for the total number of square tiles in the figure at an arbitrary step (n) of the pattern.

$$(n \times n) + 1$$

Question 3. Prove that your expression is a valid representation of the number of tiles at step n of the pattern. You may use drawings, words, numbers, and/or symbols for your proof.

Proof: Show that $(n \times n) + 1$ is a valid representation of the previous pattern shown.

Let n be the arbitrary step in the pattern. Let S equal the total number of square tiles in the pattern, then
$$(n \times n) + 1 = S$$

So let n be the 15th step, so you have $15 \times 15 = 225$ and according to our expression you add 1 to that which gives you 226, which equals the total number of tiles.

Fig. 9.3. An argument that relies solely on a particular case

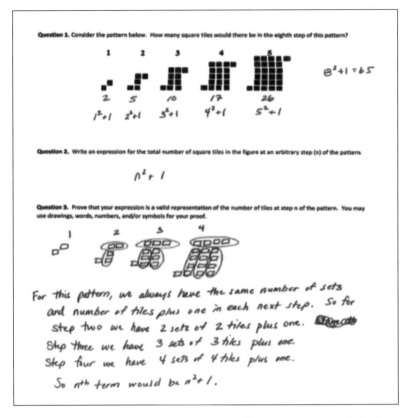

Fig. 9.4. An argument that, like that in figure 9.2, gives insight into
why a generalization holds for all integers

A volunteer from each group shared one commonality they noticed across all (or at least most) of the posters. For example, in the first group, Kiyana noticed that many of the group posters mentioned "showing why the pattern works in all cases." Because the common criteria were going to be used to create a course rubric, the instructor asked groups that had recorded a criterion similar to that identified by Kiyana to expand on what they were thinking. Groups shared reflections such as "The proof should apply to all possible values," "The proof should answer the question why, not just state the correct formula," "The conclusion should be stated in general terms rather than for a specific example or case," and "It is helpful if the proof makes connections between the examples and the general formula." Once the class as a whole decided that they understood what was meant by the descriptors in this category, the instructor asked the students to name the category. For this particular criterion, the students named the category "Generalization."

The same process was used to determine the other criteria that would be used in the initial draft of their rubric. After the class, the instructor returned to the notes recorded from the whole-class discussion and organized the students' thoughts into a draft rubric (see fig. 9.5). In addition, the instructor omitted some of the specificity of the language shared by students so that (*a*) the criteria could more easily be applied to different problem contexts and types of proofs and (*b*) the rubric would be easy to read with short, bulleted descriptors.

Proof Criterion	Clear identification of parameters, constraints, and assumptions	Generalization	Chain of Evidence, Structure, and Clarity	Validity/Correctness
Descriptors	• Define the statement of the problem and the givens. • Define all variables. • Explain the boundaries of the solution (e.g., which numbers or number systems for which the proof works). • Make explicit all assumptions.	• Proof should apply to all situations/ values within the specified parameters. • Answer the question "why?" • The conclusion should be stated in general terms. • Make connection between concrete examples and generalization.	• Demonstrate reasoning that follows a logical sequence. • Argument is clear, complete, concise, and simplified. • Consider including elements to clarify argument, such as generalized visual representations, or concrete examples.	• Proof conclusion is valid/correct/true.

Fig. 9.5. The initial draft of the rubric developed by the fall 2013 class

■ Communal Evolution of the Proof Rubric

The instructor informed the students that they would use and revise this rubric throughout the semester. Thus, the students understood that the rubric was a work in progress that could be modified if it did not adequately serve the needs of their class community. Figure 9.6 shows the final class rubric after several revisions made throughout fall 2013. The items in bold print indicate places where modifications were made.

Proof Criterion	Clear identification of parameters, constraints, and assumptions	Generalization	Chain of Evidence, Structure, and Clarity	Validity/Correctness
Descriptors	a1. Define the statement of the problem and the givens. a2. Define all variables. a3. Explain the boundaries of the solution (e.g., which numbers or number systems for which the proof works). a4. Make explicit all assumptions.	b1. Proof should apply to all situations/values within the specified parameters. b2. Answer the question "why?" **(see also, c1 and c4).** b3. The conclusion should be stated in general terms. b4. Make connection between concrete examples and generalization **(if applicable).**	c1. Demonstrate reasoning that follows a logical sequence. c2. Argument is clear, complete, concise, and simplified. c3. Consider including elements to clarify argument, such as generalized visual representations, or concrete examples. **c4. Make explicit use of definitions to aid in the precision and clarity of your argument.**	d1. Proof conclusion is valid/correct/true.

Fig. 9.6. The final version of the rubric developed by the fall 2013 class

As depicted in figure 9.6, students decided to provide a name/label for each criterion (e.g., "a1") so that they could more easily refer to the categories when discussing proofs in their group. They added "see also, c1 and c4" to b2 to remind themselves that demonstrating logical reasoning and using definitions can be useful to explain *why* a mathematical result is true. They added the phrase "if applicable" to b4 because, as the semester progressed, they recognized that concrete examples are not necessary for constructing an acceptable proof but can help clarify an argument. Finally, they added an entire subcategory (c4) pointing to the importance of explicit use of definitions to aid in the precision and clarity of proofs (a criterion of little importance in the Sticky Gum or Growing S's problems, but of greater importance in later course topics such as set theory).

Students in both semesters of the course had approximately three separate opportunities to revisit and revise the rubric as a class community. In neither semester did the students make substantial edits to their original rubric. This suggests that the original tasks (Sticky Gum and Growing S's) and the related sample students' arguments served as a good foundation for considering the criteria necessary for a complete and valid proof. Once the rubric was in place, students focused their attention on how the rubric categories related to the proofs they constructed. Through application and discussion of the rubric criteria, the class was able to further develop their communal understanding of what counts as proof.

■ Assessment Roles of the Class-Developed Rubric
Assessment *as* Learning

The class-developed rubric engaged students in assessment *as* a means to learn about proof. Through developing communal criteria for what counts as proof, students actively made sense of the complex nature of proof construction. In addition, students used the rubric to evaluate their own arguments throughout the semester. For example, figure 9.7 depicts Jalen's self-evaluation of his original argument for the Growing S's problem. (Jalen's original argument is depicted in fig. 9.4.) In returning to his original argument with the rubric categories in mind, Jalen was able to further his understanding of the class-developed criteria in a meaningful context (i.e., his own argument). Furthermore, self-evaluations provided students with the opportunity to improve their original arguments, attending to the criteria for which they scored lowest.

Students had opportunities to carefully evaluate instructor-selected sample arguments for a variety of problems throughout the semester. Additionally, small groups constructed and presented proofs during class, expecting questions and critique after the presentation. Students regularly referred to subcategories of the rubric to describe strengths of their peers' arguments or to identify areas for improvement. Because the students developed the rubric, they felt empowered to use it to communicate their reasoning and ideas.

At the end of the semester, students described the ways they used the class-developed rubric. The following is a representative description shared by Nathan:

> When writing proofs that I was struggling with at the time, I would write an argument and then use the rubric to double-check my own work. This was employed so heavily during the more difficult proofs because I felt like a lot of times I was doing something incorrectly. This rubric helped me double-check if I was or wasn't.

Nathan's reflection, together with those of his peers, suggested that the rubric was used consistently throughout the semester to self-regulate proof learning.

Question 1: Copy our class-developed criteria for a compelling/convincing argument in the first column, and then complete the remainder of the table based on your original written argument for the Growing S's Problem.		
Class-developed criteria for proof writing.	On a scale of 0-5 (0 = not at all, 5 = completely), how well does your argument meet each criterion?	Explain your rationale for your numeric rating by making explicit reference to your original argument.
Clear identification of parameters/constraints, and assumptions	1	did not give all parameters and assumptions; did not state/claim in terms of pattern remains constant.
Generalization - answer question "why"? conclusion stated in general term	2	in question 4 I state it with term but it does not come up a generalization? idea answer why?
Chain of evidence, structure, and clarity. argument is clear/complete	2	argument is not very clear, I do not clearly show chain of evidence so "argument" is not conveyed
Validity/Correctness - Proof/conclusion valid/constructive	4	Proof is valid and correct but from previous, claim of evidence is not correct

Fig. 9.7. Jalen's self-evaluation of his original argument for the Growing S's problem

■ Assessment *for* Learning and Assessment *of* Learning

Although the main role of the class-developed rubric was to facilitate students' self-regulated learning (i.e., assessment *as* learning), it was also used by the instructor to assess their work formatively (i.e., assessment *for* learning) and summatively (i.e., assessment *of* learning). For example, the instructor analyzed students' proofs prior to class and identified categories (or subcategories) of the rubric with which students struggled. This helped the instructor prepare purposeful questions and activities that would push students to deepen their understanding.

With respect to summative assessment, students received an assessment feedback sheet for each assigned problem set. The assessment sheet contained a copy of the rubric, a statement of the problem being graded, and the instructor's feedback indicating the areas of the rubric students would need to revisit. When using the rubric for assessment *of* learning, students were still encouraged to use feedback to revise their original problem sets.

■ Discussion

Most uses of rubrics related to proof have been focused on assessment *of* learning or assessment *for* learning (e.g., Brown and Michel 2010). Our instructional model positions the rubric as a tool for assessment *as* learning, where students are encouraged to become self-regulated learners. The activity involving the Sticky Gum problem and the Growing S's problem helped students actively and critically reflect on what should and should not count as proof. Therefore, the instructor did not grade these initial arguments. Instead, the students critiqued a set of their peers' arguments and developed a list of criteria to describe what constitutes proof. Students then revisited, self-evaluated, and revised their initial arguments based on the class-developed criteria.

Throughout the semester, students used the rubric as a tool to start constructing proofs, a "checklist" to consider after constructing a proof, and a prompt when critiquing peers' arguments. Students also revised the rubric based on their developing experiences and understandings of proof. Their focus on particular components of the rubric changed as the semester progressed. For example, at the beginning of the semester, students focused largely on the "generalization" category of their rubric. This might be due to the fact that some students were still trying to understand the difference between inductive and deductive arguments. Through regular negotiation of the validity of sample inductive and deductive arguments, all students in the class agreed that examples were useful to gain insight into a mathematical proposition but were insufficient as proof in their community. At this point they began to direct their attention elsewhere in the rubric. In particular, they paid more attention to the refinement and communication of their arguments, frequently referring to "chain of evidence, clarity, and structure."

As the semester progressed, students discussed the relative necessity of each criterion in the rubric. While they acknowledged, for example, that restating the problem (a1, fig. 9.6) would clarify the argument, they agreed it was not necessary for the argument to count as proof. Conversely, they discussed how attending to boundaries of the problem (a3) was critical in order for the proof to be generalized to all possible cases (b1), something the class accepted as essential for any mathematical proof. Hence, rather than simply accept written conventions of proofs (typically introduced either explicitly or implicitly by the instructor), students' consideration of the relative importance of each criterion facilitated their meaningful understanding of those conventions.

In any form of assessment, it is critical that there is consistency between instructor goals and student achievement of those goals (Nicol and Macfarlane-Dick 2006). Although the students in this study developed the rubric, their criteria were consistent with those understood by the instructor (and the larger mathematics community of practice). The selection of the task and the sample student work were critical to the achievement of such consistency. The instructor selected arguments that would highlight important distinctions and criteria for proof writing so that students' criteria would align reasonably with that of the mathematics community.

■ Conclusion

Students should be positioned with autonomy in their learning and construction of ideas related to proof within the classroom. In this chapter, we offer an instructional model that engages students in actively developing a rubric for writing proofs, as well as increases their opportunities for self-regulation in learning proof. Engaging in assessment *as* learning through the development and utilization of a rubric allowed students to learn proof as a communal, negotiated, and sense-making process.

References

Bénéteau, Catherine, Sarah K. Bleiler, and Denisse R. Thompson. "Promoting Mathematical Reasoning through Critiquing Student Work." In *Annual Perspectives in Mathematics Education 2014: Using Research to Improve Instruction,* edited by Karen Karp, pp. 151–60. Reston, Va.: NCTM, 2014.

Blanton, Maria, L., Despina A. Stylianou, and M. Manuela David. "Understanding Instructional Scaffolding in Classroom Discourse on Proof." In *Teaching and Learning Proof across the Grades: A K–16 Perspective,* edited by Despina A. Stylianou, Maria L. Blanton, and Eric J. Knuth, pp. 290–306. New York: Routledge, 2009.

Boyle, Justin D., Sarah K. Bleiler, Yi-Yin (Winnie) Ko, and Sean P. Yee. "Constructing and Critiquing Arguments: A Case of *How* to Determine What Is Proof." Under review.

Brown, David E., and Shayla Michel. "Assessing Proofs with Rubrics: The RVF Method." In *Proceedings of the 13th Annual Conference on Research in Undergraduate Mathematics Education.* Raleigh, N.C., February 25–28, 2010.

Conference Board of the Mathematical Sciences (CBMS). *The Mathematical Education of Teachers II.* Providence, R.I., and Washington, D.C.: American Mathematical Society and Mathematical Association of America, 2012.

de Villiers, Michael. "The Role and Function of Proof in Mathematics." *Pythagoras* 24 (1990): 17–24.

Earl, Lorna M. *Assessment as Learning: Using Classroom Assessment to Maximize Student Learning.* Thousand Oaks, Calif.: Corwin, 2013.

Fawcett, Harold P. *The Nature of Proof.* The Thirteenth Yearbook of the National Council of Teachers of Mathematics (NCTM), edited by W. D. Reeve. Washington D.C.: NCTM, 1938.

Harel, Guershon, and Larry Sowder. "Toward Comprehensive Perspectives on the Learning and Teaching of Proof." In *Second Handbook of Research on Mathematics Teaching and Learning,* edited by Frank K. Lester, pp. 805–42. Charlotte, N.C.: Information Age Publishing, 2007.

Healy, Charles C. "Discovery Courses Are Great in Theory, But . . ." In *The Geometric Supposer: What Is It a Case Of?,* edited by Judah L. Schwartz, Michal Yerushalmy, and Beth Wilson, pp. 85–106. Hillsdale, N.J.: Lawrence Erlbaum Associates, 1993.

Lave, Jean, and Etienne Wenger. *Situated Learning: Legitimate Peripheral Participation.* Cambridge, U.K.: Cambridge University Press, 1991.

National Council of Teachers of Mathematics (NCTM). *Principles and Standards for School Mathematics.* Reston, Va.: NCTM, 2000.

National Governors Association Center for Best Practices and Council of Chief State School Officers (NGA Center and CCSSO). *Common Core State Standards for Mathematics.* Washington, D.C.: NGA Center and CCSSO, 2010.

Nicol, David J., and Debra Macfarlane-Dick. "Formative Assessment and Self-Regulated Learning: A Model and Seven Principles of Good Feedback Practice." *Studies in Higher Education* 31, no. 2 (2006): 199–218.

Smith, Jennifer Christian. "A Sense-Making Approach to Proof: Strategies of Students in Traditional and Problem-Based Number Theory Courses." *Journal of Mathematical Behavior* 25 (2006): 73–90.

Smith, Jennifer Christian, Stephanie Ryan Nichols, Sera Too, and Kury Oehler. "Building a Community of Inquiry in a Problem-Based Undergraduate Number Theory Course: The Role of the Instructor." In *Teaching and Learning Proof across the Grades: A K–16 Perspective,* edited by Despina A. Stylianou, Maria L. Blanton, and Eric J. Knuth, pp. 307–22. New York: Routledge, 2009.

Smith, Margaret Schwan, Edward A. Silver, and Mary Kay Stein. *Improving Instruction in Algebra: Using Cases to Transform Mathematics Teaching and Learning.* New York: Teachers College Press, 2004.

Smith, Margaret Schwan, et al. *Cases of Reasoning-and-Proving in Secondary Mathematics: A Curriculum for the Professional Education of Teachers.* Manuscript in preparation, n.d.

Stylianides, Andreas. "Proof and Proving in School Mathematics." *Journal for Research in Mathematics Education* 38 (2007): 289–321.

Stylianou, Despina A., Maria L. Blanton, and Eric Knuth. *Teaching and Learning Proof across the Grades: A K–16 Perspective.* New York: Routledge, 2009.

Thompson, Denisse. R., Sharon L. Senk, and Gwendolyn J. Johnson. "Opportunities to Learn Reasoning and Proof in High School Mathematics Textbooks." *Journal for Research in Mathematics Education* 43, no. 3 (2012): 253–95.

CHAPTER 10

Secondary Teachers' Mathematical Habits of Mind: A Paper-and-Pencil Assessment

Sarah Sword, *Education Development Center, Inc., Waltham, Massachusetts*

Ryota Matsuura, *St. Olaf College, Northfield, Minnesota*

Miriam Gates, *Education Development Center, Inc., Waltham, Massachusetts*

Jane Kang, *Education Development Center, Inc., Waltham, Massachusetts*

Al Cuoco, *Education Development Center, Inc., Waltham, Massachusetts*

Glenn Stevens, *Boston University, Boston, Massachusetts*

Much more important than specific mathematical results are the habits of mind used by the people who create those results. . . . The goal is not to train large numbers of high school students to be university mathematicians. Rather, it is to help high school students learn and adopt some of the ways that mathematicians *think* about problems. . . . Although it is necessary to infuse courses and curricula with modern content, what is even more important is to give students the tools they will need in order to use, understand, and even make mathematics that does not yet exist. (Cuoco, Goldenberg, and Mark 1996, pp. 375–76)

■ Introduction

Teachers' development of mathematical habits of mind (MHoM) has been a focus of work for more than a decade. This focus is important for two reasons. First, current standards are aligned with this way of thinking (see the following section on "The Need for Mathematical Habits of Mind"). Teachers need MHoM because they are expected to provide opportunities for their students to develop those habits. Second, strong MHoM (e.g., recognizing structural similarities in different mathematical ideas) can empower teachers by bringing focus and coherence to how they think mathematically and to their work with students (Cuoco 2008; Cuoco, Goldenberg, and Mark 1996; Cuoco, Goldenberg, and Mark 2010; National Council of Teachers of Mathematics [NCTM] 2014; Seeley 2014).

Teachers have reported that developing MHoM strongly affects their teaching. Observations suggest that how these teachers talk about mathematics places less emphasis on specific mathematical results and more emphasis on ways of thinking (Lee, Baldassari, and Leblang 2006; Lee et al. 2007; Lee et al. 2009). Most important, there is evidence that MHoM are habits teachers can acquire, rather than some static you-have-it-or-you-don't way of thinking.

Recognizing the need to investigate how teachers use MHoM in their teaching, and how those habits can change over time, we began research centered on the question:

> What mathematical habits of mind do secondary teachers use, how do they use them, and how can we measure them?

Instruments to measure these habits did not exist when we began our work. We articulated habits we thought would be useful for teachers to cultivate, and we created related instruments, a paper-and-pencil assessment of teachers' MHoM, and tools for observing teaching practice. We would like to highlight three things:

1. We are creating instruments for research and development, *not* for teacher evaluation. The instruments are intended to help researchers, district leaders, and professional developers better understand and meet the mathematical needs of secondary teachers.

2. We are developing an articulation of MHoM, a paper-and-pencil assessment, and observation tools together. This has been a synergistic effort. For instance, classroom observations have suggested assessment items, and teacher work on the assessment has sharpened the articulation of habits.

3. This work is ongoing.

We want to emphasize that our research is centered on understanding the nature of MHoM and the roles these habits play in teaching. We recognize, however, that MHoM constitute just one aspect of a broad spectrum of knowledge and skills that teachers bring to their profession.

This chapter focuses on the paper-and-pencil assessment designed to measure secondary teachers' MHoM. We begin by discussing the habits we chose as foci. We then share characteristics of the assessment. Finally, we describe two assessment items to illustrate concretely *what* we are measuring and *how* we are measuring it.

The Need for Mathematical Habits of Mind

Among the eight Mathematics Teaching Practices in NCTM's *Principles to Actions* are several that depend on teachers' MHoM for implementation (NCTM 2014). For example, teachers expected to "use and connect mathematical representations" in their teaching practice must be able to create, choose, and use representations themselves. Similarly, to teach their students how to "struggle productively," teachers must have a sense of how to do that in their own mathematics practice. We see each of these as important MHoM. For detailed examples of teachers drawing on their MHoM to implement practices similar to those outlined in the Mathematics Teaching Practices, see Matsuura and colleagues (2013b).

Similarly, there is significant overlap between the Common Core Standards for Mathematical Practice for students and the conception of MHoM for teachers. For example, the seventh mathematical practice standard (MP.7) states, "Look for and make use of structure," which is also core to MHoM. Practice MP.7 is explained as:

> Mathematically proficient students look closely to discern a pattern or structure. . . . In the expression $x^2 + 9x + 14$, older students can see the 14 as 2×7 and the 9 as $2 + 7$ . . . They can see complicated things, such as some algebraic expressions, as single objects or as being composed of several objects. For example, they can see $5 - 3(x - y)^2$ as 5 minus a

positive number times a square and use that to realize that its value cannot be more than 5 for any real numbers x and y. (National Governors Association Center for Best Practices and Council of Chief State School Officers [NGA Center and CCSSO] 2010, p. 8)

Likewise, the Mathematical Education of Teachers II (MET2) report states: "Expert high school teachers should know mathematics in at least four overlapping ways" (Conference Board of the Mathematical Sciences [CBMS] 2012, p. 65). One of those ways is "as *educators*. They should understand the habits of mind that underlie different branches—arithmetic, algebra, geometry . . . and how these develop in learners" (p. 65). Another of the four ways is as *mathematicians*:

> They should have experienced a sustained immersion in mathematics that includes performing experiments and grappling with problems, building abstractions as a result of reflection on the experiments, and developing theories that bring coherence to the abstractions. (p. 65)

But what counts as evidence that a teacher "knows mathematics as a mathematician"? How can we track teacher growth or learn to improve professional development (PD) programs? How does this knowledge affect teaching practice and student outcomes? Well-aligned assessment tools allow the field to investigate these questions.

■ What Mathematical Habits Are We Assessing?

A concrete definition of MHoM drives our work:

> MHoM are the specialized ways of approaching mathematical problems and thinking about mathematical concepts that resemble the ways mathematicians employ.

The MHoM framework is one important aspect of the knowledge required in the work of teaching mathematics. Certainly, it is not the *only* aspect. We have seen that having strong MHoM is not enough for teachers to provide opportunities for students to develop those habits. Likewise, we have seen teachers who draw primarily on other kinds of knowledge and skills to do excellent work with students. However, given evolving notions of what constitutes content knowledge for students, such as in the Standards for Mathematical Practice, this way of thinking is ever more essential for teachers.

We are currently measuring mathematical habits selected using a methodological process (described in Matsuura et al. 2013a). Focusing on these habits has allowed us to create an assessment that is not too burdensome to use. In this chapter, we will emphasize our work with two such habits: EXPR (Engaging with one's experiences) and STRC (Making use of structure to solve problems). We define each in turn:

> **EXPR—Engaging with one's experiences.** This habit is about what one does when faced with new ideas. Its purpose includes (1) understanding the meaning, context, and purpose of a given situation and (2) finding general, unifying principles that provide insight and explanatory power. The habit has two main components, distinguished according to *how* understanding is sought.
>
> One component is *using language to acquire clarity and understanding of one's experience*. Language can serve to both unpack and compress complex ideas. Thus, the process of clearly describing "what's going on" facilitates sense making by organizing and framing one's experience.

Another critical component is *experimenting*. Examples of the experimental process may include (*a*) working with smaller or special cases, (*b*) seeking regularity and/or coherence in repeated calculations, (*c*) finding and explaining patterns, and (*d*) generalizing from examples.

STRC—Making use of structure to solve problems. This habit entails taking advantage of the underlying structure of a given situation to facilitate problem solving. Examples of this habit may include (*a*) creating, choosing, and/or using representations, (*b*) writing expressions in equivalent forms to solve problems, (*c*) interpreting and making use of the structure of expressions, and (*d*) "chunking" to delay or avoid thinking about certain details in order to see the big picture.

This habit is closely related to EXPR. Broadly speaking, EXPR may be viewed as being about *understanding* structure, while STRC is about *using* structure. But they are not mutually exclusive.

These habits are aligned with the MET2 recommendations and are closely related to two of the Common Core Standards for Mathematical Practice:

1. MP.7: Look for and make use of structure

2. MP.8: Look for and express regularity in repeated reasoning (NGA Center and CCSSO 2010)

While we recognize that there can be overlaps, we envision the "make use of structure" from MP.7 as primarily aligned with the habit STRC. The "look for . . . structure" from MP.7 and MP.8 are likewise closely related to the habit EXPR. Looking for structure is part of what one does when faced with new ideas, and as such is an aspect of EXPR. Looking for and expressing regularity in repeated reasoning is an example of the kind of activity one might engage as part of EXPR.

■ Features of the Assessment

The assessment has several distinguishing features:

- It focuses on MHoM—the ways of thinking through which mathematics is created, rather than on specific results.

- It focuses on teachers' *approaches* to items, and not whether they can arrive at solutions. Items are designed so that most teachers have the requisite knowledge to solve, or at least begin to solve. We will elaborate on this in the sections below on the Maximum Value and the Two Products items.

- Items are drawn from multiple sources, including classroom observation work (see Matsuura et al. 2013b for related observational work).

- We have involved mathematicians who think deeply about the implications of their own MHoM for precollege learning and teaching, education researchers who conduct similar assessment work in other contexts, and statisticians and methodologists who help us with decision making.

We have completed several rounds of field tests with a total of more than 400 teachers, and continue to field-test (Matsuura et al. 2013a). We have refined the assessment items as follows:

- Items must be accessible and situated in secondary content. If the mathematical content of an item was not accessible to most secondary teachers, we deleted or revised the item.

- If most teachers solved an item in only one way, we dropped the item. We seek items that elicit a variety of approaches.

- We deleted items for which we could not categorize teachers' approaches easily. This often meant eliminating "interesting" problems. Items eliciting many unique responses—although fun to work on—have not been useful for measurement purposes.

- Although we originally situated most items in classroom settings, we often dropped that context. Since the assessment captures *teachers'* MHoM, that may seem counterintuitive. However, we are investigating MHoM that teachers use when they are doing mathematics *for themselves*. The classroom context often proved distracting to teachers.

■ *Maximum Value* **Item**

To illustrate what we mean by capturing teachers' approaches, consider the item *Maximum Value*, intended to measure the habit STRC: *Making use of structure to solve problems*. It asks:

Find the maximum value of the function $f(x) = 11 - (3x - 4)^2$.

Note the close relationship between this item and the one described in MP.7: "they can see $5 - 3(x - y)^2$ as 5 minus a positive number times a square and use that to realize that its value cannot be more than 5 for any real numbers x and y" (NGA Center and CCSSO 2010, p. 8). We modified the item for greater accessibility and to invite more diversity in the approaches.

In field tests, most teachers solved the item correctly using some method—i.e., most knew the "content." However, we saw variation in their approaches. These approaches tended to come in "clumps," where groups of teachers used the same kinds of approaches. Using teacher responses, we developed a rubric that allows us to code how each teacher solved the problem.

For example, some recognized that $(3x - 4)^2$ represents the square of some number, so it is greater than or equal to 0. Thus in $f(x) = 11 - (3x - 4)^2$, we are subtracting a non-negative number from 11. To maximize $f(x)$, we need $(3x - 4)^2 = 0$ so the maximum value is 11. Figure 10.1 shows a sample teacher solution. This reasoning depends on the fact that x can be chosen so that $(3x - 4)^2 = 0$. We often could not tell whether the teachers noticed this, and therefore we chose not to consider it in the rubric.

$f(x) = 11 - (3x - 4)^2$. Anything squared is ≥ 0.

Therefore, $11 - (\text{stuff squared})$ must be ≤ 11. So 11 is the max.

Fig. 10.1. A sample teacher solution to the *Maximum Value* item

Some teachers used transformations of the graph of $y = f(x)$. Others used calculus. Another common approach involved finding the axis of symmetry of the graph of $y = f(x)$. Again, we are coding/categorizing teacher solutions according to the approach taken. Thus, we disregard minor errors as long as the intent of the approach is clear from their solutions (e.g., using $x = -b/a$ for axis of symmetry formula).

This item is intended to measure the habit STRC: *Making use of structure to solve problems*. In $f(x) = 11 - (3x - 4)^2$ we can immediately see the maximum value of the function. The solution in figure 10.1 shows how the teacher uses the underlying structure of this expression, demonstrating strong alignment with STRC. On the other hand, consider the approach involving expanding $f(x)$ into standard form (i.e., $f(x) = -9x^2 + 24x - 5$), and then finding the axis of symmetry using the formula $x = -b/(2a)$. Even if the solution is correct, this approach does not address the underlying algebraic structure of the expression.

The mathematical habits we described above are not mutually exclusive. When working on the assessment items, teachers may use multiple habits in conjunction, or habits that are outside the scope of the current study. However, we have aimed to develop items that *highlight* the use of a single habit.

■ *Two Products* Item

Another item, intended to measure habit EXPR: *Engaging with one's experiences*, asks:

Use the fact that $1764 \times 1765 = 3113460$ to find 1762×1767. Explain your thinking.

In field tests, most teachers found some way to approach this item. We saw a variety of solution methods:

1. Calculating 1762×1767 longhand.

2. Using simpler examples—e.g., start with 8×9 and 6×11 and notice that they differ by 6. Teachers often try several examples before noticing that the products always differ by 6. They conclude *without further justification* that the solution is 3113454.

3. Articulating an underlying algebraic structure: the original product has the form $x(x + 1) = x^2 + x$ and the new product has the form $(x - 2)(x + 3) = x^2 + x - 6$. Thus the latter must be 6 less than the former. We have seen this approach carried out to different degrees. For example, some teachers recognized and described the structure but were unsure how to *use* it to solve the problem.

4. Articulating an underlying arithmetic structure: one teacher wrote, "2 groups of 1765 removed from 3113460" and "2 groups of 1762 added," and then used the distributive property to show that the solution is 6 less than 3113460 (see fig. 10.2). We have seen many interesting versions of this approach.

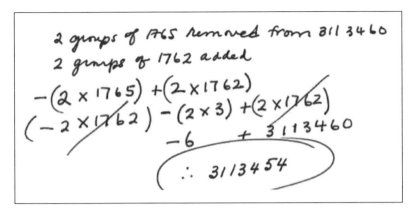

Fig. 10.2. A sample teacher solution (approach #4) to the *Two Products* item

This item is intended to measure the habit EXPR: *Engaging with one's experiences*. It gives concrete experiences—namely, the products 1764×1765 and 1762×1767—and it asks teachers to make sense of these products. Approaches #3 and #4 articulate the underlying relationship between these products. They demonstrate the use of mathematical language to describe the nature of this relationship, leading to acquisition of clarity and understanding of one's experiences. Approach #1, although dealing with the experience itself, does not take the next step to unravel the meaning and purpose of this experience. While approach #2 recreates similar experiences, clear articulation of what makes those experiences similar—a general, unifying principle that provides explanatory power—is missing.

Although the habits EXPR and STRC are closely related, we see this item as measuring the habit EXPR. Recall from the section above on mathematical habits that EXPR is about *understanding* the structure of a given situation, while STRC is about *using* structure. In this item, the underlying relationship of the two products is not readily apparent. Some work is needed (either through using language, symbols, or experimenting) to uncover this relationship. The articulations seen in approaches #3 and #4 are culminations of the *engagement* with the task at hand and thus show strong alignment with EXPR.

Challenges of building this assessment have included developing the rubrics and categorizing individual teachers' responses. The questions that arise as we consider teacher responses center around what can be inferred from written work:

- How can we ensure that we are indeed measuring MHoM and not simply capturing teachers' prior (traditional) knowledge of mathematics?

- What constitutes evidence of a "way of thinking" or "intent of an approach"? How much must a partial response include to fit into a particular category? A solution like the one in figure 10.3, with no further work shown, is not uncommon.

$$x \cdot (x+1) = x^2 + x$$
$$(x-2)(x+3) = x^2 + x - 6$$

Fig. 10.3. A common partial response to the *Two Products* item

Analyzing the Assessment Results

The rubrics development (i.e., sorting teacher responses according to approaches taken and deriving codes from these approaches) is supported by research literature (Erickson 1998; Glaser and Strauss 1967; Guba 1978). To conduct initial validity and reliability testing, two research mathematicians assigned a numerical value to each code/approach based on its alignment with the habits that each item is intended to measure. In the future, we will invite a larger panel of experts to help us with this coding process.

The assessment development involves an iterative process of design, field-testing, data analysis, and revision. We recently completed a field test involving thirty-nine secondary teachers. We also collected information such as their educational background, teaching experience, and grade levels and courses they teach.

In our analysis (Matsuura et al. 2013a) two researchers independently coded all responses, using the rubric for each item. For all but one assessment item, the Kappa value was greater than 0.80, indicating very strong inter-rater reliability (Hallgren 2012). Using data from our teacher sample, we measured the internal consistency reliability of the assessment and found Cronbach's Alpha value of 0.87, well above the generally accepted threshold of 0.7 for a reasonably reliable instrument (Nunnally 1978). We checked for construct validity of the assessment using principal component analysis, and we conducted exploratory analysis of item discrimination. We also studied the relationship between teachers' professional background and their assessment responses. Our latest field test includes a sample of more than 200 teachers.

Use of the Assessment

We re-emphasize that this is *not* an assessment to evaluate individual teachers' mathematical knowledge. Rather, it is a research tool. We are using it both to better understand what MHoM secondary teachers bring to their practice and to evaluate the impact of our own PD on teachers' mathematical thinking. A number of other groups are using it as formative assessment for teachers in selecting or designing PD, or as pre- and post-testing to measure impact of PD. The *Changing Curriculum, Changing Practice* (National Science Foundation DRL-1019945) project is using the assessment to investigate the conjecture that high school teachers' implementation of a curriculum emphasizing MHoM will lead to measurable changes in teachers' mathematical knowledge, as well as to explore the relationships among teachers' use of MHoM for themselves and their use of a particular curriculum. Concrete results from studies like these can provide information that will ultimately lead to enhancing students' experiences of learning mathematics.

■ Conclusion

With the widespread adoption of the Common Core State Standards, the notion of mathematical content has changed. *Look for and express regularity in repeated reasoning* (MP.8), for example, is now considered core content for students (NGA Center and CCSSO 2010). Learning to think mathematically is a ticket to success in a range of fields, such as business, finance, STEM-related disciplines, and even building trades. To provide students opportunities to meet the Standards for Mathematical Practice, teachers must develop their own mathematical thinking in ways that are aligned with those practices.

This paper-and-pencil research instrument is intended to help the field better understand and meet the mathematical needs of secondary teachers. As we better understand these needs and how to meet them, we can better prepare teachers to meet the ideals expressed in our opening quotation: "to give students the tools they will need in order to use, understand, and even make mathematics that does not yet exist."

(*Note:* This paper is based upon work supported by the National Science Foundation under Grants No. DRL-1222496, DRL-1222426, and DRL-1222340. Any opinions, findings, and conclusions or recommendations expressed in the paper are those of the authors and do not necessarily reflect the views of the National Science Foundation.)

References

Conference Board of the Mathematical Sciences (CBMS). *The Mathematical Education of Teachers II.* Providence, R.I., and Washington, D.C.: American Mathematical Society and Mathematical Association of America, 2012.

Cuoco, Al. "Introducing Extensible Tools in Middle- and High-School Algebra." In *Algebra and Algebraic Thinking in School Mathematics,* 2008 Yearbook of the National Council of Teachers of Mathematics (NCTM), edited by Carole Greenes, pp. 51–62. Reston, Va.: NCTM, 2008.

Cuoco, Al, E. Paul Goldenberg, and June Mark. "Habits of Mind: An Organizing Principle for Mathematics Curriculum." *Journal of Mathematical Behavior* 15, no. 4 (1996): 375–402.

———. "Contemporary Curriculum Issues: Organizing a Curriculum around Mathematical Habits of Mind." *Mathematics Teacher* 103, no. 9 (2010): 682–8.

Erickson, Frederick. "Qualitative research methods for science education." In *International Handbook of Science Education*, edited by Barry J. Fraser and Kenneth Tobin, pp. 1155–73. Dordrecht, The Netherlands: Kluwer Academic Publishers, 1998.

Glaser, Barney G., and Anselm L. Strauss. *The Discovery of Grounded Theory: Strategies for Qualitative Research.* Chicago: Aldine Publishing Company, 1967.

Guba, Egon G. *Toward a Methodology of Naturalistic Inquiry in Educational Evaluation.* Monograph Series 8. Los Angeles: UCLA Center for the Study of Evaluation, 1978.

Hallgren, Kevin A. "Computing Inter-Rater Reliability for Observational Data: An Overview and Tutorial." *Tutorials in Quantitative Methods for Psychology* 8, no. 1 (2012): 23–34.

Lee, Sabra, Carol Baldassari, and Judith Leblang. *Focus on Mathematics: Creating Learning Cultures for High Student Achievement Year 3 Evaluation Report* 2006. Available from http://focusonmath.org/FOM/PERG.

Lee, Sabra, Carol Baldassari, Judith Leblang, and Elizabeth Osche. *Focus on Mathematics: Creating Learning Cultures for High Student Achievement Summative Evaluation Report 2009.* Cambridge, Mass.: Program Evaluation and Research Group at Lesley University, 2009.

Lee, Sabra, Carol Baldassari, Judith Leblang, Elizabeth Osche, and Samara Hoyer-Winfield. *Focus on Mathematics: Creating Learning Cultures for High Student Achievement Year 4 Evaluation Report 2007*. Cambridge, Mass.: Program Evaluation and Research Group at Lesley University, 2007.

Matsuura, R., S. Sword, R. Faux, M. Gates, A. Cuoco, G. Stevens, and M. B. Piecham. "Framing and Measuring Mathematical Habits of Mind: A Component of Mathematical knowledge for Teaching." *Assessing Secondary Teachers' Habits of Mind,* 2013a.

Matsuura, R., S. Sword, M. B. Piecham, G. Stevens, and A. Cuoco. "Mathematical Habits of Mind for Teaching: Using Language in Algebra Classrooms." *Mathematics Enthusiast* 10, no. 3 (2013b): 735–76.

National Council of Teachers of Mathematics (NCTM). *Principles to Actions: Ensuring Mathematics Success for All*. Reston, Va.: NCTM, 2014.

National Governors Association Center for Best Practices and Council of Chief State School Officers (NGA Center and CCSSO). *Common Core State Standards for Mathematics*. Washington, D.C.: NGA Center and CCSSO, 2010.

Nunnally, Jum C. *Psychometric Theory*. 2nd ed. New York: McGraw-Hill, 1978.

Seeley, Cathy L. *Smarter Than We Think: More Messages about Math, Teaching, and Learning in the 21st Century*. Sausalito, Calif.: Math Solutions, 2014.

PART III

Professional Learning to Enhance Classroom Assessment

Introduction

Sandra Crespo, *Michigan State University, East Lansing*
Nicole Rigelman, *Portland State University, Portland, Oregon*

> *Never doubt that a small group of thoughtful, committed people can change the world. Indeed, it is the only thing that ever has.*
>
> —Margaret Mead

Assessing student learning is a core practice in the work of teaching. It is a practice that comes into play at different stages of the plan-implement-reflect phases of instruction and provides teachers with a window into their students' thinking which in turn is used to manage and monitor learning and growth. Although assessing students' learning is embedded within every single aspect of teaching mathematics, it is a challenging practice to develop; to do so, teachers must make a strong individual and collective commitment to their own professional learning and that of their colleagues. Learning to assess students' learning is a complex practice that is best done in the company of trusted colleagues. Hence developing effective assessment practices requires ongoing significant effort and purposeful study. The National Board for Professional Teaching Standards (NBPTS) says it best when it stated:

> Accomplished teachers critically examine their practice, seek to expand their repertoire, deepen their knowledge, sharpen their judgment and adapt their teaching to new findings, ideas, and theories. . . . Accomplished teachers contribute to the effectiveness of the school by working collaboratively with other professionals on instructional policy curriculum development and staff development. (1989, p. 4)

When schools provide teachers not only with the expectation to engage in professional learning, but also with time, space, and resources that encourage reflection, application, and collaboration, everyone wins. Teachers become students who alongside their own students learn and grow. These conditions produce generative learning (Greeno 1988; Hiebert and Carpenter 1992) and continuous growth—a space for learning in and from practice (Ball and Cohen 1999) that all teachers deserve. In the current school climate, which leans more toward efficient delivery and assessments of student outcomes, it may seem counterproductive to spend precious resources on professional learning experiences for teachers. Margaret Mead's quote above reminds us that where there is a will there is always a way, and that all great causes start small. There is no more worthy educational cause than advocating for system-wide support for teachers' professional learning as a sure means to improve students' learning.

The professional literature on school reform points to the importance of professional learning communities (PLCs) as key agents of change, especially when these are focused on students' learning (c.f., Curry 2008; Kruse, Louis, and Bryk 1994; Little et al. 2003; Murphy and Lick 2005). When teachers work in PLCs, improved teaching practice is a by-product. When teachers focus their professional learning on assessment practices, the gains in students' learning are noticeable, and so are the changes in their own repertoire of teaching practices (Sato, Wei, and Darling-Hammond 2008).

The chapters in part III provide inspiration and guidance on how teachers might improve their assessment practice and effectively measure student learning. As a collection these chapters examine a variety of professional learning approaches from university courses to job-embedded coaching and collaboration to the actual practice of teaching and reflecting on the efficacy of the approaches.

In **Developing Teachers' Ability to Be Critical Consumers of Assessments,** Hunsader, Thompson, and Zorin describe their approach and frameworks to develop teachers' skills for critically examining assessment resources. They introduced teachers to their assessment review framework in order to analyze the potential of assessments to draw out student mathematical thinking and mathematical processes or practices. Teachers were surprised by what they learned about the quality of the commercially available assessments and left with new ideas and resources about how to enhance the commercially available assessments their schools use.

In **Practicing Questioning in a Professional Learning Community: A Hub of Classroom Assessment,** Lee and colleagues describe how a group of teachers collaborated to improve their assessment practice (specifically, questioning) through work in a course-based PLC. The collaborative work focused on developing questions that assess student understanding rather than point them toward a particular answer or desired way of thinking (the focus standard). Teachers reported that this process helped them to redefine their priorities in classroom assessments and identify areas to reset goals, which ultimately served as a springboard for the improvement of their assessment practice.

In **Proficiency-Based and Problem-Based Instruction: Mutually Supporting Moves or Contradictions?,** Rigelman describes potential contradictions that exist between proficiency-based and problem-based teaching and learning. Samples of tasks and accompanying student work, as well as scoring tools and processes for their use, illustrate ways that proficiency-based and problem-based approaches can work together to develop powerful classroom assessment experiences for students. This chapter will support and guide readers as they take on the challenge of providing their students with worthwhile assessment opportunities or take up similar investigations of how different instructional methods support or conflict with their assessment practices.

In **Authentic Student Work Samples Support Formative Assessment in Middle School,** Dempsey and colleagues describe the Assessment Work Sample Method (AWSM) as a method for professional learning that encourages ongoing reflection about content and instructional practice in order to refine and improve formative assessment practices. In this model, teams of teachers review student work, examine their thinking and understanding, and consider implications for students' learning and their practice. The professional development team learned both about how to improve teachers' professional learning experience and about those areas where teacher beliefs and practice challenged their work.

In the final chapter of part III, **Formative Assessment Strategies in the Secondary Mathematics Classroom,** Marynowski provides illustrations of formative assessment strategies in secondary mathematics classrooms. Each of the featured strategies is connected to a formative assessment practice shown to make a difference in student learning. The strategies included are: formative quizzes, students working on whiteboards, self-assessment, and peer feedback. The researchers found that through this project teachers developed views of formative assessment both as a tool and a process.

As you read each of the chapters in this section we invite you to consider the following questions:

- How does learning more about assessment practices help teachers to support their students' learning?

- How does focusing teacher professional learning on assessing student learning enhance teachers' opportunities to learn in and from their practice?

- What do these chapters suggest for your learning about classroom assessment and for learning with or leading your colleagues' learning about assessment?

References

Ball, Deborah Loewenberg, and David K. Cohen. "Developing Practice, Developing Practitioners: Toward a Practice-Based Theory of Professional Education." In *Teaching as the Learning Profession: Handbook of Policy and Practice,* edited by Gary Sykes and Linda Darling-Hammond, pp. 3–32. San Francisco: Jossey Bass, 1999.

Curry, Marnie Willis. "Critical Friends Groups: The Possibilities and Limitations Embedded in Teacher Professional Communities Aimed at Instructional Improvement and School Reform." *Teachers College Record* 110, no. 4 (2008): 733–74.

Greeno, James G. *Situations, Mental Models and Generative Knowledge.* Rep. No. IRL 88-0005. Palo Alto, Calif.: Institute for Research on Learning, 1988.

Hiebert, James, and Thomas P. Carpenter. "Learning and Teaching with Understanding." In *Handbook of Research on Mathematics Teaching and Learning,* edited by Douglas A. Grouws, pp. 65–97. New York: Macmillan, 1992.

Kruse, Sharon, Karen Seashore Louis, and Anthony Bryk. *Building Professional Community in Schools.* Madison, Wisc.: Center on Organization and Restructuring of Schools, 1994.

Little, Judith Warren, Maryl Gearhart, Marnie Curry, and Judith Kafka. "Looking at Student Work for Teacher Learning, Teacher Community, and School Reform." *Phi Delta Kappan* 83, no. 5 (2003): 184–92.

Murphy, Charlene U., and Dale W. Lick. *Whole Faculty Study Groups: Creating Student-Based Professional Development.* 3rd ed. Thousand Oaks, Calif.: Corwin Press, 2005.

National Board for Professional Teaching Standards (NBPTS). *What Teachers Should Know and Be Able to Do.* Arlington, Va.: NBPTS, 1989.

Sato, Mistilina, Ruth Chung Wei, and Linda Darling-Hammond. "Improving Teachers' Assessment Practices through Professional Development: The Case of National Board Certification." *American Educational Research Journal* 45 no. 3 (2008): 669–700.

CHAPTER 11

Developing Teachers' Ability to Be Critical Consumers of Assessments

Patricia D. Hunsader, *University of South Florida, Sarasota-Manatee*
Denisse R. Thompson, *University of South Florida, Tampa*
Barbara Zorin, *University of South Florida, Sarasota-Manatee*

Classroom assessment is critical to instructional planning and should inform "teachers as they make instructional decisions" (National Council of Teachers of Mathematics [NCTM] 2000, p. 22). Indeed, assessment should be a "bridge between teaching and learning, helping teachers collect evidence about student achievement in order to adjust instruction to better meet student learning needs" (Wiliam 2007, p. 1054). Although classroom assessments often have a summative role in assigning grades, they also have a formative role in helping teachers identify ways to improve mathematics teaching and learning (Joyner and Muri 2011).

As educators, we know that "what one learns is intricately connected with how one learns it" (Crespo 2003, p. 246). That is, it is not enough to know *what* students learn (i.e., the mathematical content) unless we also know *how* students learn it (i.e., the processes they use when thinking about concepts) (Ma 1999). It is often through students' engagement with mathematical processes and practices that their depth of content understanding is made visible. Hence, assessments that engage students with mathematical practices and processes have the potential to illuminate such understanding and serve a formative role to guide future instruction. But how do teachers develop the needed expertise to engage their students in high-quality classroom assessment, particularly with the move toward implementation of the Common Core State Standards for Mathematics (CCSSM) (National Governors Association Center for Best Practices and Council of Chief State School Officers [NGA Center and CCSSO] 2010)?

In this chapter, we share an approach we use with both preservice and in-service teachers to help them become critical consumers and developers of classroom assessments. We focus on helping teachers analyze assessments objectively to gauge the extent to which they provide students opportunities to engage in mathematical practices and processes. We have collected data from both preservice and in-service teachers, but we focus this chapter on the reflections of nineteen in-service teachers enrolled in one of our mathematics methods courses. The teachers in our sample include eight teachers from elementary grades, ten from middle grades, and one from high school, with a range of experience from three to twenty-three years (mean = 11 years, std. dev. = 8.3 years). In-service teachers are uniquely positioned to reflect on how our approach to developing teachers' assessment knowledge and skills affects their classroom assessment practices and the thinking of students.

■ A Framework for Analyzing Assessments

Previous work with classroom assessments led us to question whether the unit tests accompanying published textbooks provide the level of information about student learning that they appear to give. Although it is straightforward to check an assessment for content alignment, it is more complex to evaluate the opportunities an assessment provides for students to engage with mathematical processes and practices. To provide an objective means to analyze tests for their focus on these processes and their potential to elicit student thinking, we developed a framework that focuses on all of the NCTM Process Standards (NCTM 2000) with the exception of Problem Solving (see fig. 11.1). For information about the development of the framework, refer to Hunsader et al. (2014) and Hunsader, Thompson, and Zorin (2013). We do not believe a determination of whether an assessment item represents problem solving can be made without knowledge of a specific sample of students and their prior learning, information not available in our analysis of publishers' tests. As we discuss later, teachers who analyze their own tests would be able to make such a determination.

Reasoning and Proof

N   The item does not direct students to provide justification for why they gave that response.

Y   The item directs students to provide justification for why they gave that response. ("Check your work" by itself is not justification.)

Mathematical Communication

N   The item does not direct students to communicate what they are thinking through symbols (beyond a numeral answer), graphics/pictures, or words.

Y   The item directs students to communicate what they are thinking through symbols, graphics/pictures, or words.

V   The item only directs students to record a vocabulary term or interpret/create a representation of vocabulary.

Connections

N   The item is not set in a real-world context and does not explicitly interconnect mathematical concepts (e.g., multiplication and repeated addition, perimeter and area).

R   The item is set in a real-world context outside of mathematics.

I   The item is not set in a real-world context, but explicitly interconnects mathematical concepts (e.g., multiplication and repeated addition, perimeter and area).

Representation: Role of Graphics

N   No graphic (graph, picture, or table) is given or needed.

S   A graphic is given but no interpretation is needed, and the graphic does not explicitly illustrate the mathematics inherent in the problem. (superfluous)

R   A graphic is given and no interpretation is needed, but the graphic explicitly illustrates the mathematics inherent in the problem.

I   A graphic is given and must be interpreted to answer the question.

M   The item directs students to make a graphic or add to an existing graphic.

Representation: Translation of Representational Forms (codes are bi-directional)

N   Students are not expected to record a translation between different representational forms of the problem.

SW Students are expected to record a translation between verbal and symbolic representations.

GS Students are expected to record a translation between symbolic and graphical (graphs, tables, or pictures) representations.

WG Students are expected to record a translation between verbal and graphical representations.

TG Students are expected to record a translation from one graphical representation to another.

A   Students are expected to record two or more translations among symbolic, verbal, and graphical representations.

Fig. 11.1. The framework used to analyze the extent to which test items provide opportunities for engagement with the mathematical processes (adapted from Hunsader, Thompson, and Zorin 2013)

The items in figure 11.2 are representative of items in the published tests we analyzed. Table 11.1 reports our coding according to the framework in figure 11.1.

Item 1: Draw an area model to illustrate the following product:

$$47 \times 26 = \underline{\hspace{1cm}}$$

Item 2: Chanra has 12 cookies to put into 4 bags. Write a number sentence to show how many cookies will be in each bag.

Item 3: Draw a polygon that contains an acute angle, an obtuse angle, and a pair of parallel sides. Label the acute angle, obtuse angle, and pair of parallel sides, and explain why the labels you assigned are correct.

Item 4: The perimeter (P) of a rectangular garden is 34 m. The length is 5 m longer than the width. What are the dimensions of the garden?

w

$P = 34\ m$

$l = w + 5$

Fig. 11.2. Sample items that illustrate the framework codes

Item 5: Graph the function represented by the following table of values:

x	-2	-1	0	1	2
y	0	1	4	9	16

Fig. 11.2. *Continued*

Table 11.1
The codes assigned to the items in figure 11.2

Item	Reasoning and Proof	Communica-tion	Connections	Role of Graphics	Translation of Representa-tional Forms
1	N	Y	I	M	GS
2	N	Y	R	S	SW
3	Y	Y	N	M	WG
4	N	N	R	R	N
5	N	Y	N	M	TG

Reasoning and Proof and *Communication* are connected; students cannot demonstrate reasoning without communication, yet students can communicate without sharing why they gave their answer. When students are asked to show what they are thinking with words, symbols, or graphics, we code the item as involving communication. When students are asked to justify why they gave their answer, we also code the item positively for reasoning and proof.

Items 1, 2, and 5 illustrate how a task can engage students in communication without reasoning and proof. Item 3 includes reasoning by asking students to justify why their labels are correct. If the item had only asked students to label the angles and the sides, the communication code would have been "V" for vocabulary.

The *Connections* criterion identifies items that connect mathematics to students' everyday lives through a context (items 2 and 4). The "I" code identifies items that lack a real-world context but interconnect mathematical concepts, such as multi-digit multiplication and area.

Representation is fundamental to helping students express their mathematical thinking (Diezmann and McCosker 2011; Heritage and Niemi 2007) and involves two elements. *Role of Graphics* considers how students are expected to interact with the graphics in an item (Berends and van Lieshout 2009). Items 2 and 4 illustrate the difference between codes S and R. The cookie graphic in item 2 may support struggling learners; however, by itself, the graphic is superfluous (code S) because it is not needed to solve the problem and does not cue students to the mathematics in the problem. Although the graphic in item 4 is not needed, it illustrates the mathematics of the problem (code R). If item 4 omitted the numerical data in the problem text, students would have to interpret the graphic and the code would be I. Items that ask students to make a graphic or add to an existing graphic are coded M (see items 1, 3, and 5).

The final criterion, *Translation of Representational Forms,* captures items that involve translating the essence of a problem from one representational form to another, an important skill in developing a robust understanding of concepts (Bossé, Adu-Gyamfi, and Cheetham 2011; Gagatsis and Shiakalli 2004). Items 1, 2, 3, and 5 involve some form of translation among symbols, words, and graphics.

■ Research on Applying the Framework to Published Tests

In our research (Hunsader et al. 2014), we applied the framework to the constructed-response published tests that accompanied textbook series from three publishers at each of three grade bands (119 tests from elementary grades 3–5; 91 tests from middle grades 6–8; and 104 tests from high school algebra 1, algebra 2, and geometry series). For our analyses, we used the test as the unit of analysis, believing that students should be engaged in a range of mathematical processes over the course of an entire test. Focusing on individual items as the unit of analysis may lead to a misconception that assessment items need to include multiple processes to be of value, a belief we neither hold nor want to foster.

Figure 11.3 contains box plots illustrating the range of processes we coded as evident within the tests we analyzed (Hunsader et al. 2014). With the exception of Connections at the elementary level, our results suggest that students have limited opportunities on typical assessments accompanying published textbooks to engage with many of the mathematical processes. Hence, there appears to be room for improvement. Previous research (e.g., Delandshere and Jones 1999; Senk, Beckmann, and Thompson 1997) has shown that teachers often rely on the tests accompanying their textbook as a primary source of classroom assessments. This research led us to develop experiences within methods courses for preservice and in-service teachers to help them critically evaluate their classroom tests in reference to mathematical processes, empowering them to consider how their assessments might ensure that both they and their students come to value mathematical reasoning, communication, connections, modeling, and the like.

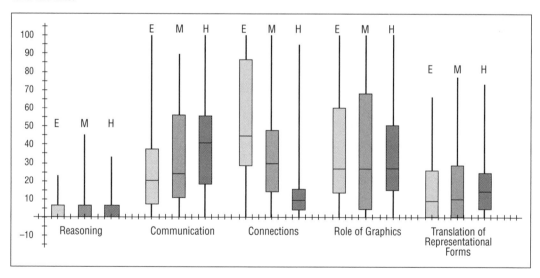

Fig. 11.3. These box plots illustrate the percent of items per test that provided students opportunities to engage with the framework criteria, with results collapsed by publisher within each grade band: Elementary (E), Middle grades (M), High School (H). Codes included in the mean percent are Reasoning (Y), Communication (Y and V), Connections (R and I), Role of Graphics (R, M, and I), and Translation of Representational Forms (SW, GS, WG, TG, and A).

■ Designing an Experience to Engage in Analyzing Classroom Tests

Our overall goal through the assessment experience was to heighten teachers' awareness of the role of assessment in instructional planning and the extent to which their current assessments (i.e., tests) elicit and reveal their students' thinking. We wanted teachers to consider how an increased focus on mathematical processes within tests might enhance the formative function of their tests to guide future instruction.

We begin with helping teachers understand the evolution of mathematics standards in the United States. In discussing the genesis of CCSSM, and specifically its Standards for Mathematical Practice [SMPs], we review standards that served as the foundation of our framework and are related to the SMPs, namely the National Council of Teachers of Mathematics' Process Standards (NCTM 2000) of problem solving, reasoning and proof, communication, connections, and representation, and the mathematical proficiencies specified in *Adding It Up* (National Research Council [NRC] 2001). We discuss the power of mathematical processes and practices to reveal student thinking, and use this discussion to introduce the framework in figure 11.1. Although our framework uses the language of the NCTM (2000) processes, the criteria get at the heart of the SMPs regarding student understanding and are applicable to the analysis of tests before student work is obtained.

After discussing the framework criteria, teachers apply the framework to sample tests from publishers' resources in small groups. We are intentional in selecting tests that represent a range of content and opportunities to engage with the processes/practices. Teachers then apply the framework to tests of their own choosing—either self-authored tests, those provided by their textbook publisher, or ones used by their district. Teachers summarize the results to obtain an overall picture of the extent to which their tests engage students with the mathematical processes/practices. Teachers are also encouraged to modify some items on tests so students have more opportunities to engage with the processes and practices.

■ Reflections on the Experience

We believe assessment focusing on processes/practices is a critical component of good instructional practice, so we typically have these assessment experiences account for 10 to 15 percent of the time in a course that covers many topics. In the specific case with the teacher reflections that are reported in this chapter, the course focus was on methods of teaching algebraic concepts and enhancing algebraic work in elementary and middle grades. We also use this assessment experience in courses that focus on current trends in mathematics education, investigating classroom assessments as well as national and international assessments, and historical perspectives with curriculum. With undergraduate preservice teachers, assessment is a topic introduced early so that appropriate assessment tasks can be discussed as part of instructional strategies used in teaching various concepts.

Because course time is always precious and there never seems to be enough time, we have been interested in whether course participants consider the time and experiences focused on assessment to be worthwhile. We asked teachers to reflect on the following:

- To what extent did using the Framework enable you to determine the extent to which tests gave students opportunities to engage in mathematical processes/practices?

- What did you conclude about the tests you analyzed?

- How might this experience influence your future assessment practices?

The reflections across these questions from the nineteen in-service teachers in our sample were coded according to theme, resulting in eighty-three responses that we classified into three themes. Each response included here is followed by the teacher's grade band and number of years of class-room teaching experience. Eleven teachers provided fourteen comments (17 percent) related to the theme *The value of the Framework for analyzing processes*:

- "Using the Framework helped me to evaluate whether or not test items aligned to the depth that is expected with Common Core." (T604, elementary, 5 years)

- "Using the Framework provided information about the type of mathematical thinking processes each question required of students. This was very informative and useful to evaluate the value of certain test questions." (T617, middle grades, 21 years)

For many teachers, this experience was the first time they had ever objectively analyzed the tests they use with students. Eighteen teachers provided thirty-five comments (42 percent) related to the theme, *The quality of the tests:*

- "It was pretty eye-opening to see the level of questions given on the standard adoption tests that our county requires us to use. Many of the questions just asked for an answer rather than asking students to use a strategy or explain how/why they got the answer they did. The questions were very surface-level and did not engage students in mathematical thinking. . . . [T]he tests I analyzed did not encourage my students to grapple with content or make meaningful arguments for their thinking. The tests do not support the ideas of Common Core." (T607, elementary, 3 years)

- "I noticed that the items that I analyzed did not aptly allow the students to reason or justify their thinking. . . . I feel like that does the student a real disservice because I can't truly interpret the data and drive my instruction if I don't know the reasoning or provide my students with the opportunity to justify their thinking." (T606, elementary, 3 years)

Teachers' reflections indicate a growing realization of the potentially negative influence of limiting classroom assessment to the tests they currently use. Eighteen teachers provided twenty-nine comments (35 percent) related to the theme *Desire to change current assessment practices*:

- "This experience might cause me to more closely scrutinize assessments provided by the textbook publisher, and I might modify at least some of the questions in order to diversify the processes tested on the assessment." (T609, middle grades, 23 years)

- "The coding and reviewing of assessments has given me a lot to think about. Do I even bother looking at publisher-based assessment or do I develop my own from scratch every time? The answer is easy, develop my tests from now on, yet the ease provided by prepackaged tests will be missed." (T612, middle grades, 7 years)

Although some teachers suggested abandoning all published tests, we encourage a more moderate approach. Given the many demands on classroom teachers' time, creating all unit tests from scratch is likely not feasible for many. We suggest that teachers use the results of their analysis to think carefully about what processes they feel are inadequately addressed and then consider the most effective means to assess those processes. One possibility is to modify a few items on an existing test; for support and examples of item modification, refer to Hunsader, Thompson, and Zorin (2014) or to Zorin, Hunsader, and Thompson (2013). Another option is to target another form of assessment for one or more processes or practices. For instance, it can be challenging within the confines of a paper-and-pencil assessment to elicit students' reasoning, and a teacher may decide that a face-to-face performance assessment or some take-home alternative assessment is preferable.

■ Extensions and Variations of the Assessment Experience

The experiences we described have been conducted within methods courses for preservice and/or in-service teachers. With preservice teachers, we usually modify the experience to focus on the analysis of individual items. Without classroom experience and an understanding of the students for whom a test is intended, it can be difficult to place value judgments on appropriate levels of processes across an entire test. One downside of this adaptation is that preservice teachers sometimes develop a misconception that an item must contain most or all mathematical processes to be valuable.

The experience described here could certainly be used as professional development in which teachers work together to analyze tests they use, perhaps by grade level or by course. In such circumstances, teachers might be challenged to add problem solving (fig. 11.4) to the framework because they will have the necessary background about students and their instruction.

Problem Solving	
N	The item is neither a problem nor an exercise. It does not require a procedure, formula, or algorithm to solve (e.g., vocabulary, recall).
E	The item is a routine exercise that can be solved by applying a procedure, formula, or algorithm currently known to the student.
P	The item is a non-routine problem that cannot be solved by applying a procedure, formula, or algorithm currently known to the student.

Fig. 11.4. Possible codes for problem solving

■ Conclusion

As we use this model with more teachers, they continue to broaden our perspective about potential uses of our framework. Teacher reflections echo prior research evidence that classroom assessment practices are key to maximizing student learning (Lukin et al. 2004), and that characteristics of high-quality assessment tasks can be applied to tasks for instructional, independent work, and group work purposes. The Common Core standards espouse instructional practice that empowers students to think more deeply and meaningfully about mathematics and to express their understanding across representations. We believe our framework can serve as a guide to help teachers select, modify, and/or create tasks that support this level of teaching and learning.

We have observed that such objective analysis can profoundly influence how teachers view the assessments they use with their students, confirming prior research findings (Mertler 2009; Zhang and Burry-Stock 2003; Zientek 2007) about teachers' ability to recognize deficits in their practice. We are not suggesting that our framework or criteria are exhaustive or that others might not value a different set of practices or processes than we chose. However, our experiences with teachers across a range of grade levels and years of experience have demonstrated the potential of professional development to impact teachers' knowledge and skills in assessment positively (Alkharusi et al. 2012) and the benefits of enhancing teachers' ability to analyze classroom assessments. A criterion-based framework such as the one we used also provides guidance to teachers in targeting test modifications to get maximum benefit from these formative assessments.

References

Alkharusi, Hussain, Said Aldhafri, Hilal Alnabhani, and Muna Alkalbani. "Educational Assessment Attitudes, Competence, Knowledge, and Practices: An Exploratory Study of Muscat Teachers in the Sultanate of Oman." *Journal of Education and Learning* 1, no. 2 (2012): 217–32.

Berends, Inez E., and Ernest C. van Lieshout. "The Effect of Illustrations in Arithmetic Problem-Solving: Effects of Increased Cognitive Load." *Learning and Instruction* 19, no. 4 (2009): 345–53.

Bossé, Michael J., Kwaku Adu-Gyamfi, and Meredith Cheetham. "Translations among Representations: Teacher Beliefs and Practices." *International Journal for Mathematics Teaching and Learning* (June 2011): 1–23.

Crespo, Sandra. "Learning to Pose Mathematical Problems: Exploring Changes in Preservice Teachers' Practices." *Educational Studies in Mathematics* 52 (2003): 243–70.

Delandshere, Ginette, and John Jones. "Elementary Teachers' Beliefs about Assessment in Mathematics: A Case of Assessment Paralysis." *Journal of Curriculum and Supervision* 14 (1999): 216–40.

Diezmann, Carmel M., and Natalie T. McCosker. "Reading Students' Representations." *Teaching Children Mathematics* 18, no. 3 (2011): 162–69.

Gagatsis, Athanasios, and Myria Shiakalli. "Ability to Translate from One Representation of the Concept of Function to Another and Mathematical Problem Solving." *Educational Psychology: An International Journal of Experimental Educational Psychology* 24, no. 5 (2004): 645–57.

Heritage, Margaret, and David Niemi. "Toward a Framework for Using Student Mathematical Representations as Formative Assessment." *Educational Assessment* 11, no. 3–4 (2007): 265–82.

Hunsader, Patricia D., Denisse R. Thompson, and Barbara Zorin. "Engaging Elementary Students with Mathematical Processes during Assessment: What Opportunities Exist in Tests Accompanying Published Curricula?" *International Journal for Mathematics Teaching and Learning* (May 2013): 1–25.

———. "Mathematical Practices: Small Changes in Assessments = Big Benefits." *Annual Perspectives in Mathematics Education* 1 (2014a): 205–14.

Hunsader, Patricia D., Denisse R. Thompson, Barbara Zorin, Amanda Loyden Mohn, Jennifer Zakrzewski, Ilyas Karadeniz, Elaine C. Fisher, and George MacDonald. "Assessments Accompanying Published Textbooks: The Extent to Which Mathematical Processes Are Evident." *ZDM: The International Journal on Mathematics Education* 46, no. 5 (2014b): 797–813.

Joyner, Jeane M., and Mari Muri. *INFORMative Assessment: Formative Assessment to Improve Math Achievement, Grades K–6.* Sausalito, Calif.: Math Solutions, 2011.

Lukin, Leslie E., Deborah L. Bandalos, Teresa J. Eckhout, and Kristine Mickelson. "Facilitating the Development of Assessment Literacy." *Educational Measurement: Issues and Practice* 23 (2004): 26–32.

Ma, Liping. *Knowing and Teaching Elementary Mathematics.* Mahwah, N.J.: Lawrence Erlbaum Associates, 1999.

Mertler, Craig A. "Teachers' Assessment Knowledge and Their Perceptions of the Impact of Classroom Assessment Professional Development." *Improving Schools* 12 (2009): 101–13.

National Council of Teachers of Mathematics (NCTM). *Principles and Standards for School Mathematics.* Reston, Va.: NCTM, 2000.

National Governors Association Center for Best Practices and Council of Chief State School Officers (NGA Center and CCSSO). *Common Core State Standards for Mathematics.* Washington, D.C.: NGA Center and CCSSO, 2010.

National Research Council (NRC). *Adding It Up: Helping Children Learn Mathematics.* Edited by Jeremy Kilpatrick, Jane Swafford, and Bradford Findell. Washington, D.C.: National Academies Press, 2001.

Senk, Sharon L., Charlene E. Beckmann, and Denisse R. Thompson. "Assessment and Grading in High School Mathematics Classrooms." *Journal for Research in Mathematics Education* 28 (1997): 187–215.

Wiliam, Dylan. "Keeping Learning on Track: Classroom Assessment and the Regulation of Learning." In *Second Handbook of Research on Mathematics Teaching and Learning,* edited by Frank K. Lester, Jr., pp. 1053–98. Charlotte, N.C.: Information Age Publishing, 2007.

Zhang, Zhicheng, and Judith A. Burry-Stock. "Classroom Assessment Practices and Teachers' Self-Perceived Assessment Skills." *Applied Measurement in Education* 16 (2003): 323–42.

Zientek, Linda Reichwein. "Preparing High-Quality Teachers: Views from the Classroom." *American Educational Research Journal* 44, no. 4 (2007): 959–1001.

Zorin, Barbara, Patricia D. Hunsader, and Denisse R. Thompson. "Assessments: Numbers, Context, Graphics, and Assumptions." *Teaching Children Mathematics* 19, no. 8 (2013): 480–88.

CHAPTER 12

Practicing Questioning in a Professional Learning Community:
A Hub of Classroom Assessment

Ji-Eun Lee, Heather Turner, Colleen Ansara, Jessica Zablocki, Cory Hincks,
and Valerie Hanley, *Oakland University, Rochester, Michigan*

Teaching, learning, and assessment are integrated parts of a cohesive practice. In light of the adoption of Common Core State Standards for Mathematics (CCSSM) (National Governors Association Center for Best Practices and Council of Chief State School Officers [NGA Center and CCSSO] 2010) and the subsequent changes in assessment instruments that emphasize higher-order skills and performance-oriented assessments, teachers face the need to refine their practices in teaching, learning, and assessment. This chapter reports on our experiences refining our own assessment practices while working together as members of a professional learning community (PLC), which was formed in a university course. We briefly share the experiences our PLC had as well as the implications of this work for teachers and educational researchers. All PLC members collaboratively wrote this chapter after finishing one cycle of PLC activity and examining all documented data. Doing so also served as another opportunity for reflection.

■Project Overview

In the following sections, we provide a brief overview of the project's context, participants, goals, and development.

Context

During the winter semester of 2014, the six authors of this chapter met in a course titled Diagnosis and Remediation in Mathematics. This was a graduate-level elective course that has been offered to students who were pursuing master's degrees in educational studies or special education. In this particular semester, because of an unusually small class size, we decided to incorporate a PLC model to replace the traditional course structure. This decision was based on the following collective beliefs that aligned with the characteristics of PLCs (Vescio, Ross, and Adams 2008): (*a*) a belief that teacher knowledge is situated in our day-to-day experiences and it is best understood through critical reflection with others who share the same experience and (*b*) a belief that our engagement in the PLC would increase our professional knowledge and ultimately enhance student learning. Our decision was also influenced by research on successful outcomes of collaborative efforts in developing assessment practices in mathematics (e.g., Koch and Suurtamm 2012; van Es 2012). PLCs that we were previously involved in were informal and usually initiated without a set of predefined goals. What distinguished this PLC was that it was formed in a university course that allowed us to purposefully strengthen professional interactions rather than social relationships. We had a semi-structured format, with the initial goal of improving assessment practice and a specific goal of improving our questioning skills in later stages. We agreed upon certain goals being completed within a certain time period (usually one to two weeks).

We brainstormed areas for improvement and decided to examine our assessment practices. Through sharing specific cases of students experiencing difficulties in mathematics, and relating our struggles with understanding their difficulties, we created a common goal of identifying students' understanding through assessment interviews, searching for intervention plans, and examining changes in their understanding. To accomplish this goal, we scheduled one on-campus meeting a week, followed by a week of fieldwork in our K–12 classrooms. This schedule alternated throughout the semester. In a typical on-campus meeting, studies related to assessment practice were examined, and we designed and shared fieldwork. In a fieldwork week, we administered assessment interviews with students and implemented the remediation activities we developed. Time spent working in the field provided an opportunity for application and reflection of what was learned and discussed in the previous on-campus session. While completing our fieldwork, we shared our field reports and other artifacts virtually via collaborative documents (e.g., Google Docs) or the course website.

Participants

Our PLC consisted of five practicing teachers and one university teacher educator. Collectively, we taught a wide range of grade levels in a variety of school settings. There were some disadvantages to this kind of group membership, such as unfamiliarity with particular school contexts or specific grade expectations. However, this make-up allowed us to have diverse discussions across topics, since each member would be able to share his or her own unique expertise and experiences (e.g., Butler et al. 2004). Table 12.1 summarizes our PLC members' background and the initial goals we set.

Table 12.1
PLC members and initial goals

Name	Teaching Grade	School Context	Initial Goals of Individual Members
Colleen	Grade 4	Public elementary	Identifying a fourth grader's difficulties in solving multistep word problems and using variables
Valerie	Grade 2	Public elementary	Identifying a second grader's difficulties in understanding place value
Cory	Grade 7	Public middle school	Assessing the impact of real-life connected instruction for a student identified as ADHD in percent concept
Heather	Grade 4	Charter school	Identifying a fourth grader's difficulties in solving contextual multiplication/division problems
Jessica	Grade 9	Private school	Identifying a ninth grader's difficulties in understanding basic fraction concepts (elementary level)

Ji-Eun, a PLC member and university teacher educator, also conducted her own Scholarship of Teaching and Learning (SoTL) project based on the individual PLC members' assessment projects. Initially, she facilitated the PLC meetings until the five teachers took on more leading roles. She also suggested relevant literature when references were needed.

■ Related Literature

Our PLC was aware of the importance of the link between theory and practice. Our examination of theoretical literature evolved throughout our project as new needs arose from PLC members. Two major themes underpinned our work: (*a*) teachers' assessment literacy and (*b*) teacher-student dialogue. We were constantly consulting research in these two areas to inform our fieldwork. We also examined the results of our own work against this body of literature.

Teachers' Assessment Literacy

Previous research studies and standards from professional organizations continually suggest teachers should increase their assessment literacy. Assessment literacy encompasses knowledge and skills educators need to identify, select, or create assessments optimally designed for various purposes and to analyze, evaluate and use the assessment data to improve teaching and learning (e.g., Kahl, Hofman, and Bryant 2013; National Council of Teachers of Mathematics [NCTM] 1995; Popham 2009; Stiggins 1991). We acknowledge that mastery of assessment literacy would require teachers' extensive effort and willingness to examine their personal knowledge and beliefs about teaching, specifically with regard to mathematics assessment (Ball 2003; Black et al. 2003). Our PLC created such a space where we could examine our own thoughts and practices.

Mathematical Discourse: Teacher-Student Dialogue

As we designed and implemented several rounds of mock and real assessment interviews, it was apparent that a more deliberate communication plan was needed. It was more difficult to ask good questions and orchestrate dialogue with students for the purpose of assessment than we had first assumed. Initially, we found ourselves approaching assessment with the "absolutist" view of mathematics (Ernest 1991), as evidenced in our questions that focused on the mathematical correctness of students' answers and steps. As we realized that effective teacher-student dialogue could provide a vehicle for ongoing assessment, we embraced the "fallibilistic" perspective of mathematics in our teacher-student dialogue, which understands mathematical knowledge as fallible and eternally open to revision (e.g., Ernest 1991; Lakatos 1976; Rowland 2000). This perspective has implications for our assessment practice in that we put more effort into unwrapping student thinking rather than simply checking the correctness of the students' answers. Researchers' explanations of clinical interviews and effective questioning allowed us to work "with" our students to gain a deeper understanding of their mathematical understanding (e.g., Ginsburg 2009; Way 2008). To improve our mathematical discourse with students in assessment contexts, we examined both theoretical and empirical studies to see how theory can be embodied in practice (e.g., Ernest 1991; Ginsburg 2009; Rowland 2000; Small 2009; Way 2008; Wood 1998).

■ Reports on Progresses

In the following sections, we share our findings and reflections around four phases of our PLC.

Phase 1 (Meetings 1–4): Focusing on Students and Standards

In the initial phase, we shared our conceptions about classroom assessment and the plan for working with individual students. We acknowledged that classroom assessments could be used to drive instruction and promote student learning, utilized to achieve various purposes, and take multiple forms that could be unique to each classroom. We also shared background information about individual students and drafts of pre-assessment items. This provided us an opportunity to exchange our expertise and experiences.

Phase 2 (Meetings 5–6): Experiencing Multiple Roles through Mock Interviews

We conducted mock assessment interviews in the PLC setting and then actual interviews with students. During mock interviews that used the draft of pre-assessment items, we each had the opportunity to act as a teacher, a student, and a professional colleague. As the teacher, we were required to ask quality questions, predict possible answers, and identify students' difficulties. We prepared a set of follow-up questions and prompts in advance. When we took on the role of a student, we were required to follow all directions and respond to the questions based on our predictions of what an actual student might do. We often intentionally provided incorrect solutions for our partner, who acted as a teacher, in order to practice the follow-up prompts. As professional colleagues, we observed the teacher-student assessment interview sessions and provided feedback. Our first mock interview session proved to be the most beneficial collaboration. It was an influential turning point because it helped to us reexamine our patterns of mathematical communication with students. The following short example (fig. 12.1) was taken from our notes during the first mock interview session. It sketches how each of us was involved in mock interview sessions and what types of issues were discussed.

This short example brought various reactions, questions, and thoughts. Some examples of these are as follows:

Colleen's debriefing. Colleen had a clear standard in her mind when she created this assessment item (e.g., from CCSSM 4.OA.3 "Solve multistep word problems posed with whole numbers. . . . Represent these problems using equations with a letter standing for the unknown quantity" [NGA Center and CCSSO 2010]). Prior to the mock interview, Colleen had indicated in the answer key that the answer should be $T = 3 \times 545$. When Heather continued writing addition sentences, which was not what Colleen had expected, Colleen felt that Heather's answer did not meet her expectation or standard.

Heather's debriefing. Heather predicted that a student would repeatedly add because she thought about a student in her fourth-grade class who always attempted to solve multiplication problems using addition.

Example 1: Colleen (teacher role) interviewed Heather (student role)

Sample question: "A school theater has 545 seats. If three performances are sold out, how many tickets are sold?"

Colleen: "Would you read this question?"

Heather: (read the question aloud)

Colleen: "What do you need to do?"

Heather: "Find how many tickets are sold."

Colleen: *"So, what is the next step to do?"*

Heather: "Add."

Colleen: *"Show your work."*

Heather: (wrote 545 + 545 = 1090, 1090 + 545 = 1635) "1635."

Colleen: "1635 what?"

Heather: "1635 tickets."

Colleen: "Is there another way you can write this problem?"

Heather: (wrote 545 + 545 + 545 = 1635)

Colleen: *"Is there a multiplication problem we can write?"*

Heather: "3 times 545?"

Colleen: "Could you write it down?"

Heather: (wrote $3 \times 545 = 1635$)

Colleen: *"Could you use a variable? Can we use T for tickets?"*

Heather: (wrote $T = 3 \times 545$).

Fig. 12.1. First mock interview session notes

PLC members' debriefing. By observing this segment of a teacher-student mock interview, we realized that asking good questions for the purpose of assessment was not as easy as we had assumed. This short mock interview on a seemingly simple multiplication question brought many questions and suggestions from the observers. Some questions arose, such as "Is a repeated addition solution acceptable? Why? Why not?" and "Was the difficulty with analyzing the context or with the size of numbers to operate?" The following observations emerged: "It seems that big numbers prevent students from focusing on the problem in context" and "Colleen's interview focused mainly on mathematical procedures and content mastery." We also gleaned suggestions for Colleen's upcoming interview with a student in her fourth-grade classroom, such as:

- "Instead of asking if there is a multiplication problem we can write, you may ask, 'What do we call it when we repeatedly add the same number?'"

- "When you define variables, make sure that the property of the object you are referring to is identified (e.g., *T* for tickets? Or, *T* for the number of tickets?)."

- "You might want to ask for the number of tickets when ten performances are sold out to see whether your student will still want to use the repeated addition method."

Our engagement in the mock interview process led us to discuss in-depth mathematical ideas. It also helped us reexamine the way we ask questions in assessment contexts as a vehicle to unwrap students' mathematical thinking.

Phase 3 (Meetings 7–11): Increased Level of Awareness of Teacher-Student Dialogue

In this phase, we developed and implemented intervention plans based on pre-assessment results and created post-assessments. We conducted another round of mock interviews using post-assessment items and found that we became more aware of the complexity involved in teacher-student dialogue in an assessment setting. Figure 12.2 shows such a shift. In this example, Heather ambitiously included an open-ended question, expecting that this question would spur much richer teacher-student dialogue and be helpful in getting meaningful assessment data. However, PLC members expressed mixed opinions. Heather and Jessica perceived that this assessment task was good because its openness allowed for multiple strategies and solutions and for the subsequent rich assessment data the teacher could get by analyzing the student's explanations (Franke, Kazemi, and Battey 2007; Stein et al. 2000). Cory and Valerie were more concerned about the pedagogical "moves" that Heather should make to elicit students' thinking in an assessment context (Smith and Stein 2011). The following example was taken from written notes, recorded in a Google Doc, after the second mock interview session.

Example 2: Discussion on Heather's assessment item

Sample Question: "Ben has 72 Legos. His friends are coming over and he needs to separate them so everyone gets the same amount to build with. How many Legos will each friend get?"

Heather: "I want this question to have many possibilities to see where my student's thoughts and strategies took him."

Jessica: "I like how you have created problems that are more open-ended and encourage critical thinking and discussion."

Valerie: "However, it might be too open-ended for your student."

Heather: "Not every question can be this way. . . . However, I believe that this will help me to gain more insight into my student's thinking."

Cory: "I really recommend that you prepare more specific follow-up questions and prompts considering multiple situations. Your student's reaction might be very different from ours in this mock interview."

Heather: "I will. In fact, this question helps me think about more follow-up prompts by predicting possible directions my student will take. I hope I can gain more insight into his thinking."

Fig. 12.2. Second mock interview notes

Phase 4 (Meetings 12–14): Reflections on Successes and Doubts

In this phase, we administered our post-assessments to the students in our classrooms. We recorded and transcribed our dialogues with students for further reflections. We also collectively reflected upon the overall process of our PLC work at the last on-campus meeting. We expressed varying degrees of satisfaction with the outcome of students' progress. In terms of our own questioning skills in assessment contexts, we found more self-criticism than self-praise, as shown in figure 12.3. In this example, Heather's self-analysis showed her perceived need for more "focusing" interaction patterns rather than "funneling" student responses (Herbel-Eisenmann and Breyfogle 2005; Wood 1998). Also, she revealed the challenges with opening up the possibility that she might provide for the student some cognitive "scaffolding" (Rowland 2000; Wood, Bruner, and Ross 1976).

Example 3: An excerpt from Heather's annotated transcript of post-assessment

Problem: Ben has 72 Legos. His friends are coming over and he needs to separate them so everyone gets the same amount to build with. How many Legos will each friend get?

S_1: This might be a bit harder because it doesn't say how many each friend will get.

T_1: That's correct it is missing information… *This story doesn't tell us how many friends Ben has or how many Legos each friend will get.*

> [T1] He only mentions the fact that it doesn't tell us how many each person gets. Did my thoughts influence his next comment?

S_2: Yeah, I don't know how many friends he has.

T_2: So what kind of Math problem do you think this is?

S_3: Division.

T_3: Why?

S_4: Because it doesn't have how many friends he has or how many Legos they get.

T_4: What does it have?

S_5: Ben has 72 Legos.

T_5: *So it tells us a total and we need to separate it but we don't know how. What if I said you could make up the missing information, either how many friends or how many Legos they will get. What do you think we should add?*

> [T5] After doing this I realize that if he had chosen how many Legos each friend got he would not be able to solve the problem because that is what he is suppose to solve for. It makes me wonder how much more information I would have learned if he had chosen the wrong option?

S_6: Ben has 4 friends.

T_6: (re-reads the story with new information) Can we solve the problem now?

S_7: Yes.

T_7: How should we start? Should we draw the Legos or the friends?

S_8: The friends just like we did in the cookies problems from class. (he draws 4 circles, one for each friend)

T_8: Are we only dividing our Legos into 4 groups?

S_9: We need to separate them one at a time so we don't make any mistakes.

Fig. 12.3. Transcript of excerpt from post-assessment analysis

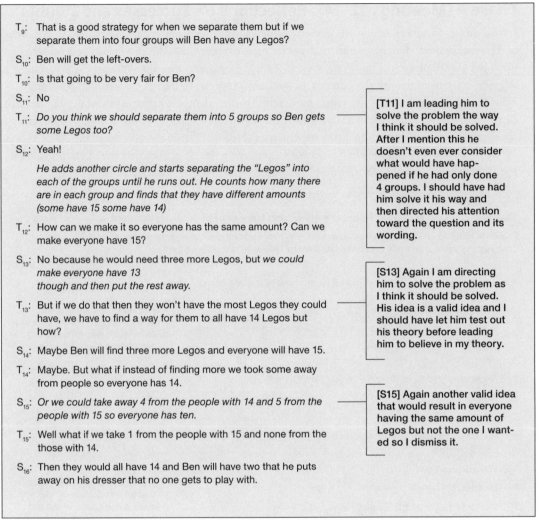

T_9: That is a good strategy for when we separate them but if we separate them into four groups will Ben have any Legos?

S_{10}: Ben will get the left-overs.

T_{10}: Is that going to be very fair for Ben?

S_{11}: No

T_{11}: *Do you think we should separate them into 5 groups so Ben gets some Legos too?*

S_{12}: Yeah!

He adds another circle and starts separating the "Legos" into each of the groups until he runs out. He counts how many there are in each group and finds that they have different amounts (some have 15 some have 14)

T_{12}: How can we make it so everyone has the same amount? Can we make everyone have 15?

S_{13}: No because he would need three more Legos, but *we could make everyone have 13 though and then put the rest away.*

T_{13}: But if we do that then they won't have the most Legos they could have, we have to find a way for them to all have 14 Legos but how?

S_{14}: Maybe Ben will find three more Legos and everyone will have 15.

T_{14}: Maybe. But what if instead of finding more we took some away from people so everyone has 14.

S_{15}: *Or we could take away 4 from the people with 14 and 5 from the people with 15 so everyone has ten.*

T_{15}: Well what if we take 1 from the people with 15 and none from those with 14.

S_{16}: Then they would all have 14 and Ben will have two that he puts away on his dresser that no one gets to play with.

[T11] I am leading him to solve the problem the way I think it should be solved. After I mention this he doesn't even ever consider what would have happened if he had only done 4 groups. I should have had him solve it his way and then directed his attention toward the question and its wording.

[S13] Again I am directing him to solve the problem as I think it should be solved. His idea is a valid idea and I should have let him test out his theory before leading him to believe in my theory.

[S15] Again another valid idea that would result in everyone having the same amount of Legos but not the one I wanted so I dismiss it.

Fig. 12.3. *Continued*

■ Discussion: Multiple Shifts and Multiple Thoughts

The final meeting of this cycle of the PLC was dedicated to the reflection of the entire processes of our PLC. Multiple shifts and thoughts were noted and four major themes emerged.

Theme 1: From Resistance to Openness

The first mock interview in the PLC setting was the most challenging and uncomfortable phase for everyone. Some were less confident about the quality of assessment items in terms of the mathematical concepts; others were uncomfortable being observed or critiquing other teachers' work. However, our initial resistance was minimal compared to the benefits we received throughout the multiple rounds of mock interviews. Our feedback became more specific as the process went on, which helped us to clarify our thoughts, demonstrate improved assessments with students, and become open to critical scrutiny. In the book *Practice Perfect,* Lemov, Woolway, and Yezzi (2012) emphasize the value of purposeful practice in an intentional setting. Through our mock assessment interviews, we experienced the transformative power of purposeful practice in a low-stakes setting.

Theme 2: Focusing on Content Standards to Practice Standards

Our initial PLC work focused on content standards identified in the curriculum documents. This tendency was noted in our typical prompts, as demonstrated in the first mock interview (e.g., "What is the next step?") where we were seeking right answers. The experience of participating in the mock interview process as a teacher, a student, and a colleague helped us realize the need for asking purposeful questions and the importance of skillfully orchestrating teacher-student interactions. This realization urged us to more seriously examine and incorporate the Standards for Mathematical Practice (NGA Center and CCSSO 2010) in the assessment context. Although "asking questions" has been a significant part of our daily work, this opportunity gave us a chance to focus more on the quality and purpose of questions as a hub of classroom assessment.

Theme 3: Scaffolding for Student Learning to Scaffolding for Teacher Development

Initially, we recognized that this type of assessment interview would be a way for the students to progress through the process of scaffolding that enables them "to solve a problem, carry out a task, or achieve a goal which would be beyond [their] unassisted efforts" (Wood, Bruner, and Ross 1976, p. 90). We tended to focus on teacher-to-student scaffolding by assuming our role as knowledgeable mentors or helpers. Later, we confirmed that this experience also helped us progress through a very similar process, teacher-to-teacher scaffolding. We were seeking feedback on our own interactions with the student as well as on our mathematical and pedagogical knowledge. The initial focus was on one-way interactions; we became aware of the importance of two-way interactions and used this assessment practice for our continued professional growth. The need for more in-depth examination of clinical interviews or teacher-student dialogue demonstrated our shift to scaffolding not only for student learning but also for teacher development.

Theme 4: Theory-to-Practice View to Practice-to-Theory View

According to our previous experiences, typical coursework or professional development sequences consist of learning some new topics and theories with the expectation that they will be implemented in the actual classrooms sometime in the future on the teachers' own time and plans. Although we had previous professional development experiences regarding assessment or effective questioning, our participation in the PLC left a distinct impact on us. In this setting, we examined our practice first, identified the questionable areas, and then examined how research studies and theories addressed the issues we experienced. This voluntary, need-based sequence allowed for a special lens through which we could see our assessment practices more meaningfully not only by knowing theories but also by making them relevant in our practices. Lemov (2013) addresses various factors that resulted in low-quality professional development such as "one and done" trainings, training that is done more "at" teachers than "by" teachers, and training that values thinking over doing. We believe that our PLC demonstrated a potential model to resolve these issues.

■ Concluding Remarks

One cycle of our PLC experience focusing on clinical interviews and questioning may be a relatively small event compared to the complex nature of our daily assessment practices. However, we can attest that there was a clear impact on our pedagogy, willingness to improve, and, ultimately, student learning. It is our hope that by establishing a PLC in a university course setting, we went outside the distinct boundaries of what is typically done in university and professional development settings. We experienced that "inquiry as stance is neither a top-down nor a bottom-up theory of action, but an organic and democratic one that positions practitioners' knowledge, practitioners, and their interactions with students and other stakeholders at the center of educational transformation" (Cochran-Smith and Lytle 2009, pp. 123–4). While jointly inquiring into our own assessment practice, examining relevant theories, creating our own assessment items, designing intervention plans, and reflecting upon our own practices, we were able to redefine priorities in classroom assessments and identify the areas to reset goals.

References

Ball, Deborah L. *Mathematical Proficiency for All Students: Toward a Strategic Research and Development Program in Mathematics Education.* Santa Monica, Calif.: RAND Institute, 2003.

Black, Paul J., Chris Harrison, Clare Lee, Bethan Marshall, and Dylan Wiliam. *Assessment for Learning: Putting It into Practice.* Berkshire, U.K.: Open University Press, 2003.

Butler, Deborah L., Helen Novak Lauscher, Sandra Jarvis-Selinger, and Beverly Beckingham. "Collaboration and Self-Regulation in Teachers' Professional Development." *Teaching and Teacher Education: An International Journal of Research and Studies* 20, no. 5 (2004): 435–55.

Cochran-Smith, Marilyn, and Susan L. Lytle. *Inquiry as Stance: Practitioner Research for the Next Generation.* New York: Teachers College Press, 2009.

Ernest, Paul. *The Philosophy of Mathematics Education.* London: Falmer Press, 1991.

Franke, Megan Loef, Elham Kazemi, and Daniel Battey. "Mathematics Teaching and Classroom Practice." In *Second Handbook of Research on Mathematics Teaching and Learning Vol.1,* edited by Frank K. Lester, Jr., pp. 225–56. Charlotte, N.C.: Information Age Publishing, 2007.

Ginsburg, Herbert P. "The Challenge of Formative Assessment in Mathematics Education: Children's Minds, Teachers' Minds." *Human Development* 52, no. 2 (2009): 109–28.

Herbel-Eisenmann, Beth, A. and M. Lynn Breyfogle. "Questioning Our Patterns of Questioning." *Mathematics Teaching in the Middle School* 19, no. 9 (2005): 484–89.

Kahl, Stuart R., Peter Hofman, and Sara Bryant. *Assessment Literacy Standards and Performance Measures for Teacher Candidates and Practicing Teachers.* Dover, N.H.: Measured Progress, 2013.

Koch, Martha, and Christine Suurtamm. "Teachers Working Collaboratively to Further Develop Their Assessment Practices in Mathematics: Turing Rubrics into Non-rubrics." Paper presented at the meeting of 12th International Congress on Mathematical Education, Seoul, Korea, July 8–15, 2012.

Lakatos, Imre. *Proofs and Refutations: The Logic of Mathematical Discovery.* Cambridge, U.K.: Cambridge University Press, 1976.

Lemov, Doug, Erica Woolway, and Katie Yezzi. *Practice Perfect: 42 Rules for Getting Better at Getting Better.* San Francisco: Jossey-Bass, 2012.

Lemov, Doug. "From 'Professional Development' to 'Practice': Getting Better at Getting Better." In *Pathway to Success*, pp. 50–65. Wisconsin Policy Research Institute, 2013. http://www.aei.org/wp-content/uploads/2013/05/-pathway-to-success_170815996739.pdf.

National Council of Teachers of Mathematics (NCTM). *Assessment Standards for School Mathematics*. Reston, Va.: NCTM, 1995.

National Governors Association Center for Best Practices and Council of Chief State School Officers (NGA Center and CCSSO). *Common Core State Standards for Mathematics*. Washington, D.C.: NGA Center and CCSSO, 2010.

Popham, James W. "Assessment Literacy for Teachers: Faddish or Fundamental?" *Theory into Practice* 48, no. 1 (2009): 4–11.

Rowland, Tim. *The Pragmatics of Mathematics Education: Vagueness in Mathematical Discourse*. London: Falmer Press, 2000.

Small, Marian. *Good Questions: Great Ways to Differentiate Mathematics Instruction*. New York: Teachers College Press, 2009.

Smith, Margaret S., and Mary Kay Stein. *5 Practices for Orchestrating Productive Mathematics Discussions*. Reston, Va.: NCTM, 2011.

Stein, Mary Kay, Margaret S. Smith, Marjorie Henningsen, and Edward A. Silver. *Implementing Standards-Based Mathematics Instruction: A Casebook for Professional Development*. New York: Teachers College Press, 2000.

Stiggins, Richard J. "Assessment Literacy." *Phi Delta Kappan* 72, no.7 (1991): 534–39.

van Es, Elizabeth A. "Examining the Development of a Teacher Learning Community: The Case of a Video Club." *Teaching and Teacher Education: An International Journal of Research and Studies* 28, no. 2 (2012): 182–92.

Vescio, Vicki, Dorene Ross, and Alyson Adams. "A Review of Research on the Impact of Professional Learning Communities on Teaching Practice and Student Learning." *Teaching and Teacher Education* 24 (2008): 80–91.

Way, Jenni. "Using Questioning to Stimulate Mathematical Thinking." *Australian Primary Mathematics Classroom* 13, no. 3 (2008): 22–27.

Wood, David, Jerome S. Bruner, and Gail Ross. "The Role of Tutoring in Problem Solving." *Journal of Child Psychology and Psychiatry* 17 (1976): 89–100.

Wood, Terry. "Alternative Patterns of Communication in Mathematics Classes: Funneling or Focusing?" In *Language and Communication in the Mathematics Classroom*, edited by Heinz Steinbring, Maria G. Bartolini Bussi, and Anna Sierpinska, pp. 167–78. Reston, Va.: NCTM, 1998.

CHAPTER 13

Proficiency-Based and Problem-Based Instruction: Mutually Supporting Moves or Contradictions?

Nicole Rigelman, *Portland State University, Oregon*

Proficiency-based and problem-based teaching and learning are two instructional approaches that can appear to be at odds with each other in the mathematics classroom. For instance, while the instructional move of clarifying and sharing learning intentions with students (Black and Wiliam 1998) that is advocated in a proficiency-based approach may improve student achievement, the way a teacher employs this move may diminish the cognitive demand of the problem-based task, a key component of a problem-based approach. Students' dispositions can also influence the implementation of proficiency-based and problem-based instruction. If a student's focus is on meeting the criteria in a proficiency-based approach merely to address "What do I need to do to get an A?" and not on "How can I show you what I know?" it can be challenging to draw out mathematical thinking and problem solving—important components of a problem-based approach. This chapter suggests that teachers who use proficiency-based and problem-based learning as mutually supporting are able to engage students with problem-based tasks to support learning, and they are also able to use tools, such as rubrics, not only for grading but also for supporting teaching and student learning. Providing students with examples of a range of student work shows what quality work looks like and supports students in understanding clear, high expectations. When students use these tools to guide self- and peer-assessment prior to the teacher providing growth-focused feedback, the tools support students during learning as opposed to merely being used summatively. Thus students understand that assessment and learning are ongoing and the student is actively involved in both processes.

■ Background

"Proficiency-based learning refers to a system of instruction, assessment, grading and reporting that is based on students demonstrating mastery of the knowledge and skills they are expected to learn as they progress through their education" (Great Schools Partnership 2014). The goal of proficiency-based teaching and learning is to ensure that students learn what they are expected to learn. Many educational stakeholders find proficiency-based teaching and learning attractive in that it can provide a more fine-grained analysis of a student's strengths and areas for improvement. It can also provide the opportunity for more detailed feedback on a student's work. Instead of receiving a holistic grade or score on a paper, communication can be about progress toward specific learning standards. In mathematics, the NCTM Standards (National Council of Teachers of Mathematics [NCTM] 1989, 2000) and Common Core State Standards (National Governors Association Center for Best Practices and Council of Chief State School Officers [NGA Center and CCSSO] 2010) inform learning standards development in states and, ultimately, in districts and schools.

Problem-based learning refers to a student-centered approach to instruction and assessment where learning of content and cognitive skills occurs through problem solving (Hiebert et al. 1997; Kazemi and Stipek 2001; NCTM 2000; National Research Council 2001, 2005). Since the release of *Agenda for Action* (NCTM 1980), mathematics educators have been focused on increasing students' opportunities to engage in problem solving with some agreement about what this can look like in the classroom (c.f., Brannan and Schaaf 1983; Bruni 1982; Kantowski 1980). Because problem-based learning is student centered, it is critical that students engage with "a question that cannot be immediately answered; [problem solving] requires some effort in making appropriate use of previously learned concepts and skills for its solution" (Bruni 1982, p. 10). Real problems typically can be approached in many ways. "Occasionally, the resulting investigations are nonproductive. Sometimes they are so productive that they lead to many different solutions or suggest more problems than they solve" (Brannan and Schaaf 1983, p. 43). Additionally, Pólya (1945) states that problem solvers "should solve problems, chose problems which are in his line, meditate upon their solution, and invent new problems" (p. 206). Similarly, the Mathematical Teaching Practices set forth in *Principles to Actions* (NCTM 2014) convey the importance of both establishing clear goals that focus learning, as well as implementing tasks that promote reasoning and problem solving. I have found that these high-leverage practices are critical for teachers interested in combining proficiency-based and problem-based instruction in mutually supportive ways.

Table 13.1 summarizes key characteristics of proficiency-based and problem-based teaching and learning. A review of this list leads one to see ways in which the approaches are mutually supportive (e.g., student-centered learning, students engaged in self-monitoring and self-assessment). However, contradictions may also arise between proficiency-based and problem-based instruction. Black and Wiliam (1998) call attention to several contradictions— places where the typical assessment practices in schools are weak and do not support high-quality teaching and learning. In mathematics classrooms, these practices include assessment tools that encourage rote learning rather than mathematical thinking and problem solving, an emphasis on quantity or presentation of written work rather than quality, and using tests to compare students to one another rather than personal improvement. My experience with proficiency-based learning is that school policies require teachers to articulate their learning targets to students, a strategy shown to positively affect student achievement (Black and Wiliam 1998). A contradiction arises when the timing of sharing of the target with students diminishes the cognitive demand of a task by communicating a solution strategy. For example, while "solve quadratics by completing the square" may be an appropriate target, if shared at the beginning of problem-based lesson, it would mean that students would not have to ponder an appropriate solution strategy for the given task. If students already know a solution path they are not problem solving; instead, they are completing exercises.

Table 13.1.

Key features of proficiency-based and problem-based teaching and learning

Proficiency-Based Teaching and Learning	Problem-Based Teaching and Learning

• Students progress at their own pace with the teacher providing the necessary supports.
 • Students progress based on their mastery of competencies.
 • Students are active in the learning process:
   – reflecting on their performance
   – taking responsibility for their learning
 • Instruction based on students' needs.
	• Students direct their own learning with teacher as facilitator.
	 • Students are active investigators:
	   – organizing and accessing prior knowledge
	   – acquiring new knowledge through investigation in small-group settings
	 • Students self-monitor and seek meaning and understanding.
	 • Instruction centered on challenging open-ended problems.

Both proficiency-based and problem-based approaches offer benefits to mathematics teaching and learning and should not necessarily be seen as contradictory. In the following sections I discuss ways to incorporate both approaches in classroom practices related to student learning and assessment.

■ Posing Worthwhile Tasks and Questions

Another assessment issue identified by Black and Wiliam (1998) relates to the types of tasks students engage with. According to Smith and Stein (1998), "The day-in and day-out cumulative effect of classroom-based tasks leads to the development of students' implicit ideas about the nature of mathematics—about whether mathematics is something about which they can personally make sense and about how long and how hard they should have to work to do so" (p. 269). If students are interacting with rote tasks, they are unlikely to experience struggle with knowing what they should do, and they come to believe mathematics is a discipline where they memorize and apply procedures. Often, because it is easier to assess a single target with a single task, proficiency-based assessment is characterized by narrowly defined tasks or those tasks where students are expected to apply a particular procedure. The implication of such an approach is that unproductive beliefs about mathematics and the students' role as a mathematician develop (NCTM 2014).

Alternatively, with problem-based learning, teachers pose worthwhile tasks designed to encourage students' inquiry and invention. Interacting with such tasks using questioning and discourse draws out student thinking and reasoning. However, worthwhile tasks are more cognitively demanding than rote tasks and have been shown to be more difficult for teachers to implement well (Stein et al. 2009). In their work through the Silicon Valley Mathematics Initiative, Foster and Noyce (2004) chose worthwhile tasks that "were of sufficient scope to allow for deep student thinking, and that could be reasonably assessed on a performance exam that lasted just a single class period" (p. 2). The tasks are characterized as ones that "require students to evaluate, optimize, design, plan, model, transform, generalize, justify, interpret, represent, estimate, and calculate their solutions" (p. 4). During these open-ended tasks students are engaged in the habits of mind of a mathematician aligned with the Common Core Standards for Mathematical Practice (NGA Center and CCSSO 2010), and students' successful performance with the tasks became a predictor of success on the state's multiple-choice exam (Foster and Noyce 2004). This problem-based approach supports students with developing more productive beliefs and experiencing more success as a mathematician.

To shift students' focus away from "What do I need to do to get an A?" and toward the perspective of "How can I show you what I know?" teachers need to pose challenging activities that promote thinking and discussion. Figure 13.1 illustrates this point with a patterning task. This task provides a context to examine a visual representation, a tile pattern, and its associated table of values. This task was posed to third graders with one of two different prompts: (1) "How many squares will be in the 25th arrangement?" or (2) "Investigate and report all you can about this pattern." The resulting student work demonstrates a contrast in the thinking elicited by each prompt. In figure 13.2, the student focuses on "answer getting" (Daro 2013), and the attention is on finding the number of squares, which reveals more about the student's computational abilities and persistence than about algebraic thinking beyond pattern recognition. On the other hand, the work shown in figure 13.3 reveals a student's more thorough investigation of the tile pattern with an extended table of values and a description of the characteristics of the tile pattern. In slowing down to investigate and make sense of the tile pattern and how it is growing, the student reveals more robust algebraic thinking than that shown in figure 13.2. The student's response in figure 13.3 provides insight into where the student is seeing the constant and the change from one figure to the next as well as the number of tiles in several larger figures through the table. Finally, the student expresses a verbal generalization, "Three plus 2 times the figure," that can be used to find the total number of tiles in any figure.

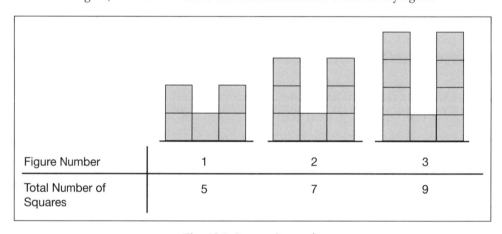

Figure Number	1	2	3
Total Number of Squares	5	7	9

Fig. 13.1. Patterning task

From a proficiency-based learning perspective, determining the learning targets associated with this later version of the task is more complex. With the first version of the task, determining the targets prior to implementing the task is more straightforward, as a teacher lists "analyze a pattern represented with a visual model and table" and "find a value for a larger figure in the pattern." With the second version of the task, anticipating what students might do with the task is necessary. Both targets listed previously are possible, but with the openness of the task a student may provide additional representations of the pattern (i.e., words, tables, or graphs), describe ways the pattern is staying the same and changing from one figure to the next, and make conjectures and generalizations about larger figures and/or any figure. A teacher may generate this initial list as potential targets while preparing to see evidence of additional targets when reviewing student work. These targets may even include aspects of cognitive skills such as those in the Standards for Mathematical Practice. A teacher may look for evidence of "make sense of problems and persevere

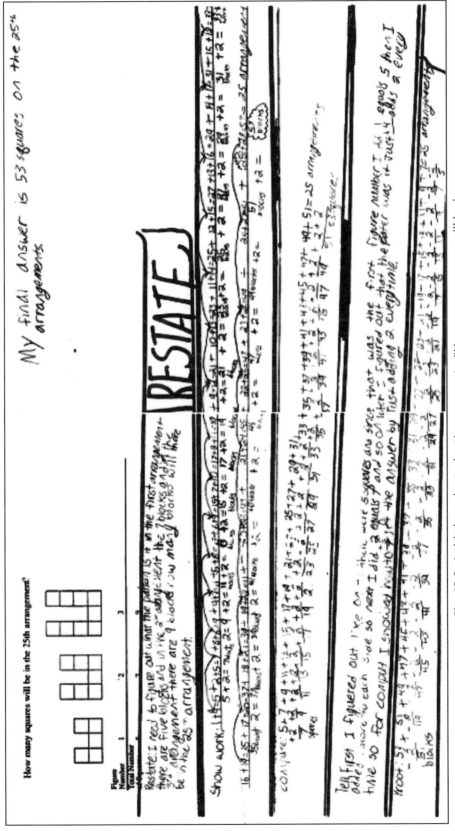

Fig. 13.2. A third-grade student's response to "How many squares will be in the 25th arrangement?"

in solving them" as the student explains correspondence among the various representations or "use appropriate tools strategically" as the student makes decisions about which representations of the task are most useful when investigating the pattern (NGA Center and CCSSO 2010).

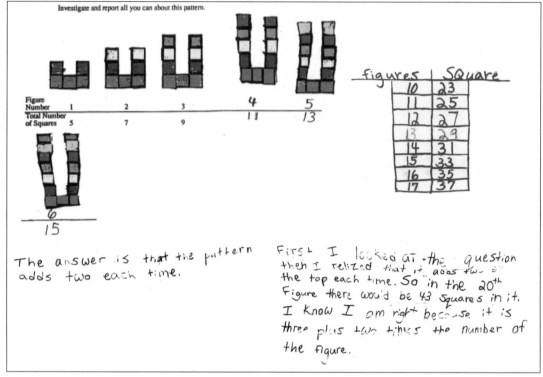

Fig. 13.3. A third-grade student's response to "Investigate and report all you can about this pattern."

Establishing Norms for *Doing* Mathematics

Students hold differing views of what it means to know and do math. The two versions of the patterning task and the associated student work provide an example of the how the openness of a task influences students' interaction with that task. To develop the mathematically proficient students described in the Standards for Mathematical Practice, it is helpful to consider what it looks like and/or sounds like to *think* and *work* like a mathematician. Once articulated, these habits of mind can be highlighted for students, thus helping to guide their work on open-ended tasks in mathematically productive ways.

Communicate Expectations about Student Performance

If teachers desire explanations that include mathematical arguments (such as in fig. 13.3) and not simply procedural summaries of the steps taken to solve the problem (such as in fig. 13.2), they need to support students in seeing the difference between the responses. Specific ways that teachers can establish these norms are described below.

For example, collectively examining exemplars for areas of strength and improvement, a common practice in a proficiency-based approach, can help students develop a critical eye for the difference between explanation and argumentation in their work (Orsmond, Merry, and Reiling 2002; Schoenfeld 1992; Wood 1999). Such a move provides students with a better understanding of the expectations, promoting a vision of what to strive for. The opportunity to examine the mathematical thinking of others helps students see relationships among multiple strategies, which can deepen their understanding and improve their work.

Another proficiency-based strategy to support students with understanding of what it looks like to engage in *doing* mathematics is to provide a "rubric" or "scoring guide" that communicates clear and high expectations for exemplary work and encourages the student to bring richness to the task. Table 13.2 includes an example of such a scoring guide. The top portion of this table is a "study guide" that conveys to students the learning targets addressed in the exam. Students use this to focus their preparation. The bottom portion is the "scoring guide" that is used to score each item on the exam. The Comparing Quadrilaterals task (shown in fig. 13.4) is a task from an eighth-grade exam. Note that this task, like the second version of the patterning task, is an open task that encourages investigation. A difference is that the students, in this case, were provided with the "study guide," the top portion of table 13.2, and were encouraged to use these ideas to prompt their thinking as they investigated this pair of quadrilaterals. This move positions the scoring guide as a teaching tool as it reinforces the expected detail for a top-level response. That is, students understand that they need to explore multiple strategies, justify their thinking, and generally show all that they know as they explore this task. A teacher reviewing the student work in figure 13.5 could consider both the learning targets addressed through the student's response as well as the level of thinking revealed in the work. It communicates to students a concept articulated in a recent TED Talk by Messerman (2012): "Show me what you know and I will assess it, I will help you learn."

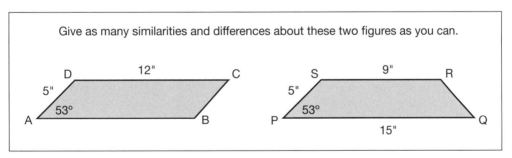

Give as many similarities and differences about these two figures as you can.

Fig. 13.4. Comparing Quadrilaterals task

Table 13.2
Exam study/scoring guide

Measurement	Geometry
• Understand measurable attributes and the idea of a unit—observe and predict the effects of changing the unit on given measurement. • Develop and use formulas to determine circumference of circles, and the area of triangles, rectangles, parallelograms, trapezoids, and circles. • Develop strategies to find the area of more complex shapes.	• Identify, compare, classify, and analyze attributes of two-dimensional shapes. • Make and test conjectures about geometric properties and relationships, and justify conclusions. • Identify, describe, and prove that objects are congruent and/or are symmetrical. • Use terminology accurately and precisely.

Exceptional
- Reflects all the criteria of Quality and goes above and beyond in one or more of the following ways…
  - Provides multiple examples and/or approaches to solving the problem.
  - Justifies by providing mathematical reasoning behind the process and solution.
  - Shows relationships to prior learning.
  - Poses and investigates "what if" questions and "I wonder" statements.

Quality
- Shows understanding of the problem's mathematical concepts and principles
- Reflects an appropriate and systematic strategy for solving the problem that is complete and correct.
- Is easy to follow, giving a clear indication of the solution process through diagrams/sketches, words, and/or numbers and math symbols.
- Provides a complete response with clear, unambiguous explanations and/or descriptions.

In Development
- Shows nearly complete understanding of the problem's mathematical concepts and principles.
- May contain computational errors.
- Provides clear evidence of the solution process, and the process is complete or nearly complete and systematic.
- Provides a fairly complete response with reasonably clear explanations and/or descriptions.

Rethink
- Misunderstood major portions of the problem.
- Contains major mathematical errors.
- Provides incomplete, ambiguous explanations and/or descriptions.

No Evidence
- Major portions of the problem are partially complete or not attempted.

Encourage Student Reflection and Goal Setting

A teacher who provides students with tools to support productive reflection and self-assessment also contributes to the development of classroom norms and habits of mind for students (Orsmond, Merry, and Reiling 2002; Schoenfeld 1992; Wood 1999). Expectations, such as those communicated in the scoring guide example from table 13.2, could be regularized behaviors as students engage in classroom tasks, group activities, and discussions. It serves to encourage a student to interact with the goals, use them to motivate their performance, and evaluate their work before submission. Also, once students receive feedback about their performance, they may have an opportunity to revise their work or set goals for their future work. The intention would be to use student reflection and self-assessment along with feedback to encourage continued growth. Whether the teacher is reporting progress relative to learning targets that are content-focused, cognitive-skill-focused, or both, the student is receiving feedback to grow on.

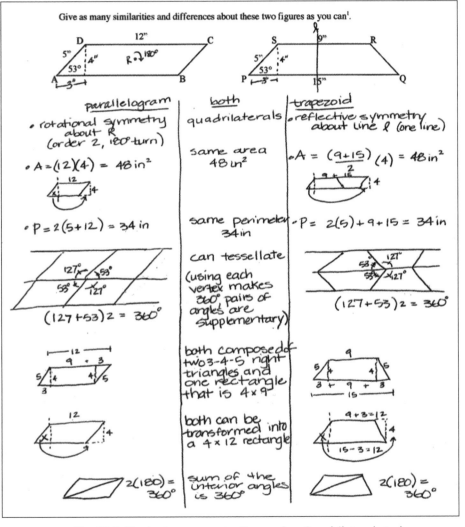

Fig. 13.5. Student response to Comparing Quadrilaterals task

■ Conclusion

The importance of the selected tasks is specifically highlighted in this chapter, as the task influences each of the other phases in the teaching and learning process. If the task is not an open task, it may not provide the opportunity for the students to show all that they know. It is critical to recognize the essential nature of this planning decision; mathematical tasks influence not only *how* students come to view mathematics but also *what* they have the opportunity to learn through the task. In addition, these tasks and the tools that teachers use to communicate expectations—such as student reflection tools, scoring criteria, and samples of exemplary work—further develop the norms for *doing mathematics,* but they should not reduce the cognitive demand of the task.

While proficiency-based and problem-based instructional moves may have features that appear contradictory to one another, there are also ways that the two approaches can support each other. Attention to clear learning goals is present in a proficiency-based environment. This focus can provide guidance for a teacher facilitating a problem-based lesson. Students actively reflecting on their performance, relative to exemplars or scoring guides, supports continued growth in knowledge and habits of a productive problem solver. When teachers recognize the potential contradictions that exist between proficiency-based and problem-based approaches and purposefully plan to avoid such contradictions, they can support students with reconsidering their role in the classroom and move them toward the reality of engaging as the mathematically proficient students described in the Standards for Mathematical Practice.

References

Black, Paul, and Dylan Wiliam. "Inside the Black Box: Raising Standards through Classroom Assessment." *Phi Delta Kappan* 80, no. 2 (1998): 139–48.

Brannan, Richard, and Oscar Schaaf. "An Instructional Approach to Problem Solving." In *The Agenda in Action.* edited by Gwen Shufelt and James R. Smart, pp. 41–59. Reston, Va.: NCTM, 1983.

Bruni, James V. "Problem Solving for the Primary Grades." *Arithmetic Teacher* 29, no. 6 (1982): 10–15.

Daro, Phil. "Against Answer Getting." Strategic Education Research Partnership, video, 17:04, 2014. http://serpmedia.org/daro-talks/.

Foster, David, and Pendred Noyce. "The Mathematics Assessment Collaborative: Performance Testing to Improve Instruction." *Phi Delta Kappan* 85, no. 5 (2004): 367–74.

Great Schools Partnership. *Proficiency-Based Learning.* The Glossary for Educational Reform. Accessed May 10, 2014. http://edglossary.org/proficiency-based-learning/.

Hiebert, James, Thomas P. Carpenter, Elizabeth Fennema, Karen C. Fuson, Diana Wearne, Hanlie Murray, Alwyn Olivier, and Piet Human. *Making Sense: Teaching and Learning Mathematics with Understanding.* Portsmouth, N.H.: Heinemann, 1997.

Kantowski, Mary Grace. "Some Thoughts on Teaching for Problem Solving." In *Problem Solving in School Mathematics,* edited by Steven Krulik and Robert E. Reys, pp. 195–203. Reston, Va.: NCTM, 1980.

Kazemi, Elham, and Deborah Stipek. "Promoting Conceptual Thinking in Four Upper Elementary Mathematics Classrooms." *Elementary School Journal* 102, no. 1 (2001): 59–80.

Messerman, Craig. "Standards-Based Grading and the Game of School." TEDxMCPSTeachers. (2012). https://www.youtube.com/watch?v=bn_sCLoQNVs&feature=youtu.be.

National Council of Teachers of Mathematics (NCTM). *An Agenda for Action,* Reston, Va.: NCTM, 1980.

———. *Curriculum and Evaluation Standards for School Mathematics,* Reston, Va.: NCTM, 1989.

———. *Principles and Standards for School Mathematics.* Reston, Va.: NCTM, 2000.

———. *Principles to Actions: Ensuring Mathematics Success for All.* Reston, Va.: NCTM, 2014.

National Governors Association Center for Best Practices and Council of Chief State School Officers (NGA Center and CCSSO). *Common Core State Standards for Mathematics.* Washington, D.C.: NGA Center and CCSSO, 2010.

National Research Council (NRC). *Adding it Up: Helping Children Learn Mathematics,* edited by Jeremy Kilpatrick, Jane Swafford, and Bradford Findell. Washington, D.C.: National Academies Press, 2001.

———. *How Students Learn: History, Mathematics, and Science in the Classroom.* Committee on *How People Learn,* A Targeted Report for Teachers, edited by M. Suzanne Donovan and John D. Bransford, Division of Behavioral and Social Sciences and Education. Washington, D.C.: National Academies Press, 2005.

Orsmond, Paul, Stephen Merry, and Kevin Reiling. "The Use of Exemplars and Formative Feedback when Using Student Derived Marking Criteria in Peer and Self-assessment." *Assessment & Evaluation in Higher Education* 27, no. 4 (2002): 309–23.

Pólya, George. *How to Solve It.* Princeton University Press, 1945.

Schoenfeld, Alan H. "Learning to Think Mathematically: Problem Solving, Metacognition, and Sense-Making in Mathematics." In *Handbook for Research on Mathematics Teaching and Learning,* edited by Douglas A. Grouws, pp. 334–70. New York: Macmillan, 1992.

Smith, Margaret Schwan, and Mary Kay Stein. "Selecting and Creating Mathematical Tasks: From Research to Practice." *Mathematics Teaching in the Middle School* 3, no. 5 (1998): 344–50.

Stein, Mary Kay, Margaret Schwan Smith, Marjorie A. Henningsen, and Edward A. Silver. *Implementing Standards-Based Mathematics Instruction: A Casebook for Professional Development.* 2nd ed. New York: Teachers College Press, 2009.

Wood, Terry. "Creating a Context for Argument in Mathematics Class." *Journal for Research in Mathematics Education* 30, no. 2 (1999): 171–91.

CHAPTER 14

Authentic Student Work Samples Support Formative Assessment in Middle School

Kathleen Dempsey, *McREL International*

Andrea D. Beesley, *Impaq International, LLC*

Tedra Fazendeiro Clark, *McREL International*

Anne Tweed, *McREL International*

It was March, and teachers had been learning about the AWSM (Learning to Use Formative Assessment with the *A*ssessment *W*ork *S*ample *M*ethod) formative assessment process since August, but evidence of its impact on teacher practice was not yet clear. Mark shared his student work sample with the professional learning community (PLC), and as he described how he implemented a simple peer feedback protocol using student-generated success criteria, we realized this might be a turning point. Moving from *learning about the process* to actually *owning the process* is a long journey, but as Mark shared his approach, others began to realize that they too could implement this process. It was not a complex process. It was about clarity—clear learning goals, clear criteria for success, and specific feedback to move the learning forward. The AWSM formative assessment process was starting to affect teacher practice.

■ Why Focus on Formative Assessment?

Assessment has profound effects on student learning and motivation. Well-designed formative assessment is associated with major gains in student achievement across all ages and subjects, and has the greatest positive impact on struggling students (Black and Wiliam 1998a and b). Formative assessment is an evidence-based process of gathering information on three questions—(1) Where am I going?, (2) How am I doing now?, and (3) Where do I go next?—to support a learning cycle (Hattie and Timperley 2007; Sadler 1989). Therefore, the most important formative assessment practices involve (1) students' *understanding of their learning target*, (2) the criteria by which they will know *how they are doing on that target*, and (3) the *feedback* they receive to help them understand next steps. These literature-supported practices form the three dimensions of AWSM's formative assessment process (see fig. 14.1). Strategies for formative assessment include sharing learning goals and success criteria for meeting the goals with students, fostering student self- and peer-assessment in relation to success criteria, and providing descriptive feedback on ungraded practice assignments.

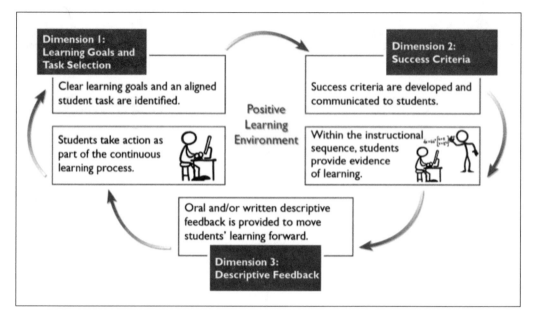

Fig. 14.1. The formative assessment process as used in AWSM

■ What Is AWSM?

Learning to Use Formative Assessment in Mathematics with the Assessment Work Sample Method (AWSM) is a professional development (PD) program that focuses on the power of formative assessment to improve teacher practice and increase student learning. It builds middle school mathematics teachers' understanding of the characteristics of high-quality formative assessment and increases their ability to use it in their classrooms. We were inspired to create AWSM following results from previous research (Randel et al. 2011) on a program that did not change teacher practice and had few mathematics examples. By contrast, AWSM provides PD that integrates mathematics pedagogical content knowledge and formative assessment practices. AWSM is embedded in everyday teacher practice and uses actual student and teacher work along with peer review and support. The challenge was to provide PD experiences that focused on *showing* rather than *telling* teachers why and how to implement formative assessment in mathematics. The AWSM work sample provided the tool and the PD format provided the mechanism by which to meet this challenge. Using the work sample, teachers could assess work from an anonymous teacher; discuss student understanding and thinking about mathematics; relate the work sample to his and her own practice; and, with guidance from an experienced session facilitator, take action for improved teaching and student learning.

AWSM was designed to encourage ongoing reflective practice that avoids the "halo" effect of many PD experiences where teachers talk about instructional processes but are unable to implement the reform in their classrooms (Weiss 1997). AWSM places teachers in collaborative learning groups, features ongoing meetings throughout the school year, and uses work samples to connect the PD to content, instructional practice, and local context. The sessions prompted teachers to examine their current assumptions, discuss differences in the formative assessment process and their current beliefs and practices, and decide on aspects of their practice to change. Then the sessions provided time to learn new approaches and stimulated reflection that led to strategy implementation, all of which are consistent with the principles for transformative learning experiences (Thompson and Zeuli 1999).

AWSM is structured around thirteen face-to-face meetings comprising an extended introductory session and twelve sessions of about forty-five minutes each. During the introductory session, participants build their understanding of formative assessment as one component of a larger assessment system. Participants discuss the characteristics of positive classroom culture, explore why it is essential for implementing this process, and consider structures that will help them create such a culture.

Sessions 1–8 target the three dimensions of the AWSM process through the examination of authentic student work. Dimensions 1 and 2 represent the foundation for AWSM, as teachers identify the goal for student learning and specific criteria for meeting that goal. This process includes an examination of student work to ensure that the learning goal, success criteria, and tasks are all well aligned to both academic content and the inferred cognitive demand of the learning goal. These dimensions also require teachers to clearly communicate learning expectations so that students can track their own progress and make learning adjustments (see fig. 14.1). For example, during the first two AWSM sessions, teachers discuss why the learning goal and the formative task must be clearly aligned, and they consider attributes that signal misalignment. They determine whether all components of the learning goal are addressed by the task or whether the task merely represents the more general learning topic. They also examine the cognitive complexity of the task and the learning goal to check for this alignment. Using criteria, teachers determine whether the learning goal and task are strongly aligned, partially aligned, or weakly aligned. These discussions lead to conversations about the mathematics content of the learning goal, the quality of the task, the level of student understanding as shown in the students' work, and recommendations for improvement. Figure 14.2 is an excerpt from a work sample used in AWSM that shows part of the teacher's cover sheet. The sheet was filled out by a teacher after the completion by students of an assigned formative task. Participants use this information to determine if the learning goal and formative task are strongly aligned, partially aligned or weakly aligned and then make recommendations for improvement.

During sessions 5–8, participants investigate dimension 3 and learn how to provide effective oral and written feedback. Participants learn that cues, questions, and recommendations for next steps help students take more responsibility for learning than does providing step-by-step directions, which leaves the responsibility with the teacher. Participants also learn strategies for implementing effective self- and peer-assessment through the use of clear success criteria and structures for student interaction.

Sessions 9–12 ask participants to share their instructional practice more directly as they generate student work samples, present the work to colleagues, and request feedback on how to improve their own implementation of the process. The process is fully integrated as participants reflect on their own progress and identify next steps.

5. What were your learning goals for the students for this assignment? In other words, what skills , concepts, or facts did you want students to learn, practice or demonstrate understanding of as a result of completing this assignment? (Students will know and understand that: ...)

I wanted students to demonstrate an understanding of unit rates and be able to calculate unit rates fluently ... or be able to make comparisons when the rates were not the same.

6. Check the type of learning goal/target this assignment addresses (check all that apply):
   - ☑ Knowledge (facts/details to be memorized)
   - ☑ Skill (algorithmic procedures)
   - ☑ Conceptual Understanding (reasoning, generalizing, explaining, etc.)
   - ☑ Problem Solving within a Context (multiple procedures; solution strategy)

11. a. How was this assignment assessed? If there is a rubric, student reflection, etc., please attach it. If you are not attaching a rubric, please explain your criteria for determining if students met the learning goal of the assignment.

The rubric is attached (on back of assignment) and shows the assignment is worth a total of 5 points (which I doubled and told the students I would do ahead of time).

11. b. Did you share these criteria with the students? ☑ Yes   [ ] No

Student shows an accurate comparison of costs of coffee pods at each of the three stores by calculating unit rates or other common ratios.	Student shows an accurate comparison of costs of coffee at two of the three stores by calculating unit rates or other common ratios.	Student calculates only one correct unit rate or common ratio.
	Student gives a clear written explanation for where the coffee should be purchased.	Student gives an unclear (or incorrect) written explanation for where the coffee should be purchased.)

Fig. 14.2. Excerpt from teacher's cover sheet

■ AWSM Evaluation

We implemented AWSM twice while evaluating its promise for improving teacher practice and student achievement. In 2012–2013 we worked with one middle school in a large urban district in Colorado, and in 2013–2014 with six more middle schools in the same district. Table 14.1 identifies the research questions and data sources of the evaluation.

Table 14.1

The alignment of AWSM research questions with data sources

Research Questions	Data Sources
To what extent can AWSM be implemented with fidelity in an authentic education setting?	PD observations, teacher questionnaires, teacher focus groups, facilitator debriefs
To what extent does AWSM show promise for improving teacher practice of mathematics formative assessment?	Teacher work sample pre- and posttest scores
To what extent does AWSM show promise for increasing student achievement in mathematics?	Student pre- and posttest scores on mathematics assessments

Impact on Teacher Knowledge

In focus groups and conversations during sessions, teachers indicated that they knew the formative assessment process, had learned formative assessment strategies, and were able to communicate with others about formative assessment. They also reported that their ability to provide descriptive feedback and their understanding of student self-assessment and peer-assessment had increased because of AWSM.

Impact on Teacher Classroom Practice

At the outset of AWSM, teachers completed a work sample to serve as the pretest measure of their assessment practice. After completing AWSM, teachers provided a final work sample to serve as the posttest. Work samples were scored on a rubric ranging from 1 to 4 by two trained content analysts. Data from the complete teacher sample (n = 47) indicated that scores significantly increased from pretest to posttest, with "feedback integrates student involvement" showing the greatest effect size (Cohen's d = 2.42) and "focus of goals on student learning" showing lowest effect size (Cohen's d = .16). The average effect size across all of the work sample dimensions was high (Cohen's d = 1.77). Figure 14.3 shows the estimated marginal means and effect sizes for each rubric dimension as a function of time (pretest to posttest).

In focus groups and surveys, teachers reported four specific formative assessment strategies that they implemented: using nongraded quizzes, so that students knew where they were in relation to the learning goal and success criteria; providing descriptive feedback to students; providing students with immediate oral feedback; and clearly communicating learning goals and success criteria to students. Teachers reported that this helped clarify their teaching and let students know what they should expect to learn. Further, having clear learning goals and success criteria facilitated communication with students and parents.

Teachers said that formative assessment data helped them to work with students at various levels of understanding in the following ways: by changing the structure of the classroom so that students were working on different assignments based on their level of mastery; by using supplemental programs and tutors to provide additional assistance; and by grouping students for instruction based upon where they were in relation to achieving the learning goal. This helped each student group focus on where they were in the learning progression.

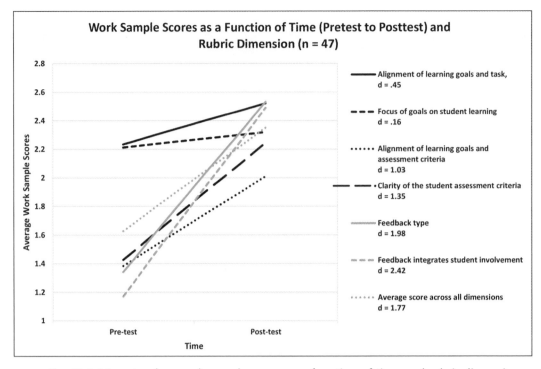

Fig. 14.3. Mean teacher work sample scores as a function of time and rubric dimension. Pretest work samples were submitted at the beginning of the school year at the outset of the AWSM program; posttest work samples were submitted at the end of the school year at program completion. Work samples were scored on a scale from 1 (lowest) to 4 (highest); d = Cohen's d effect size from pretest to posttest.

According to teachers, AWSM helped them realize that students should be involved in the formative assessment process to increase student understanding and accountability. For example, teachers used the success criteria as a checklist for students to determine their level of understanding relative to the learning goal, and they paired students for more formal peer assessment. This required teachers to teach students how to provide feedback to one another and to monitor the peer feedback process. As teachers had more practice involving students in the formative assessment process, they reported more successes.

Impact on Student Achievement

To examine the impact of the AWSM PD on student achievement in the pilot schools, the study team will acquire scores from the mathematics subtest of the Measure of Academic Progress (MAP) assessment administered twice per year (Northwest Evaluation Association 2009). After we collect these data from the school district, we will examine student achievement results using a difference-in-differences approach wherein students who were exposed to AWSM will be compared to the previous year's students who were not exposed to AWSM.

■ Lessons Learned during the AWSM Pilot

Although the AWSM study had specific research questions for investigation, much was gleaned about the challenges of implementing formative assessment practices beyond the scope of the study questions. The following list represents lessons learned along the way.

1. Because teachers come with numerous pedagogical questions and dilemmas, we learned that *facilitators of formative assessment PD must be prepared with suggestions and examples at a moment's notice.* This means that PD facilitators must have knowledge of current mathematics pedagogy and formative assessment, as well as extensive classroom experience from which to draw examples and anecdotes. One dilemma that many teachers voiced was how to flexibly group students, particularly when their classrooms were organized in ways that did not invite student collaboration. Facilitators provided specific advice that helped participants build mental pictures of how to incorporate grouping strategies before attempting this with their own students. Subsequent peer sharing of success stories made the changes seem more feasible.

2. When planning for formative assessment PD, include both orientation and job-embedded learning sessions. Teachers said they wanted to see the "big picture" of the process before diving into each formative assessment dimension. They recommended an orientation session scheduled prior to the school year to establish PD working agreements and provide a more in-depth discussion of the formative assessment process. The job-embedded sessions were critical for transferring teacher knowledge into teaching practice. We learned that *meeting regularly during the school year builds team cohesion, maintains focus on the formative assessment process, allows for intersession activities, fosters discussions with grade-level teams, and supports implementation with students.*

3. Teacher beliefs can impact professional learning. We learned that *many teachers have strongly held beliefs about grading, and the idea that formative assessment focuses on feedback rather than grades or points can be in conflict with current practice.* Teachers wondered what to do when the district and parents expect multiple grades to be posted weekly to the online grade book. Facilitators must be ready to engage in this conversation from a research perspective and ready to provide practical ideas for documenting student progress. It was interesting to note how students responded to receiving feedback rather than grades on formative tasks. It was a learning process, but as it became more routine, students, teachers, and parents realized the benefit. Changes like these require school and district support to be sustainable.

4. Mathematics teachers understand the value of using student peers as resources while learning is progressing, and of empowering students to be more aware of and accountable for their own learning. Teachers reported that, consistent with formative assessment research, struggling students benefited the most from using peer-assessment strategies. We learned that *teachers saw peer assessment as a way to get students involved in the feedback process but wondered how to help student feedback be more useful.* Teachers expressed concern about the possibility of faulty peer feedback, as correcting misconceptions or relearning skills requires time they don't have. To mitigate these issues, facilitators provided a scaffolded approach to help students become better assessors. The process begins with teachers establishing and communicating clear success criteria; it then incorporates modeling how students should work in pairs (including providing sentence starters to initiate conversation), whole-class review of anonymous student work to identify characteristics of quality, and developing checklists and other feedback protocols to help students assess one another's work.

5. Mathematics students, even those who are struggling, will be more invested in their own learning when they truly understand learning goal(s) and success criteria, their own current level of mastery, and the next steps toward meeting the goal. What we learned was that *teachers rarely developed success criteria for students or with students.* Teachers provided sample problems but felt that they didn't have time to develop success criteria. Learning about success criteria was a significant "a-ha" for some teachers who had believed that modeling a problem led directly to increased student skills and/or mathematical understanding. In AWSM, teachers were pleased to learn that students will care about mathematics and invest energy in assignments when they understand the learning goal and how to get there.

6. Similarly, mathematics students are capable of and willing to engage in cognitively demanding tasks when supported by teachers through a formative assessment process. What we learned is that *many teachers don't know how to develop or find rich tasks that require a higher level of cognitive demand unless they are provided in their text-based materials.* Much of the work that teachers assigned involved low-level, algorithmic processes rather than cognitively complex tasks. Facilitators provided examples of rich tasks and discussed how to change more routine problems into more complex ones. In AWSM, teachers who assigned complex problems and provided support found that students were able to explain and justify how they approached the work.

7. Administrative support positively influences teacher engagement in formative assessment PD and practice. Sustained administrator support seems necessary for long-term instructional change, because administrators can reinforce teachers' formative assessment strategies and alter policies (such as those for grading) that could otherwise unintentionally undermine formative assessment. We learned *that in schools where the principal or assistant principal was an active member of the team, teachers were more committed to AWSM and formative assessment.* As a result, they tried more strategies with students and developed plans at the school level for how to continue with formative assessment practices beyond the completion of the AWSM project.

At the conclusion of the pilot, participants shared some thoughts on the AWSM process:

> "I used to think formative assessment was about the teacher knowing where students are in the learning process. Now I know that formative assessment must include students so that they understand how to improve their own learning."

> "I used to think I had to grade everything. Now I know I can provide descriptive feedback and allow students to take action."

> "It's the dimensions of clear learning goals and success criteria that have most impacted my instruction. I think I was always clear about what was being learned, but I needed to be more explicit about sharing this information with my students."

Statements such as these offer insights into how formative assessment practices may impact teaching and learning and encourage the researchers and developers to continue this work.

References

Black, Paul, and Dylan Wiliam. "Assessment and Classroom Learning." *Assessment in Education* 5 (1998a): 7–74.

———. "Inside the Black Box: Raising Standards through Classroom Assessment." *Phi Delta Kappa* 80 (1998b): 139–44, 146–48.

Hattie, John, and Helen Timperley. "The Power of Feedback." *Review of Educational Research* 77 (2007): 81–112.

Northwest Evaluation Association. *Technical Manual for Measures of Academic Progress™ and Measures of Academic Progress for Primary Grades™*. Lake Oswego, Ore.: Northwest Evaluation Asssociation, 2009.

Randel, Bruce, Andrea D. Beesley, Helen Apthorp, Tedra F. Clark, Xin Wang, Louis F. Cicchinelli, and Jean M. Williams. *Classroom Assessment for Student Learning: The Impact on Elementary School Mathematics in the Central Region*. Washington, D.C.: National Center for Education Evaluation and Regional Assistance, Institute of Education Sciences, U.S. Department of Education, 2011.

Sadler, D. Royce. "Formative Assessment and the Design of Instructional Systems." *Instructional Science* 18 (1989): 119–44.

Thompson, Charles L., and John S. Zeuli. "The Frame and Tapestry: Standards-Based Reform and Professional Development." In *Teaching as the Learning Profession: Handbook of Policy and Practice,* edited by Linda Darling-Hammond and Gary Sykes, pp. 341–75. San Francisco: Jossey-Bass, 1999.

Weiss, Iris R. "The Status of Science and Mathematics Teaching in the United States: Comparing Teacher Views and Classroom Practice to National Standards." *NISE* (National Institute for Science Education) *Brief* 1, no. 3 (1997): 1–7. (ERIC Document Reproduction Service No ED411158.)

CHAPTER 15

Formative Assessment Strategies in the Secondary Mathematics Classroom

Richelle Marynowski, *University of Lethbridge, Alberta, Canada*

Formative assessment has garnered much attention in research and professional journals over the last fifteen years. However, the evolving definition of formative assessment has caused confusion among teachers about what exactly formative assessment is and how to incorporate it into their practice. A project was undertaken to support secondary mathematics teachers in incorporating formative assessment strategies into their practice by providing them with access to a coach over the course of a year. Eighteen teachers participated in having a coach observe lessons and provide feedback on how each teacher was already incorporating formative assessment and on how he or she might further implement formative assessment in the classroom. In this chapter, I first clarify how formative assessment is currently being considered, and I provide descriptions of strategies that secondary mathematics teachers incorporated into their practice as they participated in this project. In addition, some benefits and drawbacks that teachers experienced with implementing such strategies are presented.

■ What Is Formative Assessment?

For this project, formative assessment was considered to be any "process by which instruction might be improved" (Wiliam 2011, p. 38). The focus was on articulating formative assessment as a *process* for improving instruction and on improving learning, rather than on a specific instrument or tool. Several teachers who participated in this project initially thought that formative assessment needed to be something formal they did in their class with a product that they collected. Through engaging in this project, every teacher noted that their understanding of formative assessment grew to include all types of feedback for both students and teachers that are present in the classroom.

Some of the formative assessment strategies being used by the teachers could be further delineated as *assessment for learning* and *assessment as learning*. Assessment *for* learning is assessment that assists teachers in making adjustments to their practice in order to facilitate student learning (Western and Northern Canadian Protocol for Collaboration in Education [WNCP] 2006). Assessment *as* learning is assessment that encourages students to reflect on their own learning in order to make adjustments to their thinking or metacognition (WNCP 2006). Thus formative assessment encapsulates both of the processes involved in assessment *for* and *as* learning.

The formative assessment strategies that teachers used in their classrooms were framed around the five key strategies that Wiliam (2011) presented in his book *Embedded Formative Assessment*. These strategies are:

1. Clarifying, sharing, and understanding learning intentions and criteria for success so that "students know where they are going in their learning and what counts as quality work" (p. 69).

2. Engineering effective classroom discussions, activities, and learning tasks that elicit evidence of student learning, including asking "high-quality questions" (p. 104) that can enable the teacher to make effective instructional decisions based on student responses.

3. Providing feedback that moves learning forward, causes thinking, and "directs attention to what's next rather than focusing on how well or badly the student did on the work" (p. 128).

4. Activating students as instructional resources for one another, which forces students to "internalize the learning intentions and success criteria" (p. 144) in order to provide effective feedback to their peers.

5. Activating students as owners of their own learning to help students reflect "critically on one's own learning" (p. 158) using self-assessment and metacognitive strategies.

Formative assessment has been shown by many researchers to improve student learning in many different contexts (e.g., Black and Wiliam 1998; Clark 2012; James and Folorunso 2012; Stronge, Ward, and Grant 2011; Wiliam 2007). A challenge that has been noted is how to provide support for teachers to incorporate formative assessment practices into their teaching. One particular study by Wiliam and colleagues (2004) reported on the use of formative assessment strategies in classrooms in conjunction with targeted professional development support for teachers. They found that students in the classrooms where teachers had received professional support scored better than comparison groups on selected standardized academic assessment (effect size = 0.32). In addition, teachers reported that the benefits of the project not only spread to all of their classes, but "fundamentally altered their views of themselves as professionals" (p. 7). The formative assessment strategies proved to increase student achievement, and the professional support that teachers received supported the implementation of those strategies.

In light of the above study, a project was undertaken to offer teachers professional learning opportunities embedded in their daily work with respect to integrating formative assessment strategies into their practice. Secondary mathematics teachers were chosen as the group to ask to participate in this project. The next section of this chapter describes the specific strategies that were used by these teachers and their reflections on those strategies.

■ Formative Assessment Strategies

In the course of the project, teachers were observed implementing a variety of formative assessment strategies. What follows is a description of how four formative assessment strategies— *formative quizzes, students working on whiteboards, self-assessment,* and *peer feedback*—were implemented in teachers' classrooms. Included in the descriptions is an articulation of how that practice demonstrates various aspects of Wiliam's key strategies, along with any benefits or challenges teachers experienced in implementing the practice.

Formative Quizzes

Charles, an experienced secondary mathematics teacher and mathematics lead in his school, started giving students formative quizzes that included descriptive feedback or comments on the work without a grade or mark attached. He administered the formative quizzes near the end of a unit of study, as he normally would have done. The purpose of the formative quiz was to provide students with feedback on how to improve their understanding of the concepts in the unit. Once the formative quizzes were returned to students, they were given opportunities to work with each other or to ask questions of Charles "to figure out what they did wrong, to move forward, and to make corrections," not for the purpose of resubmitting the quiz, but in order to increase their understanding.

Charles commented that, at first, students questioned where the mark was. His response was to tell them that instead of focusing on the mark, they needed to focus on what they needed to do to improve. He asked his students how they felt about not having a mark on their quizzes, and they responded that they felt like they had to do something with the quiz, that the quiz was not an end to the learning but a continuation of learning. When Charles was asked if he saw a change in his students once he began incorporating formative quizzes, he said, "The biggest thing I noticed right away was the students aren't taking assessments back and throwing them in their binder; they're taking assessments back and they're working at it, so is that a change in learning? I believe that it is." In this formative assessment activity, Charles incorporated three of Wiliam's key strategies: clarifying learning intentions and criteria for success, providing feedback that moves learning forward, and activating students as resources for one another.

Self-Assessment

Kris, a younger teacher with experience in both junior and senior high school, incorporated a self-assessment component in many of his activities with students. He had students use the following categories to self-assess their understanding:

- **E**—*excellent:* I understand what to do and can do it accurately without help

- **S**—*satisfactory:* I need some guidance, or I am not always accurate

- **L**—*limited:* I am not sure where to begin, or I often experience difficulty

Kris incorporated this self-assessment into a lesson where he had students in groups moving through five stations, with each station focusing on a different operation with polynomials. Students rotated through the stations completing the activities at each station and then assigning themselves an E, an S, or an L for how well they understood the concepts and could perform the activities at each station. Once students evaluated their abilities, they then developed a plan for how they would increase their understanding or ability with any area where they deemed their level to be an S or an L.

Once students rotated through each activity, Kris briefly met with each student to discuss both the self-assessment rankings and the plan the student had developed. The information that Kris gathered during these conversations provided him with a clear understanding that many students were struggling with division of polynomials, which he addressed in his next class.

Present in Kris' lesson were three of Wiliam's five key strategies: activating students as resources for each other as they moved through the stations in groups, activating students as owners of their learning as they created a plan for how to improve their understanding, and engineering classroom activities that elicit evidence of student learning. One challenge Kris noted with having students assess themselves was that some students did not accurately assess their abilities. He commented that some students were too hard on themselves while others consistently gave themselves E's even when they encountered difficulty. Kris remarked that providing students with a clear description of what performance in each category might look like and providing feedback on the ratings that students gave themselves improved their ability to self-assess.

Students Working on Whiteboards

Teachers in this project used both mini-whiteboards and larger classroom whiteboards for formative assessment purposes. Jolene, a mid-career teacher with the majority of her teaching in grades 9–12, explored having students work on trigonometric proofs in pairs or groups of three on large classroom whiteboards. She assigned the groups one proof to complete, and while students were working on the task she stood back and surveyed the work of the class. She saw where a particular group was having difficulty and directed them to look at the work of the group next to them to get an idea of how to continue. Jolene also noticed that two groups were engaging in a debate over which group's proof was correct. At this point, she paused the class and had all students gather around and consider both proofs by asking the questions: Where are there similarities? And where are there differences? Through the discussion the students noticed that each proof was correct even though they were different. At the end of the discussion, students were given the option of continuing on with the proof they had been working on or starting a new one.

After the lesson, Jolene commented that having students write on the large whiteboards served to open up student work and thinking to make "doing mathematics" less private. She noted that students would occasionally step back from their own work to see what someone else was doing and then reengage with what their own group was working on. Jolene also found that with a quick scan she could easily see everyone's work at once, which was more efficient than walking around the class or having students line up at her desk. Within this lesson, Jolene incorporated two of Wiliam's five strategies: she had students engage in tasks that elicited evidence of student learning, and she activated students as instructional resources for each other as they commented on others' work and visibly saw how their classmates were working through a proof.

Peer Feedback

Many teachers who participated in this project purposefully created opportunities during class for students to connect with their peers about their work. In any given class, Nadine, a mid-career teacher, had her students check understandings, processes, solutions, and answers with other students in the class in many different ways. After Nadine had worked through a few examples during instruction, she asked her students to work through a question and compare solutions with their table groups, where students sat in groups of three or four. She then asked one group to write their solution on the board and invited other groups to make comments or ask questions about the solution. Nadine next asked her students to work through a second example; when they were done this time, she had them move to mixed groups where none of the members could be from their original table group. Students returned to their table groups, and Nadine again asked one group to write its solution on the board. Students were then given a series of questions to work through on their own. As the students were working, Nadine would periodically have them get up and move to check their solutions and answers with someone they had yet to talk to in class that day.

The main formative assessment strategy that was evident in Nadine's class was activating students as instructional resources for one another. Nadine found that having her students talk to each other about their solutions opened up "more communication between groups that wouldn't communicate before." She found that students were less concerned about sharing their ideas in front of the whole class as well. Nadine also noted that "some of them don't always understand the way I explain things, and so by opening that door and getting more comfortable about going to some of their other peers, even if they weren't moving very far, they found other ways of explaining things" and found a way to talk about mathematics that made sense to them. An additional benefit Nadine found from getting students talking to each other about mathematics was "they're more motivated and they're actually doing more math and playing less with their cell phones than they had been previously." She noticed that students were more actively engaged in their work than they had been before, which was an unexpected benefit of having students communicate with each other more in class.

Not all of the strategies that teachers were using are described above, nor could all of them possibly be described in a single chapter. The variety of implementation of each of the above strategies—formative quizzes, self-assessment, whiteboards, and peer feedback—was enlightening in that teachers took a strategy that they had heard about and adapted it to meet their needs and their students' needs.

■ Benefits of Formative Assessment on Teaching and Learning

At the end of the year, teachers in the project were asked if they found any benefits to either their teaching or their students' learning from incorporating formative assessment practices in their lessons. The most common comment from teachers was that formative assessment provided students with immediate feedback about their learning. Susan commented, "By the time I mark an assignment and get it back to them we've done so much more that it's meaningless." By incorporating different formative assessment strategies, she found she could give feedback to students either in the moment or the next day. This increased the number of times her students received information about their learning, which, as Susan noted, made that feedback more meaningful.

Besides providing information to students about their learning, the formative assessment practices also, as the teachers discovered, held students more accountable for their learning. As he provided immediate feedback, Charles told his students, "I'm putting it back on your shoulders now; it's easy for me to mark your quiz and give you a mark and say that you got 75 percent." With specific written feedback instead of a mark, Charles noted that students "should be excelling or striving" to want to know how to do better and where they can improve. Charles felt there was no excuse now for his students not to be excelling, because they were being given focused feedback on what they needed to do in order to improve their understanding.

Additionally, teachers noted that formative assessment provided immediate feedback to them about student learning. Dennis, a veteran teacher who taught using traditional methods, was initially resistant to incorporating formative assessment strategies into his lessons. From conversation with the coach, he decided to give students a formative unit test before their summative one.

He was excited about how well students achieved on the summative test after being given feedback and opportunities to revisit concepts through the formative test. Dennis noted that the biggest change occurred for students who had previously been experiencing difficulty. Dennis articulated how having students complete a formative quiz informed his teaching:

> The formative assessment's not only formative for students, but it's formative for me because then I can see [that] if they didn't get it, maybe I need to go over something or review something, maybe my explanation was weak or they didn't get as much practice as necessary, so I'll know ahead of time and it will inform me that this is something we better work on prior to the test, and so I think it's formative for the class, but it's also formative for the teacher.

Dennis was convinced that providing students a formative opportunity before the summative one benefited both the students and himself. He planned to incorporate formative opportunities before summative ones throughout the rest of his teaching.

The benefits that teachers noted in implementing formative assessment were many and varied. These ranged from having less marking, being able to help those students who are shy and don't speak up in class, to students having mathematical conversations that would not have happened previously. Every teacher who participated in the project noted a benefit, a change in student learning or behavior, or a change in his or her teaching from incorporating formative assessment into lessons. One teacher summed it up this way: "I believe that formative assessment is great work, it's beautiful work with what it can do for students."

■ Challenges in Implementing Formative Assessment

Though the benefits of formative assessment were prominent in the conversations, integrating formative assessment into practice also presented some challenges. Teachers noted that there was resistance on the part of the students to fully participate in some of the formative assessment activities. Natalie's comments about students resisting having conversations and learning from each other was that "they've still been really, really trained to learn from the teacher and it's going to take some time" for the students to get comfortable talking about mathematics. Susan echoed Natalie's observation and said, "The next time I teach the course I would definitely implement some of those strategies right from the beginning, so that they realize, that oh, this is her expectation, this is what we do in this room." Teachers also understood the importance of maintaining a balance for those students who prefer working on their own and for those students who prefer to have conversations about mathematics and learn from each other. A variety of formative assessment strategies that allowed each student to be able to express his or her understanding was noted as being essential to effective formative assessment.

Teachers also noted challenges within themselves when trying to integrate formative assessment into their practice. Teachers found that time to prepare or to think up formative assessment activities was a challenge. Kris commented, "A lot of times it's just tough to physically set up the groups and the stations. I think it's something you can build over years with activities, but it's tough." A few other teachers worried that incorporating some of the formative assessment strategies might take too long and they "feel the time crunch" with the curriculum. Even when a teacher noted benefits from integrating formative assessment activities, there were still challenges to overcome to seamlessly embed new strategies into his or her practice.

So Where to Begin?

What was interesting about many of the teachers in the project was that they were already incorporating elements of formative assessment into their practice, but they did not view what they were doing as formative assessment. Once teachers were opened up to the idea that formative assessment is not necessarily a written artifact that you collect, but a process for informing teaching and learning, they were more receptive to making small adjustments in their planning to gather information they could use to inform their practice.

For example, incorporating focused exit slips is a noninvasive way to begin incorporating formative assessment into one's practice. This could begin by asking students to write at the end of a class a "one sentence summary" of what they learned during that class. This information could then be used as the introduction to the next day's lesson: "What you said you learned from last class was . . ." Students then realize that attention is being paid to their learning, that what they are saying is being honored, and that teachers have a clear sense of what they are taking away from the class. Exit slips do not have to be done every class period, and they work well when the prompt that students are responding to elicits information that will inform the teacher of specific student understanding.

For teachers considering incorporating formative assessment elements into their practice, Wiliam (2011) cautioned against making several changes to teaching practice all at once. He notes that "when teachers try to change more than two or three things about their teaching at the same time, the typical result is that their teaching deteriorates and they go back to doing what they were doing before" (p. 161). Following Wiliam's suggestion, in this setting we encouraged teachers to choose one technique to incorporate in their teaching, and if they found it successful, to continue with that one technique until it is a seamless part of their practice.

References

Black, Paul, and Dylan Wiliam. "Inside the Black Box: Raising Standards through Classroom Assessment." *Phi Delta Kappan* 80, no. 2 (1998): 139–44, 146–48.

Clark, Ian. "Formative Assessment: A Systematic and Artistic Process of Instruction for Supporting School and Lifelong Learning." *Canadian Journal of Education* 35, no. 2 (2012): 24–40.

James, Ajogbeje Oke, and Alonge Micheal Folorunso. "Effect of Feedback and Remediation on Students' Achievement in Junior Secondary School Mathematics." *International Education Studies* 5, no. 5 (2012):153–62. doi: 10.5539/ies.v5n5p153.

Stronge, James H., Thomas J. Ward, and Leslie W. Grant. "What Makes Good Teachers Good? A Cross-Case Analysis of the Connection between Teacher Effectiveness and Student Achievement." *Journal of Teacher Education* 62 (2011): 339–55. doi: 10.1177/0022487111404241.

Western and Northern Canadian Protocol for Collaboration in Education (WNCP). *Rethinking Classroom Assessment with Purpose in Mind: Assessment for Learning, Assessment as Learning, Assessment of Learning.* Winnipeg: Manitoba Education, Citizen and Youth, 2006.

Wiliam, Dylan. "Content *Then* Process: Teacher Learning Communities in the Service of Formative Assessment." In *Ahead of the Curve*, edited by Douglas B. Reeves, pp. 183–206. Bloomington, Ind.: Solution Tree, 2007.

———. *Embedded Formative Assessment.* Bloomington, Ind.: Solution Tree, 2011.

Wiliam, Dylan, Clare Lee, Christine Harrison, and Paul Black. "Teachers Developing Assessment for Learning: Impact on Student Achievement." *Assessment in Education: Principles, Policy & Practice* 11, no. 1 (2004): 49–65.

PART IV

Assessment as Reasoning from Evidence

Introduction

Edward Silver, *University of Michigan, Ann Arbor*

The seminal report on educational assessment, *Knowing What Students Know: The Science and Design of Educational Assessment* (National Research Council [NRC] 2001), treats educational assessment as a process of reasoning from evidence:

> Although assessments used in various contexts and for differing purposes often look quite different, they share certain common principles. One such principle is that assessment is always a process of reasoning from evidence. By its very nature, moreover, assessment is imprecise to some degree. Assessment results are only estimates of what a person knows and can do. (p. 2)

The chapters in this section of the volume all illustrate somewhat different facets of the core idea of assessment as reasoning from evidence.

To set the context for the chapters in this section, it is useful also to think about them in light of another contribution of *Knowing What Students Know* (NRC 2001): namely, the so-called assessment triangle:

> Three foundational elements, comprising what is referred to in this report as the "assessment triangle," underlie all assessments. These three elements— cognition, observation, and interpretation—must be explicitly connected and designed as a coordinated whole. If not, the meaningfulness of inferences drawn from the assessment will be compromised. (p. 2)

The first element, cognition, refers to the importance of having a coherent model of learning and desired domain knowledge: "A model of cognition and learning should serve as the cornerstone of the assessment design process. This model should be based on the best available understanding of how students represent knowledge and develop competence in the domain" (NRC 2001, p. 3). The authors of the NRC report drew heavily on the research available from cognitive science and used language consistent with that theoretical perspective in this report, but it is certainly possible to have a model of desired domain knowledge and competence that is framed instead from sociocultural or situative theoretical perspectives. What the NRC report emphasizes is how critical it is that educational assessment be anchored by a sound conceptualization of what it means for a person to know and be able to perform competently within the domain of interest.

Two chapters in this section specifically reference the NRC report, and the authors of these chapters tie the assessment described in their chapters to core ideas from that report. Specifically, in their chapter **Embedding Formative Assessment in Curriculum Design: A Research-Based Approach**, Gearhart and colleagues describe in some detail the research on students' use of mathematical representations, such as the number line, that undergirded the design of both their instructional intervention and their assessment. In **Conducting Classroom Assessment Based in Cognition: The Case of Proportional Reasoning,** Carney and colleagues describe the research on students' thinking and reasoning with and about ratios and proportions that formed the basis for the design of their assessment methods. In this chapter, the authors use the other vertices of the assessment triangle to frame their presentation of additional information about their method of assessing proportional reasoning.

Though other chapter authors do not specifically cite the NRC report, most were explicit about the perspective on mathematical domain knowledge and competence that guided their assessment. For example, in **Learning, Teaching, and Assessing the Standards for Mathematical Practice,** Scherrer offers a situative perspective on mathematical competence that emphasizes the importance of participation in mathematical practices, and he describes how that perspective can be enacted in classroom assessment. In another chapter, **Applying CCSSM's Definition of Understanding to Assess Students' Mathematical Learning,** Albert and Kim use ideas from the Common Core State Standards for Mathematics (National Governors Association Center for Best Practices and Council of Chief State School Officers [NGA Center and CCSSO] 2010), and some related research, to identify three categories of mathematical understanding that illustrate mathematical competence. They then report and analyze the work of a group of South Korean teachers who constructed assessment items to assess young students' mathematical proficiency with respect to each category of understanding and analyzed students' responses to those items. In the chapter by Walcott and colleagues **(What NAEP Tells Us about the Relationship between Classroom Assessment Practices and Student Achievement in Mathematics),** the model of student competence in mathematics is presumably the framework used to construct the National Assessment of Educational Progress (NAEP).

The chapters in part IV all reveal some interesting facet of how assessment can be used as evidence to make inferences. In chapters 18 through 20 (from Scherrer; Carney et al.; and Gearhart et al.), the focus is on using assessment evidence to make reasonable inferences about what students know and can do, in each case with a focus on a different aspect of the domain of mathematics. In chapter 21, from Albert and Kim, the focus is on how the teachers who wrote the items and analyzed the corresponding student responses interpret the information in order to make inferences not only about what students know and can do but also about how instruction might need to be modified to promote students' development of understanding across the various categories.

Walcott and colleagues, in chapter 16, focus explicitly on the use of assessment evidence to guide decisions about classroom practice. They illustrate how an analysis of evidence from student performance results and teacher questionnaire data can be coordinated and used to make inferences about teacher classroom assessment practices that are likely to support or hinder student achievement. And in chapter 17 **(Guidelines for Analyzing Assessment Data to Inform Instruction),** Rankin discusses a range of assessment data that is available to teachers and educational decision makers, and she carefully delineates possible ways to use the data as sources of evidence from which to make inferences that could guide education decision making.

The chapters in this section cover a wide-ranging territory of educational assessment, and they each shine light on a different aspect of the assessment landscape. Yet, they all illustrate the core truth articulated by the NRC (2001): assessment is always a process of reasoning from evidence. Their authors offer interesting examples of how to design assessments to gather high-quality evidence—linked to a model of what students should know and be able to do—and how to use such evidence to make valid inferences that undergird sound educational decisions.

As you read the chapters in this section, consider the following questions:

- What conceptualization is presented of what it means for a person to know mathematics and be able to perform competently with respect to the topic(s) of interest?

- How do these chapters position assessment to enhance mathematics teaching and learning?

References

National Governors Association Center for Best Practices and Council of Chief State School Officers (NGA Center and CCSSO). *Common Core State Standards for Mathematics.* Washington, D.C.: NGA Center and CCSSO, 2010.

National Research Council (NRC). *Knowing What Students Know: The Science and Design of Educational Assessment,* edited by James W. Pellegrino, Naomi Chudowsky, and Robert Glaser. Washington, D.C.: National Academies Press, 2001.

CHAPTER 16

What NAEP Tells Us about the Relationship between Classroom Assessment Practices and Student Achievement in Mathematics

Crystal Y. Walcott, *Indiana University-Purdue University Columbus*
Rick Hudson, *University of Southern Indiana*
Doris Mohr, *University of Southern Indiana*
N. Kathryn Essex, *Indiana University-Bloomington*

Every teacher has faced a dilemma regarding assessment. This dilemma is encompassed by a phrase that has developed a negative connotation in education today—"teaching to the test." The curriculum and assessment choices teachers make in the classroom are complex in nature and directly affect student performance. The meaning of this phrase, "teaching to the test," is specific to particular classroom contexts. In classrooms where rich, concept-based assessment practices are commonplace, "teaching to the test" entails the enactment of rich, concept-based instruction. On the other hand, in classrooms where assessments heavy in rote procedure are commonplace, the phrase denotes the enactment of rote procedure-based instruction. Most classrooms fall somewhere within the continuum described above, and in this chapter we hope to identify some general characteristics of assessment practices that apply to the majority of classrooms. Gleaned from the results of the National Assessment of Educational Progress (NAEP) Main Mathematics Assessment (NCES 2014), the results we will share here will shed light on characteristics and trends in current classroom assessment practices over the ten-year period from 2003 to 2013. In addition, we will explore the relationship between students' achievement on standardized assessments and the characteristics of classroom assessment practices employed.

With a wealth of commercial test preparation materials that target standardized test preparation in mathematics available (including resources supplied by textbook publishers), how should teachers go about determining which types of curricular activities influence students' performance in standardized assessment environments? Existing research sheds some light on what works, in general, when preparing students for standardized assessment. Five effective standardized test preparation strategies identified in research include (1) grounding instruction in rigorous academic standards that aligns to the content and the ways in which students will be tested; (2) using various types of assessment methods and item formats; (3) providing opportunities for students to develop test-taking strategies; (4) preparing in regular intervals rather than cramming during the weeks leading up to the testing; and (5) motivating students to do their personal best on standardized testing (Miyasaka 2000; Turner 2009).

In this chapter, we explore one of these strategies in depth: using various types of assessment methods and item formats. The overall goal of this exploration is to provide insights to teachers regarding research-based best practices for choosing assessment methods and types of items to implement in the classroom. Existing research provides some insight into teachers' classroom assessment beliefs. For instance, research has shown that 51 percent of teachers in high-stakes assessment states (states where observable student consequences resulted from performance on the state-mandated tests) reported that their classroom testing formats closely aligned to the state test formats, compared to a figure of 17 percent of teachers in low-stakes assessment states (states where no observable consequences resulted from performance on the state-mandated test). Furthermore, almost twice as many teachers in high-stakes states reported using weekly multiple-choice tests than did their low-stakes states' counterparts (31 percent and 17 percent, respectively) (Abrams, Pedulla, and Madaus 2003).

These findings imply that the higher the stakes of a given assessment, the better the chance that classroom assessment mirrors the format of the state assessment and, thus, will include the frequent implementation of multiple-choice items. This practice seems to be based on the belief that if students are routinely tested using the same methods as the state-mandated tests, student performance will be positively impacted. But is this the case?

This chapter provides insights into this question by analyzing student performance on the National Assessment of Educational Progress (NAEP) Main Mathematics Assessment and by disaggregating NAEP Math performance results by teacher-reported assessment practices. The NAEP Main Mathematics Assessment is administered to a nationally representative sample of fourth- and eighth-grade students every two years. NAEP is similar to many state-mandated tests in that students are asked to complete multiple-choice as well as short and long written-response items in the content areas of number and operations, algebra, measurement, geometry, and data analysis and probability.

■ NAEP Teacher Questionnaire

The teachers of students participating in the NAEP assessment complete a questionnaire that gathers information on teacher demographics, preparation and professional development, and instructional practices. In both the fourth- and eighth-grade questionnaires, teachers are asked how often they use multiple-choice tests, problem sets, short or long written responses, and individual or group projects or presentations to assess student progress in mathematics (see fig. 16.1). This question appeared on the 2003, 2007, 2009, 2011, and 2013 fourth-grade teacher survey, as well as on the 2009, 2011, and 2013 eighth-grade survey. For the purposes of this study, we focus on only two of the four teacher questionnaire items mentioned above—use of multiple-choice and short or long written-response assessments—with the rationale that the other two categories are rarely, if ever, found in standardized tests.

How often do you use each of the following to assess student progress in mathematics?
Fill in one oval on each line.

	Never or hardly ever	Once or twice a year	Once or twice a month	Once or twice a week	
a. Multiple-choice tests	Ⓐ	Ⓑ	Ⓒ	Ⓓ	HE001131
b. Problem sets	Ⓐ	Ⓑ	Ⓒ	Ⓓ	HE001132
c. Short (e.g., a phrase or sentence) or long (e.g., several sentences or paragraphs) written responses	Ⓐ	Ⓑ	Ⓒ	Ⓓ	HE001133
d. Individual or group projects or presentations	Ⓐ	Ⓑ	Ⓒ	Ⓓ	HE001134

Fig. 16.1. NAEP teacher questionnaire excerpt on assessment practices

■ Teacher-Reported Classroom Test Use

A look at the fourth-grade data shows that the percentage of students whose teachers reported use of multiple-choice assessments has increased; however, use of written-response assessments has also increased over time. The percentage of students whose teachers use multiple-choice assessments one to two times per week increased from 19 percent in 2003 to 24 percent in 2013, and the percentage of students whose teachers marked "never" or "hardly ever" fell from 19 percent to 13 percent over the same time period. In 2013, the majority of fourth graders had teachers who reported using multiple-choice assessments one to two times per month (53 percent in 2013, up from 48 percent in 2003). At the same time, the largest group of fourth graders had teachers who reported the use of written-response assessments one to two times per week, increasing from 37 percent in 2007 to 44 percent in 2013. Conversely, the percentage of students whose teachers reported "never" or "hardly ever" using written-response assessments decreased by 6 percent since the 2003 administration. The second largest group reported using short or long written-response assessments one to two times per month (40 percent in 2013, down from a high of 42 percent in 2011 and up from a low of 39 percent in 2003). In short, as of the 2013 administration the trend data indicate that more fourth graders have teachers who are reporting the use of multiple-choice (77 percent) and written-response assessments (84 percent) on a frequent basis (defined for this study as one to two times per week or one to two times per month). See tables 16.1 and 16.2 for fourth-grade teacher-reported data (National Center for Education Statistics [NCES] 2014).

Table 16.1
Frequency of use of multiple-choice assessments

Frequency	Grade	2013	2011	2009	2007	2003
1–2 times per week	Gr. 4	24	23	23	20	19
	Gr. 8	11	12	11	N.A.	N.A.
1–2 times per month	Gr. 4	53	52	51	49	48
	Gr. 8	52	52	50	N.A.	N.A.
1–2 times per year	Gr. 4	9	11	11	12	14
	Gr. 8	22	22	22	N.A.	N.A.
Never or hardly ever	Gr. 4	13	14	15	19	19
	Gr. 8	15	14	17	N.A.	N.A.

Table 16.2
Frequency of use of short or long written-response assessments

Frequency	Grade	2013	2011	2009	2007	2003
1–2 times per week	Gr. 4	44	39	37	37	39
	Gr. 8	30	27	26	N.A.	N.A.
1–2 times per month	Gr. 4	40	42	42	42	39
	Gr. 8	46	45	45	N.A.	N.A.
1–2 times per year	Gr. 4	7	9	10	9	14
	Gr. 8	14	15	17	N.A.	N.A.
Never or hardly ever	Gr. 4	9	10	11	12	16
	Gr. 8	10	13	12	N.A.	N.A.

Given that only three administrations of data are available for eighth grade, it is noteworthy that about half of eighth graders' teachers reported administering multiple-choice assessments one to two times per month (52 percent in 2013, up from 50 percent in 2009). In addition, the largest group of teachers of eighth graders reported using short or long written-response assessments one to two times per month (46 percent in 2013, and 45 percent in 2009 and 2011). Perhaps the most important information that can be inferred from the data is that in 2013 a majority of eighth graders had teachers who reported using multiple-choice (63 percent) or short/long written-response (76 percent) assessments at least one to two times per month. See tables 16.1 and 16.2 for eighth-grade teacher-reported data (NCES 2014).

Findings from our study should be viewed in light of existing research (Abrams, Pedulla, and Madaus 2003; Miyasaka 2000; Turner 2009) indicating that teachers tend to implement item types that mirror the forms of standardized assessments given to their students. When combining the frequency categories of "1–2 times per week" and "1–2 times per month," at both grade levels and within both assessment formats reported here, between 63 percent and 84 percent of students are administered multiple-choice or short/long written response assessments on a frequent basis. The NAEP teacher survey does not collect data regarding the rationale for the teachers' assessment decisions; however, the frequency of classroom assessment may be in response to standardized test preparation. If this is the case, is this good practice? Does the frequency of use of multiple-choice or short/long written-response assessments relate to student performance on standardized measures?

■ Performance Trends on NAEP

NAEP releases overall scale scores to the general public via the NCES website (nces.ed.gov) following each test administration. Fourth- and eighth-grade scores are reported on a continuous scale, with scores ranging from 0 to 500 scale points. The NAEP Online Data Explorer (http://nces.ed.gov/nationsreportcard/naepdata/) is a tool that allows users to group scale score data by various student, teacher, and school demographic variables. We generated scale score data at fourth- and eighth-grade disaggregated by the two teacher testing practice variables discussed earlier. These results help to explore the question of whether or not frequent use of multiple-choice or short or long written-response assessments is related to student performance. As these data are shared, keep in mind that a scale score increase of eleven scale points is roughly equivalent to one grade-level gain at fourth grade and an increase of eight scale points is equivalent to one grade-level gain at eighth grade (Kloosterman and Walcott 2007).

■ Scale Scores by Multiple-Choice Assessment Use

An analysis of scores from 2003 to 2013 reveals fourth graders' scale scores have increased significantly across all categories of classroom multiple-choice assessment use. Most notably, students whose teachers reported never or hardly ever using multiple-choice assessments realized a nine-point increase in the NAEP average scale scores from 2003 to 2013 (nearly a gain of one grade level), while those students whose teachers reported using multiple-choice assessments one to two times per week realized a gain of seven points (a gain of more than one-half of a grade level). At eighth grade, scale scores increased by one to three scale points in each group from 2009 to 2013. These were statistically significant increases, but with only three years of data it is difficult to identify particular trends within categories.

The bigger story for multiple-choice test use lies not in the trends over time, but in scale scores across categories within a given testing year. Figure 16.2 shows fourth-grade scale score trends from 2003 to 2013 disaggregated by multiple-choice test-use categories. The greatest performance gap between the categories appears when comparing scale scores for the 2011 administration. Here, students of teachers who reported never or hardly ever using multiple-choice assessments scored on average eleven scale points higher than students whose teachers reported using them one to two times per week. With an eleven-point gain representing a one-grade level gain, these data indicate that, in 2011, fourth graders whose teachers reported never or hardly ever using multiple choice assessments outperformed their counterparts described above by a full grade level. However, it is important to remember that these results are correlational, not causal. The 2011 eighth-grade data reveal a larger gap between scale scores of these two groups (see fig. 16.3), with students whose teachers reported never or hardly ever using multiple-choice assessments outperforming their frequently tested counterparts by nineteen scale points, an equivalent of over two grade levels.

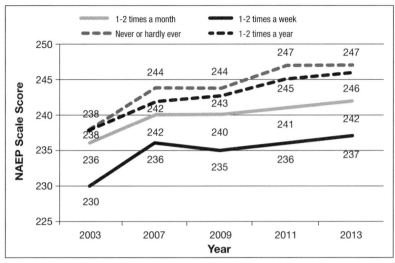

Fig. 16.2. NAEP scale scores of fourth-grade students by categories of multiple-choice assessment use

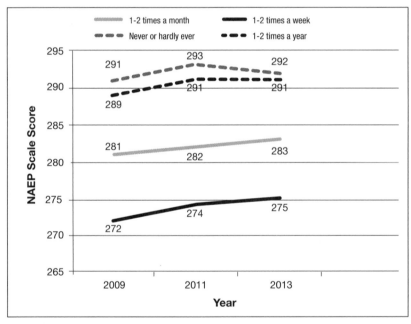

Fig. 16.3. NAEP scale scores of eighth-grade students by categories of multiple-choice assessment use

■ Scale Scores by Short or Long Written-Response Assessment Use

In terms of short and long written-response assessment use, trends in scale scores from 2003 to 2013 show that across all categories, fourth-grade scores are on the rise, with the highest gains in the "1–2 times per week" and "1–2 times per month" categories. The trends in eighth grade are not as clearly differentiated. The highest scale score, 286, is associated with students whose teachers reported administering short or long written-response assessments one to two times per month or one to two times per year. Here, too, eighth-grade trend lines are impossible to establish with only three years of data.

Although the data regarding written-responses are not as clear as the multiple-choice data, the data seem to suggest that fourth-grade students who never or hardly ever have assessments requiring written responses do not do as well as their peers who experience short and/or long written-response assessments more frequently. Figure 16.4 shows that in 2013, fourth-grade students whose teachers reported using short or long written-response assessments either one to two times per month or one to two times per week outperform their counterparts whose teachers reported using them never or hardly ever by five to six scale points, about a one-half grade-level gain.

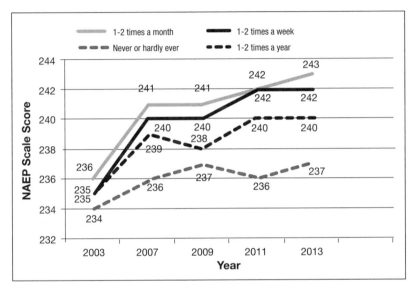

Fig. 16.4. NAEP scale scores of fourth-grade students by categories
of short or long written-response assessment use

■ Item-Level Performance

Following each assessment administration, NAEP releases sets of items to the public via the Online Questions Tool (http://nces.ed.gov/nationsreportcard/itmrlsx/landing.aspx). The tool allows users to view questions as they were presented to students in their test booklets, as well as scoring rubrics and performance data for each item. Our research team has access to a secure database of items that allows for additional analysis of data not available through the online tool. The secure database allows us to group item-level data by various demographic variables collected as part of the NAEP assessment. We were interested in what we could learn from student performance at the item level when analyzed from the perspective of assessment frequency categories. In many instances we found substantial gaps between the categories of "never" and "one to two times per week." For this chapter, we intentionally selected two released items where these gaps exist. As shown in the following two examples, performance advantages were seen in those cases where students less frequently experienced multiple-choice assessments and frequently experienced short and long written-response assessments. The data reported about the two items below were accessed using the secure database from the 2011 NAEP assessment teacher questionnaire.

Task 1: Division Story Item (Multiple-Choice)

The first task example is shown in figure 16.5. In this multiple-choice item, fourth-grade students were asked to determine the number of students on a team if 316 students are to be equally partitioned into four teams. To complete this problem, students had access to a calculator.

> Park School has 316 students. For field day, the students are put into 4 teams with the same number of students on each team. How many students are on each team?
>
> A.   79
>
> B.   312
>
> C.   320
>
> D.   1,264
>
> Did you use the calculator on this question?
>
>   ◯ Yes   ◯ No

Fig. 16.5. Division story item (2011-4M8 #4)

This item was fairly easy for all fourth-grade students, with 75 percent of students responding with the correct answer of A (79). However, students' success on this item seems to correlate with the frequency with which their teachers reported using multiple-choice assessments. As the data in table 16.3 demonstrate, the more frequently students engaged in multiple-choice assessments, the less likely they were to answer the problem correctly. Based on our analyses, we have found that this trend was evident across many, but not all, of the NAEP items. Approximately 80 percent of students whose teachers never or hardly ever used multiple-choice assessments responded to this item correctly, while 71 percent of students whose teachers reported using multiple-choice assessments once or twice a week responded correctly. This difference is statistically significant, and quite substantial for a large-scale assessment such as NAEP. Similarly, in general, students whose teachers reported never or hardly ever using assessments requiring short or long written responses performed worse than those students whose teachers did use this type of assessment.

Table 16.3

Student data on the division story item grouped by frequency of assessment categories

Frequency Category	Percentage of Students Responding Correctly in Multiple-Choice Categories	Percentage of Students Responding Correctly in Short or Long Written-Response Categories
Never or hardly ever	80%	70%
1–2 times per year	79%	75%
1–2 times per month	74%	76%
1–2 times per week	71%	75%

Task 2: Unit Conversions Problem Solving Item (Short Constructed Response)

The second example task is shown in figure 16.6. In this open-response task, eighth-grade students were asked to solve a problem in which the student had to convert a rate given in ounces per day to a rate of quarts per week (described in the task as seven days). Although there are several ways to solve this problem accurately, one method is to multiply the number of ounces by 7 to determine the total number of ounces consumed in one week. Then, a student could divide by 32 to find the number of quarts Tyler drank in seven days. Students were also prompted to show their work. This item was scored as "Correct" if the student responded 5.25 and showed correct work. The item was scored "Partial" if the correct answer was given with insufficient work, if an incorrect answer was given with a correct process, or if the student responded "5."

Tyler drinks 24 fluid ounces of milk each day for 7 days. How many quarts of milk does he drink in the 7 days? Do not round your answer. (1 quart = 32 fluid ounces)

Answer: _____ quarts

Show how you found your answer.

Fig. 16.6. Unit conversions problem solving item (2013-8M7 #9)

This item was moderately difficult for eighth-grade students, with 41 percent of students in the national sample responding with the correct answer, 14 percent of students providing a partially correct response, and 42 percent of the national sample responding with an incorrect response. However, as shown in the second column of table 16.4, students' success on this item seems to be correlated with the frequency in which their teachers reported using multiple-choice tests in the classroom. Like the division story task above, students whose teachers reported commonly using multiple-choice assessments did not perform as well on this item as their peers who never or rarely experienced multiple-choice classroom tests. The difference between the percent of students' correct responses (18 percent) was significant and, again, quite substantial for a large-scale assessment. Students whose teachers reported giving more classroom tests requiring long or short responses scored slightly higher on this item than did their peers whose teachers reported less frequent use of long or short response tests, as shown in the third column of table 16.4.

Table 16.4

Student data on the unit conversions problem solving item grouped by frequency of assessment categories

Frequency Category	Percentage of Students Responding Correctly in Multiple-Choice Categories	Percentage of Students Responding Correctly in Short of Long Written-Response Categories
Never or hardly ever	53%	43%
1-2 times per year	50%	44%
1-2 times per month	43%	46%
1-2 times per week	35%	45%

■ Connections to the Classroom

As states begin to implement Common Core State Standards (National Governors Association Center for Best Practices and Council of Chief State School Officers [NGA Center and CCSSO] 2010), the assessment landscape is bound to change. New technologies will become more prevalent in the standardized assessment landscape as assessments developed by PARCC (Partnership for Assessment of Readiness for College and Careers [PARCC] 2014) and Smarter Balanced (Smarter Balanced Assessment Consortium 2014) are implemented. These technologies will allow for different types of item formats, as well as new manners in which to score items. Teachers need sound advice regarding instructional strategies to help their students navigate this new assessment landscape, one that includes computer-based testing environments and scoring via artificial intelligence. In addition to the strategies mentioned in the beginning of this chapter, teachers will need to use additional assessment methods incorporated with new student test-taking strategies to prepare students for the online testing environments of PARCC and Smarter Balanced.

In light of these changes, how might our findings influence teachers' decisions in determining what types of curricular activities affect student performance? First, our data seem to refute the commonly held belief that teachers' frequent use of multiple-choice tests will better prepare students for standardized assessments that include them. Indeed, it appears from the data that students who experienced the most multiple-choice testing in their classrooms tended to fare worse on NAEP than students who rarely took such exams. However, we know little about the actual assessments that the teachers were giving their students. It seems possible that many were produced by textbook publishers, and it may be that the quality of these assessments, including their alignment to classroom instruction, plays a role in how well students do on other multiple-choice tests.

We admit that our findings should be viewed as tentative in nature, and there are obvious limitations with the data we report in this chapter. The assessment practices are self-reported, and individual teachers may have interpreted the survey question in different ways. For example, we believe that the phrase "short or long written-responses" may include a wide variety of question types, including fill-in-the-blank items, essays, tasks prompting reasoning, and open-ended, problem-solving tasks. Such discrepancies may account for the lack of clarity in regard to the student achievement results. Additionally, in interpreting these data, it is important to clarify that the student achievement and assessment practice data are correlational, not causal. As such, alternative interpretations of our results could be that the types of assessments teachers use are reflective of their instructional practices, which, in turn, affect student achievement, or that low-performing students are more likely to be exposed to multiple-choice tests.

Furthermore, socioeconomic status may be a confounding variable, as students from lower socioeconomic backgrounds (as measured by eligibility for national school lunch programs) tend to score lower on the mathematics portion of the NAEP assessment and may also be more likely to have teachers who frequently use multiple-choice assessments. For example, between 2009 and 2013, fourth-grade students identified as eligible for the national school lunch program (NSLP) scored 21 to 22 points lower than those not eligible and were 50 percent more likely to have teachers who assess mathematics using multiple-choice assessments 1–2 times per week. During the same time period, eighth-grade students identified as eligible for the NSLP scored approximately 21 to 25 points lower than those not eligible and were twice as likely to have teachers who assess mathematics using multiple-choice assessments 1–2 times per week. Regardless of the reasoning, it is alarming that socioeconomically disadvantaged students are more likely than their peers to be assessed using multiple-choice items.

Regarding use of short/long written-response assessments, the results for both fourth and eighth grade were somewhat surprising. Fourth-grade students identified as eligible for the NSLP scored 23 to 24 points lower than those not eligible, and yet they were slightly more likely as those not eligible to have teachers who used short/long written response assessments 1–2 times per week. Eighth-grade students identified as eligible for the NSLP scored 26 to 27 points lower than those not eligible, but they were roughly 10 to 20 percent more likely to have teachers who used short/long written response assessments 1–2 times per week. These results seem counterintuitive and suggest that other factors beyond those investigated here are contributing to the findings.

The results shared in this study provide data that have the potential to inform classroom teachers about choosing methods to assess students. If, as previous research suggests, teachers are to use instruction that aligns to the content and to the ways in which students will be tested, use a variety of assessment methods and item formats, and provide opportunities to students to develop test-taking strategies (Miyasaka 2000; Turner 2009), then it follows that teachers should use some multiple-choice testing. In the case of multiple-choice testing, just as with open-ended response assessments, care must be used to ensure that the tests are well-written and appropriately aligned with the content.

The results shared in this chapter are particularly interesting considering that the majority of NAEP items are multiple-choice in nature. It is notable that in completing the item analysis, students who were rarely tested with multiple-choice assessments performed better on all types of assessment items. Our research is consistent with the findings of Newmann, Bryk, and Nagaoka (2001), who found that students in Chicago who engaged in high-quality, authentic assignments tended to show greater learning gains than their peers who experienced low-quality classroom assignments. Additionally, the use of high-quality assignments in mathematics, in particular, was somewhat more beneficial for low-achieving students than high-achieving students.

As teachers, we want to ensure that the types of items students encounter on standardized assessments are familiar. However, NCTM has advocated for alternative assessment measures and for an increased emphasis on reasoning and communication in the K–12 classroom. Assessing such mathematical processes and practices is difficult to do using multiple-choice assessments, and the assessment of reasoning and communication is not reflected in many publisher-generated tests or testing resources (Hunsader et al. 2014). Our analyses and interpretations suggest that students need opportunities to write about mathematics and be assessed on this work. For examples of what this looks like, a variety of assessment resources are available online, offering various item types, including those involving writing about mathematics. These include the NAEP Questions Tool, the PARCC sample questions, Smarter Balanced sample items and performance tasks, as well as numerous state-specific item resources.

References

Abrams, Lisa M., Joseph J. Pedulla, and George F. Madaus. "Views from the Classroom: Teachers' Opinions of Statewide Testing Programs." *Theory into Practice* 42, vol. 1 (2003): 18–29.

Hunsader, Patricia D., Denisse R. Thompson, Barbara Zorin, Amanda Loyden Mohn, Jennifer Zakrzewski, Hyas Karadeniz, Elaine C. Fisher, and George MacDonald. "Assessments Accompanying Published Textbooks: The Extent to Which Mathematical Processes Are Evident." *ZDM: The International Journal on Mathematics Education* 46, vol. 5 (2014): 797–813.

Kloosterman, Peter, and Crystal Walcott. "The 2003 NAEP Mathematics Assessment: Overall Results." In *Results and Interpretations of the 2003 Mathematics Assessment of the National Assessment of Educational Progress*, edited by Peter Kloosterman and Frank K. Lester, Jr., pp. 289–309. Reston, Va.: NCTM, 2007.

Miyasaka, Jeanne R. "A Framework for Evaluating the Validity of Test Preparation Practices." Paper presented at the Annual Meeting of the American Educational Research Association, Chicago, 2000.

National Center for Education Statistics (NCES). "NAEP Data Explorer" (2014). http://nces.ed.gov/nationsreportcard/naepdata/.

National Governors Association Center for Best Practices and Council of Chief State School Officers (NGA Center and CCSSO). *Common Core State Standards for Mathematics.* Washington, D.C.: NGA Center and CCSSO, 2010.

Newmann, Fred M., Anthony S. Bryk, and Jenny K. Nagaoka. *Authentic Intellectual Work and Standardized Tests: Conflict or Coexistence?* Chicago: Consortium on Chicago School Research, 2001.

Partnership for Assessment of Readiness for College and Careers (PARCC). "The PARCC Assessment" (2014). http://www.parcconline.org/parcc-assessment.

Smarter Balanced Assessment Consortium. "Smarter Balanced Assessments" (2014). http://www.smarterbalanced.org/smarter-balanced-assessments/.

Turner, Steven L. "Ethical and Appropriate High-Stakes Test Preparation in Middle School: Five Methods That Matter." *Middle School Journal* 41, vol. 1 (2009): 36–45.

CHAPTER 17

Guidelines for Analyzing Assessment Data to Inform Instruction

Jenny Grant Rankin, *Northcentral University, Prescott Valley, Arizona*

■ Introduction and Problem

In education, student assessment feedback in the form of data is used to inform decisions concerning instruction and to determine how best to meet students' diverse learning needs. Educators' data-informed decisions can lead to improved student learning (Sabbah 2011; Wohlstetter, Datnow, and Park 2008). Thus educators commonly analyze mathematics assessment data to inform decisions that impact students' mathematics performance.

Provincial, territorial, state, and other mathematics assessment data often look simple to interpret. However, assessment data is commonly much more complex, and its proper analysis often involves assessment-dependent steps that are counterintuitive. This issue is compounded by the misleading manner in which data is frequently displayed in data systems and reports. For example, according to Harvard Graduate School of Education professor Thomas Kane, data analysis problems often relate to the data not being organized in a way that can answer questions (Davis 2013).

Fortunately, research findings can be applied to improving the way in which data is communicated to educators. For example, in a quantitative study of 211 educators of varied backgrounds at nine schools with varied demographics, educators' data analyses were shown to be 205 percent to 436 percent (two to four times) more accurate when text-based guidance made appropriate data analyses easier for educators (Rankin 2013). Likewise, considering best practices for mathematics assessment data analyses can help educators appropriately use the data to inform decisions to help students.

■ Common Types of Mathematics Assessment Data Analyses

Educators have many different objectives when using mathematics assessment data to gain understanding and help guide decision making. Some of the most common analysis objectives are featured below and paired with potential assessment characteristics ("Check"), analysis guidelines ("Analyze"), and a sample conclusion ("Example") that can help mathematics educators perform successful analyses. Summative analyses tend to be especially tricky, and thus there is a summative focus to this section. However, many of the issues raised should be considered when using mathematics assessment data for formative purposes. Assessing students on a formative basis is one of the most powerful applications of assessments and data, and its import is not to be overlooked. Likewise, the types of assessments to which this section refers are not limited to multiple-choice tests, as the same guidelines can be applied to project-based assessments and other formats for measuring student learning.

Grade-to-Grade Comparisons

To help determine how one grade level is performing in mathematics compared with another, such as one at the same school, educators make grade-to-grade comparisons using mathematics assessment data. For example, the Response to Intervention (RTI) Framework and Progress Monitoring Process involves comparing grade levels' mathematics test scores (Adams 2013); it involves comparing different editions of a test, just as a test program can feature different editions from one *test* year to the next. A testing program can feature consistency in score interpretation from one test edition to the next if its scores are scaled, which involves transforming raw test score points into a set of different values to establish consistent meaning for all students taking the test (Tan and Michel 2011).

Check

In order to understand assessment-specific data guidelines, educators should consult literature published in concert with the assessment's results. For example, educators can search the website of the entity that oversees the assessment's production and/or dissemination, such as a state department of education (e.g., www.cde.ca.gov), publisher (e.g., www.ets.org), or consortium (e.g., www.smarterbalanced.org). Running a search of the website for the assessment name or following links like "Testing" will often lead to a posttest guide for the assessment. If the assessment or an account of its results is distributed in hard copy form, some sort of "District Administrator's Test Guide" often accompanies it, and this can provide assessment analysis information. If these approaches fail, educators can call the test provider and be connected with a staff member who can answer questions concerning the assessment's structure and analysis.

In the case of grade-to-grade comparisons, the above-described resource can be used to verify whether or not the assessments are vertically scaled in the assessment series, meaning the difficulty remains constant (in relation to students tested) from one grade level to the next. Change in difficulty is more common in mathematics than in subjects like English (e.g., reading or writing), as the type of mathematics being tested from one grade level to the next can differ completely (e.g., algebra versus geometry versus calculus). For example, a ninth-grade level geometry test might be easier for ninth graders than a tenth-grade level calculus test is for tenth graders.

Analyze

If the assessments *are* vertically scaled, it might be appropriate to subtract the average mathematics assessment score of students in one grade level from the average mathematics assessment score of students in another grade level on tests from a series to determine how much one grade level outperformed the other. If the assessments are *not* vertically scaled, the calculation described above would be inappropriate. An alternate calculation, such as subtracting the state/territory grade level mathematics average from the school grade level mathematics average for each grade level, and then comparing these two values, *might* be possible. In either case, consulting the specific assessment's technical/analysis guidelines is essential. While inappropriate calculations are easy to demonstrate in each example (below) in this chapter, appropriate calculations are dependent on the particular assessment being examined and its own analysis guidelines.

Example

An educator might seek to use the mathematics assessment as one of multiple measures in determining how grade levels 6 and 7 compared on mathematics performance. While it might be tempting to draw the following conclusion, doing so would not work if tests in this series varied in difficulty from one grade level to the next (e.g., the sixth-grade test is not equally difficult for sixth graders as the seventh-grade test is for seventh graders):

> 352 was the average score of grade 7 students at my school on the 2014 Grade 7 Standardized Math Test, whereas 368 was the average score of grade 6 students at our feeder school on the 2014 Grade 6 Standardized Math Test. Since our school's students had the lower score, they must have performed more poorly than our feeder school's students.

Year-to-Year Comparisons

Longitudinal student data, which is collected over time, facilitates more thorough analyses of student performance than partial histories can offer (U.S. Department of Education, Office of Planning, Evaluation and Policy Development 2010). To help determine how an educational entity performed in mathematics during one school year compared to how it performed in a previous school year, educators make year-to-year comparisons using mathematics assessment data. When assessments utilize different items (e.g., test questions, prompts, rubrics, etc.) from one test year to the next, their scores are often scaled in order to ensure consistent difficulty from year to year. When mathematics assessment scores are *not* scaled in this way, there is increased potential to misunderstand the data's longitudinal implications.

Check

It is important to verify whether or not the assessments are scaled from one test year to the next. As noted earlier, scaling results in a scale score, which is a raw score that has been altered/scaled to account for differing difficulties from one administration year to the next so that performance from different years on the same test may be compared (California Department of Education 2011).

Analyze

If the assessments *are* scaled from year to year, it might be appropriate to subtract an average mathematics assessment score of students from one test year (e.g., 2013) from the average mathematics assessment score of different students the next year (e.g., 2014) on the same test to determine which school year's students performed better on the same test. The average *raw* score, however, would remain inappropriate for such a comparison (Tan and Michel 2011). If the assessments are *not* scaled from year to year and they featured different items, the calculation described above would be inappropriate. An alternate calculation, such as subtracting the state/territory average from the class average for each particular year, and then comparing these two values, *might* be possible. In either case, the specific assessment's analysis guidelines should be consulted.

Example

An educator might seek to use the mathematics assessment as one of multiple measures in determining whether mathematics performance was higher during one school year than another. It might be tempting to draw the conclusion in the example below, but doing so would not work if the assessment items varied from one year to the next, even if this assessment's scores had been scaled (in which case, a scale score is preferable to a raw score for comparisons):

> My 2014 tenth graders had a 345 average raw score on the 2014 Grade 10 Standardized Mathematics Test, whereas my 2013 tenth graders had a 321 average raw score on the 2013 Grade 10 Standardized Mathematics Test, so I probably improved my mathematics teaching skills.

Cohort Growth

Cohort data is used to determine how a specific group of students changed over time, as cohort data involves data from the same group over time (particularly *limited cohorts*, which exclude students not tested both years). For example, an educator might look at how student group A performed in grade 2 in 2013, and then how that same student group A performed when they were in grade 3 in 2014. As established earlier, score scaling can lead to consistency in score interpretation (Tan and Michel 2011).

Check

Educators should verify whether or not the assessments are vertically scaled (as explained earlier). Vertically scaled assessments maintain the same level of difficulty (in relation to students tested) from one year to the next. Scaling is particularly important if cohort comparisons are intended, as assessment items will typically differ when the grade level of students answering/using them differs.

Analyze

If the assessments *are* vertically scaled, it might be appropriate to subtract a cohort's scores from one year (e.g., 2013) from their scores the next year (e.g., 2014) on tests from a series to determine growth. If the assessments are *not* vertically scaled, the calculation described above would be inappropriate. An alternate calculation, such as subtracting the state/territory average from the cohort's average for each test year, and then comparing these two values, *might* be possible. In either case, the specific assessment's analysis guidelines can be used to determine a recommended measure of cohort growth.

Example

An educator might seek to use the mathematics assessment as one of multiple measures in determining whether students improved in mathematics over time. The conclusion in the example below would not be valid, however, if this assessment's scores were not vertically scaled:

> My grade 3 students' average score was 382 on the 2014 State Math Test when they were in grade 3 (with me), and these same students averaged 373 on the 2013 State Math Test when they were in grade 2 (with previous teachers), so my students' performance improved.

Subdomain-to-Subdomain Comparisons

Some assessments' performance is reported by domain, sometimes called *content cluster* or *test area*, which means the performance on assessment items tied to topics or standards within particular categories is averaged or otherwise aggregated into a series of domain scores. Sometimes these test areas are called *subdomain*s, as they are for the Pan Canadian Assessment Program (PCAP), for which Mathematics is already referred to as its own, single domain (Nova Scotia School Boards Association 2012). The same is true of the Mathematics domain and subdomains of the internationally administered Programme for International Student Assessment (PISA) (Organisation for Economic Co-operation and Development 2009).

Check

Investigation can help one verify whether or not the assessment's subdomains (i.e., items aligned to them) differ in difficulty, meaning some subdomains (such as Number Properties) are harder than others (such as Quadratics and Polynomials) within the same mathematics test. This is not to be mistaken as determining whether subdomain *topics* vary in difficulty, but rather determining whether the collections of *items* that assess these subdomains vary in difficulty.

Analyze

If the assessment's subdomains *are* equal in difficulty, it could be appropriate to compare performance in one subdomain of the test to performance in another subdomain of the same test to determine potential strengths and weaknesses. If the assessment's subdomains are not equal in difficulty, such a calculation would be inappropriate. An alternate calculation, such as subtracting the state/territory average from the district or school board average for each domain, and then comparing these two values, might be possible. In either case, consulting the specific assessment's analysis guidelines is again paramount.

Example

An educator might seek to use the mathematics assessment as one of multiple measures in determining where students' strengths and weaknesses lie. The following conclusion would not work if this assessment's subdomains varied in difficulty:

> My grade 9 students averaged 76 percent correct in the Number Properties subdomain (on test A in 2013), and the same group of students averaged 65 percent correct in the Quadratics and Polynomials subdomain (on test A in 2013). Since my students scored higher in Number Properties, I did a better job teaching Number Properties than I did teaching Quadratics and Polynomials.

When 211 educators were questioned about a school's strengths and weaknesses as measured by an assessment with differing subdomain difficulty, 87 percent of the incorrect answers were incorrect because of the analysis error exemplified above (Rankin 2013).

Year-to-Year Subdomain Growth

Just as educators use longitudinal data to determine how an educational entity performed overall in mathematics during one school year compared to a previous year, it is useful to learn how performance changed in a particular subdomain. Largely because of the narrowed nature of subdomain scores, such comparisons are especially tricky and for some assessments they are not recommended.

Check

Educators should verify whether or not the same subdomain (i.e., assessment items aligned to it) varies in difficulty from one year to the next. This means the subdomain can get harder or easier for students taking the test (e.g., because of a change in assessment items).

Analyze

If an assessment has maintained the same items from one year to the next and has maintained security for these items, it might be appropriate to subtract students' average score for a particular subdomain one year from students' average score for the same subdomain the next year to determine how much instruction for the subdomain at that grade level might have improved. If the assessment's subdomains are equal in difficulty from year to year because of *scaling*, this calculation could be inappropriate because of the strain on scaling that occurs when the number of assessment items narrows, since a subdomain contains fewer items than as assessment as a whole. If the assessment's subdomains are *not* equal in difficulty from year to year, the calculation described above would definitely be inappropriate. In any case, educators consult the specific assessment's analysis guidelines.

Example

An educator might seek to use the mathematics assessment as one of multiple measures in determining whether scores went up for a particular subdomain from one year to the next. While it might be tempting to draw the following conclusion, doing so would not work if this assessment's subdomains varied in difficulty from year to year:

> My students averaged 74 percent correct in the Volume and Area subdomain in 2013, and my next year's class of students averaged 74 percent correct in the Volume and Area subdomain in 2014, so my students' performance remained the same for the Volume and Area subdomain.

Cohort Subdomain Growth

Like year-to-year subdomain growth, measuring cohort subdomain growth can be tricky. Determining such growth involves measuring how a specific group of students changed over time in a particular subdomain. For example, an educator might seek to understand how student group A performed in the Numbers and Operations subdomain in grade 7 in 2013, and then how that same student group A performed in the same subdomain when they were in grade 8 in 2014.

Check

It is important to verify whether or not the same subdomain varies in difficulty (in relation to students tested) from one grade level to the next. For example, the ninth-grade Algebra subdomain may not be equally difficult for ninth graders as the tenth-grade Algebra subdomain is for tenth graders.

Analyze

If an assessment used for multiple grade levels has maintained the same items from one year to the next and has maintained security for these items (or, as is the case for some physical fitness assessments, test security does not impact outcomes), it *might* be appropriate to subtract students' average score for a particular subdomain one year from the same group of students' average score for the same subdomain the next year (i.e., in the next grade level) to determine growth. If the assessment's subdomains were individually scaled, this calculation could be inappropriate for reasons explained earlier. If the assessment's subdomains are *not* equal in difficulty from grade to grade, the calculation described above would definitely be inappropriate. In any case, educators' specific assessment's analysis guidelines should be consulted.

Example

An educator might seek to use the mathematics assessment as one of multiple measures in determining if the same group of students improved in a particular test area. Drawing the conclusion in the example below would not be appropriate if this assessment's subdomains differed in difficulty grade to grade:

> My grade 7 students averaged 76 percent correct in the Numbers and Operations subdomain in 2013, and they averaged 67 percent correct in the Numbers and Operations subdomain when they were in grade 6. This shows the same group of students grew by 9 percentage points within a single subdomain, so I have improved their Numbers and Operations skills.

■ Data Reporting Standards for Which Educator Leaders Should Advocate

The quantity of considerations educators must navigate when analyzing mathematics assessment data can be daunting, and referring to each assessment's published guidelines can strain educators' already demanding work schedules. Meanwhile, a study by the U.S. Department of Education found data systems are frequently of limited use in informing instruction because of limitations in terms of the system's data, interface, or tools (Faria et al. 2012). Thus it is critical that educator leaders advocate for improvements to data systems and tools that will more actively facilitate easy and correct data use. If done correctly, a data system's report design can readily provide educators with relevant information and thus allow teachers to focus on instruction and students (Hattie 2010).

Educator leaders can advocate for their data providers to embed assessment-specific data analysis support *directly within* the data system and reports. For example, in the Rankin (2013) study noted earlier, assessment-specific data analysis guidance like that shared in this chapter was embedded *within* reporting environments, much like usage guidance is required to accompany over-the-counter medicine so people know how best to use it. This embedded guidance, which frees educators from the need to consult assessment analysis guides, rendered educators' data analyses 307 percent more accurate when a report footer was present, 205 percent more accurate when a system-embedded reference sheet was present, and 273 percent more accurate when a system-embedded reference guide was present, with improvements as high as 436 percent when respondents specifically indicated they used one of these supports. Data reporting standards based on that study and a synthesis of over 300 similar sources are available at www.overthecounterdata.com/s/OTCDStandards.pdf (a noncommercial research website). Educator leaders can advocate for their data systems and reports to adhere to these research-based reporting practices in order to make assessment data easier to use successfully.

This enhanced use can help mathematics assessment feedback to be something that effectively informs teacher practice and encourages student learning.

References

Adams, Jarrod G. *Response to Intervention Framework and Progress Monitoring Process: K–3 Regular Education Teachers' Perceptions.* Electronic Theses and Dissertations (1125) (2013). http://dc.etsu.edu/etd/1125.

California Department of Education. *California Standards Tests Technical Report.* Concord, Calif.: Educational Testing Service, 2011.

Davis, Michelle R. "Managing the Digital District: Intelligent Data Analysis Helps Predict Needs." *Education Week,* October 1, 2013, 33, no. 6 (2013): 20–21.

Faria, Ann-Marie, Jessica Heppen, Yibing Li, Suzanne Stachel, Wehmah Jones, Katherine Sawyer, Kerri Thomsen, Melissa Kutner, and David Miser. *Charting Success: Data Use and Student Achievement in Urban Schools.* Washington, D.C.: Council of the Great City Schools and the American Institutes for Research, 2012. http://www.cgcs.org/cms/lib/DC00001581/Centricity/Domain/87/Charting_Success.pdf.

Hattie, John. "Visibly Learning from Reports: The Validity of Score Reports." *Online Educational Research Journal* (2010). http://www.oerj.org/View?action=viewPaper&paper=6.

Nova Scotia School Boards Association. *Student Performance in Nova Scotia: A Compilation of Results from National and International Assessments.* February 2012.

Organisation for Economic Co-operation and Development. *PISA 2009 Assessment Framework: Key Competencies in Reading, Mathematics and Science* (2009). http://www.oecd.org/pisa/pisaproducts/44455820.pdf.

Rankin, Jenny Grant. "Over-the-Counter Data's Impact on Educators' Data Analysis Accuracy." *ProQuest Dissertations and Theses,* 3575082 (2013). http://pqdtopen.proquest.com/doc/1459258514.html?FMT=ABS.

Sabbah, Faris M. "Designing More Effective Accountability Report Cards." *ProQuest Dissertations and Theses,* AAT 3469488 (2011). http://search.proquest.com/docview/893068662?accountid=28180

Tan, Xuan, and Rochelle Michel. "Why Do Standardized Testing Programs Report Scaled Scores? Why Not Just Report the Raw or Percent-Correct Scores?" *R&D Connections* 16. Princeton, N.J.: Educational Testing Service (ETS), 2011.

U.S. Department of Education. Office of Planning, Evaluation and Policy Development. *Use of Education Data at the Local Level from Accountability to Instructional Improvement.* United States Department of Education (ERIC Document Reproduction Service No. ED511656) (2010).

Wohlstetter, Priscilla, Amanda Datnow, and Vicki Park. "Creating a System for Data-Driven Decision-Making: Applying the Principal-Agent Framework." *School Effectiveness and School Improvement* 19, no. 3 (2008): 239–59.

CHAPTER 18

Learning, Teaching, and Assessing the Standards for Mathematical Practice

Jimmy Scherrer, *North Carolina State University, Raleigh*

One of the most striking features in mathematics education over the past few decades has been the sharp shift in what it means to be mathematically literate. In today's Common Core era, becoming mathematically literate is as much a matter of acquiring mathematical practices as it is of acquiring any defined set of content standards. These new criteria for mathematical literacy are illustrated with the articulation of the Standards for Mathematical Practice, henceforth referred to simply as *mathematical practices* (National Governors Association Center for Best Practices and Council of Chief State School Officers [NGA Center and CCSSO] 2010).

Different conceptions of what it means to learn these mathematical practices correspond to different assumptions about how to teach and, ultimately, how to assess them. When educators discuss what it means to be mathematically literate, the articulation of these different conceptions of learning matter, and considerations of consistency and coherence across learning, teaching, and assessing come into the discourse.

In this chapter, I present one approach to teaching and assessing mathematical practices, where one conceptualizes learning them as the increased ability to effectively participate in them. I begin the chapter by reviewing three learning perspectives: the behaviorist, the cognitivist, and the situative. I then consider the degree of fit between present-day notions of mathematical literacy and certain persisting traditions of teaching and assessment. By positioning conceptions of learning, teaching, and assessment in this manner, I hope to convince the reader that traditional assessment practices do not adequately measure the criteria associated with present-day notions of mathematical literacy.

■ Learning, Teaching, and Assessing from Three Perspectives

The following subsections compare three learning perspectives: the behaviorist, the cognitivist, and the situative. For each perspective, learning is defined; teaching methods that yield that type of learning are discussed; and assessments that capture that type of learning are presented.

The Behaviorist Perspective

Learning

Traditional views of education adopt a behaviorist perspective. From this perspective, learning is an attribute of an individual and is viewed as the process of accumulating and strengthening associations and skills (Thorndike 1906). A key assumption of this perspective is that learning how to complete "simple" tasks is a prerequisite for learning how to complete "complex" tasks (Gagné 1968).

Teaching

From a behaviorist perspective, teaching consists of direct instruction of skills and follows a carefully sequenced curriculum of increasingly advanced skills (Gagné 1968). The hallmark of this style of teaching is the active role assumed by the teacher—the "sage on the stage"—and the passive role assumed by the student. Through receptive learning and drill, this type of learning environment encourages students to become adept at practices that result in efficient performance on traditional standardized assessments (Gagné 1968; Thorndike 1906).

Assessing

Assessments crafted from a behaviorist perspective include independent samples of knowledge—that is, components of knowledge that have been intentionally decoupled from other components, with the belief that independent components of knowledge can be measured most objectively—to estimate how much of a domain an individual has acquired (Greeno, Collins, and Resnick 1996; Shepard 2000). These assessments contain questions that ask students to recall basic facts or apply basic procedures. For example, a mathematics assessment designed from a behaviorist perspective would test a student's ability to subtract 5 from 12 and to add 5 to 7; it would be less apt to assess the student's ability to notice and explain the relationship between those two problems. Such conceptual understanding of material is associated with the cognitivist perspective.

The Cognitivist Perspective

Learning

From a cognitivist perspective, learning is characterized in terms of growth of conceptual understanding and general strategies of thinking and reasoning (Greeno 1998). This is viewed as an unobservable process that causes a reorganization of concepts in the learner's mind that leads to increased "meaning making" (Bruner 1990; Koedinger, Corbett, and Perfetti 2012).

Teaching

Teaching styles associated with the cognitivist perspective generally have pedagogical principles associated with Piaget's theory of knowledge development, known as constructivism. Constructivist theories are grounded in the belief that conceptual understanding occurs through intellectual activity rather than by absorption of information (Bransford, Brown, and Cocking 2000; Piaget 1970). The teacher often serves as a "guide on the side" who creates activity settings that provide students with opportunities to build relationships between old and new knowledge. Thus, what distinguishes teaching styles associated with the cognitivist perspective from direct teaching is the active role that the student plays in the learning process; this role may entail, for example, more problem solving, comprehending, and active inquiry into the meanings and significance of concepts (Greeno 1998).

This type of learning environment encourages students to become adept at constructing conceptual understanding on the basis of general ideas and connections between concepts.

Assessing

Assessments crafted from a cognitivist perspective include questions that go beyond the recall of basic facts and application of procedures. These assessments include questions that test students' conceptual understanding, sense making, and ability to reason and make connections, among others. For example, similar to the questions presented above, a mathematics assessment would test a student's ability to subtract 5 from 12 and to add 5 to 7, but it would go on to assess the student's ability to notice and explain the relationship between those two problems.

The Situative Perspective

Learning

In the situative perspective, learning and cognition are viewed as inseparable from the activities in which students engage. Thus, the situative perspective shifts focus from the individual to systems of activity that include individuals interacting with each other and their environment (Greeno 1998). Learning is said to occur when individuals have more effective participation in the practices of a specific community (Lave and Wenger 1991).

Teaching

From a situative perspective, a teacher's role is to create activity settings that provide students with legitimate opportunities to participate in the practices that are to be learned, in an approach that is akin to apprenticeship (Lave and Wenger 1991). In this practice-oriented approach, the basic skills and knowledge associated with the behaviorist perspective, and the sense making associated with the cognitivist perspective, are "anchored" in authentic activities that address larger conceptual problems that are being solved (Greeno 1998; Jurow 2005). This type of learning environment encourages students to become adept at practices that result in effective participation within specific communities of practice.

Assessing

Assessments crafted from a situative perspective are practice oriented and capture practices *in situ*. Unlike traditional standardized assessments, assessments crafted from a situative perspective do not decouple skills and concepts from the authentic activities in which they are used. I will spend the rest of this chapter discussing how practice-oriented activity systems enable the assessment of mathematical practices *in situ*.

■ Assessing Mathematical Practices *in Situ*

When adopting a situative perspective, there is a commitment to focus on participation in activity settings. To take this commitment seriously, significant changes to our current assessment and reporting system need to be made—namely, mathematical practices need to be emphasized in both what is assessed and what is reported.

Although some past curricula emphasized activities that included various practices, qualitative accounts of implementation suggest that only content was assessed and reported (e.g., Smith 2004).

Smith (2004) reports on the *Mathematics in Context* curriculum, which asked students to, among other things, justify their thinking and question the reasoning of others. Although the students did indeed participate in these practices while working on classroom activities, the teacher's feedback to the students remained limited to the judgment about whether the work on their *papers* was satisfactory, with little to no mention of the practices in which they engaged. Further, the official reporting that the teacher did (e.g., grades) was no different from the official reporting of those teachers who taught using the traditional textbook. Any assessment of mathematical practices must focus on process, not just the final product. Thus, assessing mathematical practices needs to be done *in situ*, where skills and concepts are anchored in the practices in which they are used. If practices are assessed in any other fashion we risk not knowing if students can naturally participate in the practices or if they simply possess what Whitehead (1929) referred to as *inert knowledge*. This refers to knowledge that can be used when individuals are prompted to recall specific content or perform a specific skill, but not spontaneously used in natural problem-solving situations where the knowledge should be applied. Consider the following task claiming to assess students' ability to employ the mathematical practice that asks them to *critique the reasoning of others* (MP.3; NGA Center and CCSSO 2010, p. 6):

> Bill found out that both his father and mother received a 10% raise at work. Bill's father told him that his raise was $5,000. Since his mother also received a 10% raise, Bill reasons that his mother's raise was $5,000. Critique Bill's reasoning.

This task explicitly prompts students to "critique Bill's reasoning." Hence, it is dubious to use students' responses to infer their ability to participate in this practice. Part of knowing how to critique the reasoning of others includes knowing when to do so. Therefore, assessing mathematical practices should be done in situations where the opportunity to participate in them naturally arises. I refer to these situations as *Intact Interactive Systems of Activity*; in this construct, *Intact* emphasizes that skills and concepts are not decoupled from the practices in which they are used; *Interactive System* makes salient that all of the components mutually shape each other; *Activity* brings student participation to the foreground.

■ Intact Interactive Systems of Activity

Intact Interactive Systems of Activity have three major components: (1) a task that is being worked on, (2) a person or persons working on the task, and (3) the resources available to help complete the task (cf. Engeström 1987). These resources include, among others, the skills and knowledge of concepts that the person or persons use to participate successfully.

From a situative perspective, skills and concepts are valued and maintained in a community because they are useful in conducting the community's activities (Greeno 2012; Hall and Greeno 2008). They are useful, of course, because they help solve tasks, but they are also useful because they provide common ground. Simply stated, skills and concepts help communities communicate more efficiently (Clark and Schaefer 1989; Hutchins 2005). To perform this role, a large portion of the community must know the skills and understand the concepts. Thus, when considering participation in the practices of a community, the learning of skills and concepts is paramount. However, the hallmark of Intact Interactive Systems of Activity is that skills and concepts are not decoupled from the practices in which they are used. In the next section, I will describe what one such system looks like in the mathematics classroom.

A Classroom Example: The Antarctica Project

Part of the Middle-School Mathematics through Application Project at Stanford, *Antarctica* is a unit specifically crafted using the situative perspective on learning (Bushey 1997; Jurow 2005; Moschkovich 1998), and it serves as a good example of how to teach and assess mathematical practices in an Intact Interactive System of Activity. *Antarctica* provides students with opportunities to participate in actual mathematical practices, and it presents mathematics primarily as a resource for real-world problem solving. In the project, students take on the role of architects designing a new Antarctica research station to meet the needs of four scientists who will live and work there. The students receive a series of memos from the Frozen Scientific Group, a fictitious design firm requesting the students' help, which articulate various design considerations. While each memo has students focus their attention on different aspects of the design, they all adhere to the same theme: students are asked to meet the needs of the scientists in a manner that will minimize the cost of building and heating the station. For example, Memo 1, which is given to students on official letterhead from the Frozen Scientific Group, reads:

> We are asking for proposals from several companies, and will accept the proposal that best meets our needs at the most reasonable cost. We need a design for a scientific research station on the Antarctic coast. The site for the station is a small flat field of dry rock 17 meters wide and 30 meters long. The station should provide lab space, housing, and recreational facilities for four scientists. . . . Your design proposal report should include a floor plan of the design, along with a proposed budget for building and heating costs over the two years. Of course, you will want to include materials that explain why your design best meets our needs. (Moschkovich 1998, p. 4)

In *Antarctica*, as with most curricula used in Intact Interactive Systems of Activity, mathematical skills and concepts emerge as students work on their project. For example, while working on Memo 1, students have to consider the proportional relations between lengths of lines in their diagram and the physical lengths and widths of the rooms being represented on the diagram. Although they are not explicitly told to do so, students often begin to take meter sticks and measure actual spaces in the classroom. (This is an example of MP.5: *Use appropriate tools strategically* [NGA Center and CCSSO 2010, p. 7].) Then, predictably, the concept of scale, which is one of the unit's main content objectives, emerges as students try to accurately represent the length and width of a large room on a small piece of paper or computer screen. At this point, in order to continue with the design, it becomes functionally necessary for students to learn the mathematical content. All activities in the unit are designed in this fashion—that is, the mathematics is situated in the specific problems that emerge while students participate in the design. Likewise, the classroom discussions during the project are about issues that arise when trying to solve the problem, and not about isolated skills and concepts. Skills and concepts are indeed discussed, but those topics emerge as students grapple with issues that arise in the design of the buildings (Greeno 1997; Jurow 2005).

The practice-oriented tasks in *Antarctica* create problem spaces that provide both reasons and resources for learning mathematics. For example, in Memo 3, students are tasked to see if they can reduce the heating costs of their station by altering their design. This gives the students a reason to start exploring the relationship between surface area and heat loss. (It also enables them to participate in MP.7: *Look for and make use of structure* [NGA Center and CCSSO 2010, p. 9]. That is, students come to see that the "more square" their floor plan is the less surface area will be exposed on outside walls.) But the problem space also gives the resources to learn the mathematics, and becomes part of the solution—for example, the concept of scale can be explored by measuring physical objects in the classroom, such as a student-desk chair, and comparing them to objects that will be represented on their floor plan, such as a toilet. The mathematics needed to solve the task is thus both generated out of the activity and at the same time generates the activity. When these types of activity systems are examined, we see that the components—task, students, and resources—mutually shape one another (Goodwin and Goodwin 1996).

■ Assessing Mathematical Practices within an Intact Interactive System of Activity

When considering the process of learning primarily from the point of view of students' participation in practices, the assessment of these practices needs to occur while students participate in activity settings designed to enable various practices of interest. To be clear, there are no specific activity settings designated as "assessment activities." Rather, assessing mathematical practices is done while students participate in their everyday classroom activities. The challenge, however, is designing activity settings that enable participation in the practices of interest (Shepard 2000): to make valid inferences about a student's competency with a specific mathematical practice, the students must be engaged in an activity system that provides an opportunity for the student to naturally participate in the practice. To meet this challenge, it is useful, I believe, for educators to take a situative approach, where lessons and units are designed around mathematical practices, not content. Furthermore, because learning is defined as an increase in participation, mathematical practices are not assessed during one culminating activity. It is expected that students' participation will follow some sort of trajectory, where students move from peripheral participation to fuller participation in the practices of interest (Lave and Wenger 1991). Thinking of learning as a trajectory encourages a focus on assessment as a process occurring over time.

For example, an assessment tool similar to the one displayed in figure 18.1 (on p. 206) can be used to capture types of participation associated with MP.3: *Construct viable arguments and critique the reasoning of others* (NGA Center and CCSSO 2010, p. 6). Figure 18.1 lists text from the CCSS document in the left-hand column. The other columns include space where a user can record evidence of the practice across multiple tasks. Once again, *Antarctica* can be used to illustrate. While working on Memo 2, which is designed to have students explore the relationship between area and perimeter, groups are asked to build a floor area using 12 square units. Adhering to the goal of keeping the cost of construction as low as possible, students begin designing various configurations of the 12 square units and calculate the construction cost of each. After a bit of tinkering and discussion, one student makes the conjecture that the closer the area is to a square, the smaller the perimeter. The group reasons that smaller perimeters would result in fewer exposed surfaces and would be cheaper to build and heat (Jurow 2005). Their various designs and calculations confirm these conjectures. Another student conjectures that his group's designs will never have a perimeter that is larger than the area. (It should be noted that both conjectures made in these examples include important mathematical concepts. However, as is the norm in Intact Interactive Systems of Activity, these concepts emerged as students worked on their designs, rather than being explicit topics of discussion.) Assuming the teacher were interested in capturing this practice, he or she could use a tool similar to figure 18.1 to record the conjectures being made and judge the quality of them, perhaps by asking the student what evidence her conjecture is based on or how she might go about exploring the truth of her conjecture. Then, as students participate in other activities that enable them to make conjectures, the teacher could assess in the same manner. Learning would be defined as, for example, an increase in the number of conjectures and an increase in the quality of the conjectures. Similar to the assessment tool presented in figure 18.1 (on following page), an app could be created for a tablet that displays a recording matrix for each child that a teacher uses while circulating. This app could aggregate the data across students and generate a visualization of student participation in various practices over time. This would be an efficient way for teachers to know if they need to design activity systems that enable participation in specific practices.

■ Conclusion

This chapter discussed the utility of adopting the situative perspective when thinking about teaching and assessing mathematical practices. I discussed students participating in an Intact Interactive System of Activity—the *Antarctica* project—to illustrate an activity setting that enables the type of interactions needed to assess mathematical practices *in situ*. I argued if practices are assessed in any other fashion, we risk arriving at conclusions that do not generalize beyond school mathematics.

Different perspectives bring different aspects of learning into focus, and those different foci should correspond to significantly different emphases in teaching and assessment. As it currently stands, the degree of fit between present-day notions of mathematical literacy and certain persisting traditions of assessment is rather poor. Traditional standardized assessments have been developed almost entirely within the behaviorist perspective, where skills and concepts are decoupled from the practices in which they are used. This has caused a tension between how it is believed that teachers ought to teach and how their students are actually assessed. This tension is further stressed now that a set of mathematical practices has been formally articulated and emphasized in the Common Core. If being mathematically literate is indeed as much a matter of acquiring mathematical practices as it is of acquiring any defined set of content standards, then teaching and assessing need to be as much about providing opportunities to participate in mathematical practices as they are about providing opportunities to master and demonstrate basic skills and concepts. To be in better accord with the epistemological assumptions of the situative view on learning, I encourage our community to foster the sharp shift in what it means to be mathematically literate by teaching and assessing the Standards for Mathematical Practice within Intact Interactive Systems of Activity.

Notes

In addition to the editorial panel, I want to thank Paola Sztajn and Tamar Avineri for their thoughtful comments on earlier versions of this work. I would also like to thank Jim Greeno for taking the time to send me invaluable materials that helped provide context for the argument presented in this chapter.

The Antarctica project can be downloaded from https://web.stanford.edu/group/redlab/cgi-bin/materials/Antarctica%20Project%E2%80%93Design%20Thinking%20version.pdf.

Standards for Mathematical Practice—MP.3: Construct viable arguments and critique the reasoning of others

Student Name	Date and Activity	Date and Activity	Date and Activity	Date and Activity	Date and Activity	Date and Activity
Understands and uses stated assumptions, definitions, and previously established results in constructing arguments						
Makes conjectures and builds a logical progression of statements to explore the truth of the conjectures						
Analyzes situations by breaking them into cases, and can recognize and use counterexamples						
Is able to justify conclusions to others						
Reasons inductively about data, making plausible arguments that take into account the context from which the data arose						
Compare the effectiveness of two plausible arguments, distinguish correct logic or reasoning from that which is flawed						
Asks useful questions to clarify or improve others' arguments						

Scoring: Indicate the date of the activity and then score the practice as a 1, 2, or 3. A score of 1 indicates that the evidence you observed suggests that the student has no more than limited proficiency with the practice. A score of 3 indicates that the evidence you observed suggests that the student has proficiency with the practice. Write "NA" in a cell if a given activity does not provide the opportunity for the student to participate in the practice.

Fig. 18.1. Example assessment tool for MP.3

References

Bransford, John D., Ann Brown, and Rodney Cocking. *How People Learn: Brain, Mind, Experience, and School.* Washington, D.C.: National Academies Press, 2000.

Bruner, Jerome. *Acts of Meaning.* Cambridge, Mass.: Harvard University Press, 1990.

Bushey, Beverly J. "Student Reflection in Emergent Mathematical Activity." PhD diss., Stanford University, 1997.

Clark, Herbert, and Edward Schaefer. "Contributing to Discourse." *Cognitive Science* 13 (1989): 259–94.

Engeström, Yrjo. *Learning by Expanding: An Activity-Theoretical Approach to Developmental Research.* Helsinki: Orienta-Konsultit, 1987.

Gagné, Robert. "Learning Hierarchies." *Educational Psychologist* 6, no. 1 (1968): 1–9.

Goodwin, Charles, and Majorie Harness Goodwin. "Seeing as Situated Activity: Formulating Planes." In *Cognition and Communication at Work*, edited by Yrjo Engeström and David Middleton, pp. 61–95. New York: Cambridge University Press, 1996.

Greeno, James G. "Theories and Practices of Thinking and Learning to Think." *American Journal of Education* 106, no. 1 (1997): 85–126.

_____. "The Situativity of Knowing, Learning, and Research." *American Psychologist* 53 (1998): 5–26.

_____. "Concepts in Activities and Discourses." *Mind, Culture, and Activity* 19, no. 3 (2012): 310–13.

Greeno, James G., Allan Collins, and Lauren B. Resnick. "Cognition and Learning." In *Handbook of Educational Psychology*, edited by David Berliner and Robert Calfee, pp. 15–46. New York: Macmillan, 1996.

Hall, Rogers, and James G. Greeno. "Conceptual Learning." In *21st Century Education: A Reference Handbook*, edited by Thomas Good, pp. 212–21. London: Sage, 2008.

Hutchins, Edwin. "Material Anchors for Conceptual Blends." *Journal of Pragmatics* 37 (2005): 1555–77.

Jurow, Susan. "Shifting Engagements in Figured Worlds: Middle School Mathematics Students' Participation in an Architectural Design Project." *Journal of the Learning Sciences* 14, no. 1 (2005): 35–67.

Koedinger, Kenneth R., Albert T. Corbett, and Charles Perfetti. "The Knowledge-Learning-Instruction Framework: Bridging the Science-Practice Chasm to Enhance Robust Student Learning." *Cognitive Science* 36, no. 5 (2012): 757–98.

Lave, Jean, and Etienne Wenger. *Situated Learning: Legitimate Peripheral Participation.* New York: Cambridge University Press, 1991.

Moschkovich, J. "Rethinking Authentic Assessments of Student Mathematical Activity." *Focus on Learning Problems in Mathematics* 20, no. 3 (1998): 1–17.

National Governors Association Center for Best Practices and Council of Chief State School Officers (NGA Center and CCSSO). *Common Core State Standards for Mathematics.* Washington, D.C.: NGA Center and CCSSO, 2010.

Piaget, Jean. *Science of Education and the Psychology of the Child.* Translated by Derek Coltman. New York: Orion, 1970.

Shepard, Lorrie. "The Role of Assessment in a Learning Culture." *Educational Researcher* 29, no. 7 (2000): 4–14.

Smith, Marvin. "Practices in Transition: A Case Study of Classroom Assessment." In *Standards-Based Mathematics Assessment in Middle School*, edited by Thomas Romberg, pp. 60–80. New York: Teachers College Press, 2004.

Thorndike, Edward. *Principles of Teaching Based on Psychology.* New York: AG Seiler, 1906.

Whitehead, Alfred. *The Aims of Education.* New York: Macmillan, 1929.

CHAPTER 19

Conducting Classroom Assessment Based in Cognition: The Case of Proportional Reasoning

Michele B. Carney, Gwyneth R. Hughes, Jonathan L. Brendefur, Angela R. Crawford, and Tatia Totorica, *Boise State University, Idaho*

The standards from the National Council for Teachers of Mathematics (NCTM 1989, 2000) and the more recent U.S.-based Common Core State Standards (National Governors Association and Chief Council of State School Officers [NGA Center and CCSSO] 2010) have called for shifting the focus of classroom mathematics instruction. In the United States, mathematics instruction has traditionally focused on developing and demonstrating fluency with particular procedures, algorithms, and facts. Calls for reform over the last three decades have aimed to shift the focus to developing students' understanding of the mathematics and their fluent and flexible use of mathematical ideas and procedures across a wide range of applications.

From a mathematics assessment perspective, U.S. classrooms have traditionally concentrated on measuring students' abilities to generate or select correct solutions. In this chapter, we argue that construction of assessments and analysis of results also need to illuminate students' thinking processes so teachers can better understand how students arrive at solutions. The work from the Cognitively Guided Instruction (CGI) project provides one example of focusing assessment and classroom instruction around student cognition (Carpenter et al. 1999) The CGI problem types provide teachers with a framework through which to examine students' thinking around the concepts of addition, subtraction, multiplication, and division. Several years ago, the National Research Council (NRC 2001) advocated for shifting the focus of assessments in order to highlight the cognitive process students use to solve problems:

> Assessments should focus on identifying the specific strategies children are using for problem solving, giving particular consideration to where those strategies fall on a developmental continuum of efficiency and appropriateness for a particular domain of knowledge and skill. . . . To this end, assessments, especially those conducted in the context of classroom instruction, should focus on making students' thinking visible to both their teachers and themselves so that instructional strategies can be selected to support an appropriate course for future learning. (p. 4)

The NRC report (2001) provided a three-part framework to structure the construction of assessment instruments: (*a*) research on student cognition, (*b*) observation of students' cognitive processes, and (*c*) interpretation of evidence from observation. However, despite the success of projects such as CGI (Fennema et al. 1996) and recommendations from the NRC (2001), there is little evidence of such a shift in assessment practices. The purpose of this chapter is to describe such an assessment utilizing the NRC framework by focusing on students' thinking around the topic of proportional reasoning.

We focus on proportional reasoning because it is a linchpin for future success in mathematics and science (Lesh, Post, and Behr 1988). Lamon (2005) states:

> Clearly many people who have not developed their proportional reasoning ability have been able to compensate by using rules in algebra, geometry, and trigonometry courses, but, in the end, the rules are a poor substitute for understanding. They are unprepared for real applications in statistics, biology, geography, or physics—where important, foundational principles rely on proportionality. (p. 3)

Therefore, it is imperative that students develop meaningful understanding of proportional reasoning and demonstrate fluency *and* flexibility in proportional reasoning situations. An assessment designed to make students' proportional reasoning strategies visible would support teachers in making strategic decisions about classroom instruction. Figure 19.1 provides a visual organizer for the information in the chapter highlighting the integration of the NRC framework with the topic of proportional reasoning.

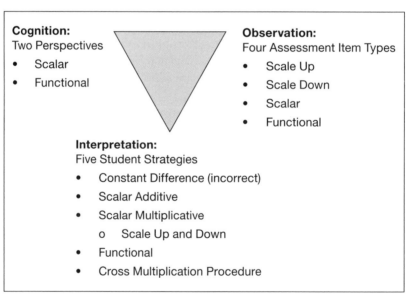

Fig. 19.1. NRC framework elements with the associated proportional reasoning areas

■ Cognition in Proportional Reasoning

The NRC (2001) framework stresses the importance of utilizing research on student cognition in the construction of mathematics assessments. Research indicates that students must fluently and flexibly use the *scalar* and *functional* perspectives in proportional reasoning situations (Lamon 2005; Lobato and Ellis 2010). A scalar perspective entails recognizing a ratio as a composed unit that can be scaled up or down by multiplying each quantity in the ratio by a constant factor. For example, given the problem "Callie bought 7 cookies for $3. How many cookies can Callie buy for $12?" a student may recognize that the original 7 cookies to $3 ratio can be scaled up by multiplying each quantity in the ratio by 4 to generate the 28 cookies for $12 ratio (see figure 19.2a). A functional perspective, on the other hand, entails recognizing and using the constant multiplicative relationship between the two quantities within the ratio and applying this relationship to create equivalent ratios. For example, given the similar context "Callie bought 6 cookies for $2. How many cookies can Callie buy for $13?" a student may recognize that the number of cookies to be purchased is 3 (6 ÷ 2) times the number of dollars paid. This understanding allows the student to quickly realize Callie can purchase 3 × 13 or 39 cookies (see fig. 19.2b).

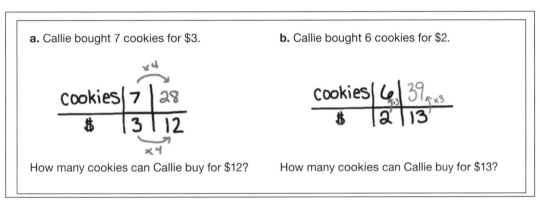

a. Callie bought 7 cookies for $3.

How many cookies can Callie buy for $12?

b. Callie bought 6 cookies for $2.

How many cookies can Callie buy for $13?

Fig. 19.2. Ratio table depiction of different number relationships and potential strategy choices

In addition to recognizing and fluently applying these relationships, students need to flexibly choose which relationship to use depending upon the situation or number relationship presented. For example, ideally a student would be able to realize that applying a scalar perspective to the situation presented in figure 19.2a (simply multiplying by 4) would be more efficient than applying a functional perspective, needing to multiply by 2 1/3 (after recognizing that this is the number you need to multiply by 3 to make 7).

These two perspectives are not only useful for efficiently solving proportional missing value problems, but they also represent two essential mathematical concepts that extend across secondary mathematics. For example, the concept of scaling and scale factor in geometry requires a scalar perspective, whereas the functional perspective gives students access to the input/output concept of mathematical function, a cornerstone of high school algebra.

■ Observation of Proportional Reasoning

The observation component within the NRC framework involves creating a set of assessment tasks designed to elicit responses from students, illuminating the cognitive processes identified as important within the domain. For proportional reasoning this involves designing tasks that highlight students' fluency and flexibility from scalar and functional perspectives. The operationalization of these perspectives into assessment tasks involved examining the research on how students' understanding develops over time. Steinthorsdottir and Sriraman (2009) identified a potential trajectory for the development of students' proportional reasoning involving the manipulation of number relationships to focus students' thinking on different facets of the proportional relationship. Using aspects of their trajectory in conjunction with the two perspectives from cognition on proportional reasoning, we developed our assessment framework, with the intention the tasks serve two objectives: (1) illuminate students' thinking strategies along a trajectory and (2) identify whether students had achieved fluency and flexibility with the scalar and/or functional relationships. Table 19.1 provides four example problems, from a similar context, with the number relationships manipulated to provide insight into students' cognitive processes in proportional reasoning. We anticipated the *scale up* and *scale down* problems would help us to locate where students were along a trajectory if they had not yet achieved fluency with the scalar and/or functional perspectives. The scalar and the functional problems were designed to provide insight into students' fluency and flexibility with each of these perspectives. The anticipated strategy is what we expected a student fluent in both perspectives to use for the particular number set.

The manipulation of the number relationships involved highlighting a particular proportional reasoning perspective by providing a relatively easy whole number relationship in one direction, while creating a more difficult non-whole number relationship for the other perspective. The exception was the scalar problem that involved a times 2.5 relationship in an effort to increase the difficulty level from the *scale up* problem. In hindsight, we would now add an additional functional relationship problem with a similar relationship to the times 2.5 to determine whether one perspective is inherently more difficult for most students to see.

Based upon previous research, we anticipate changes in students' levels of fluency and flexibility with these two perspectives on proportional reasoning as the situations become more complex (Tourniaire and Pulos 1985). It is important to note that our assessment item framework is based on manipulating the number relationships while the context is kept relatively constant to avoid introducing extraneous variables that might influence a student's approach. Our full assessment included both a discrete (cookies and dollars) and continuous (hiking and hours) context across multiple problems. Because of space limitations, we only present the continuous problems in the current analysis.

■ Interpretation of Proportional Reasoning

After conceptualizing and operationalizing proportional reasoning, the third domain within the NRC framework involves the interpretation of evidence from assessments. For classroom-based assessments, this involves gathering student work samples to construct a rubric and using the rubric to provide a consistent and meaningful interpretation of the evidence provided from an assessment.

The student work we used to create our interpretation rubric came from a convenience sample of 101 ten- to fifteen-year-old students. The assessment items were administered prior to formal instruction in proportional reasoning to focus on how students initially demonstrate cognitive understanding (versus procedural knowledge) in these situations. Older students in our sample should have received instruction around proportional reasoning during middle school, and we would expect more efficient strategies from these students. However, review of curricular materials, previous state standards, and contact with teachers in our study indicated that instruction was based primarily on algorithmic implementation of cross-multiplication, with little or no instruction emphasizing a scalar or functional perspective of proportion.

Our goal in analyzing the data was to determine what information the items provided (or did not provide) about the students' cognitive processes in solving the problems. We present this analysis with the caveat that additional information is likely needed to determine students' exact placement along a continuum of strategies, but that closely analyzing student work can provide us with reasonable insight into students' progress toward understanding the scalar and the functional perspectives. The following section highlights the identified student strategies for the four problem types provided in table 19.1. Five student strategies, one incorrect and four correct, were identified from the student work on the assessment items: *constant difference* (incorrect), *scalar additive, scalar multiplicative, functional,* and *cross multiplication*. In addition, within scalar multiplicative a distinct sub-strategy was identified for the scalar and the functional problem types, highlighting an important distinction in terms of instruction and students' level of fluency and flexibility with this perspective. The following sections provides a brief description with associated examples for each strategy.

Table 19.1

Assessment items highlighting manipulation of number relationships

Problem Type		Problem	Anticipated Strategy
Scalar	Scale Up	Jane estimates she takes 4 hours to hike 6 miles. Approximately how far can she hike in 12 hours?	x 3 Miles 6 | ? Hours 4 | 12 x 3
	Scale Down	Sonya estimates she hikes 16 miles in 6 hours. How much time would it take Sonya to hike 4 miles?	÷ 4 Miles 16 | 4 Hours 6 | ? ÷ 4
	Scalar	Angie estimates she hikes 8 miles in 3 hours. How much time would it take Angie to hike 20 miles?	x 2.5 Miles 8 | 20 Hours 3 | ? x 2.5
Functional		**A:** Lexi estimates she hiked 15 miles in 5 hours. How far could she hike in 8 hours? **B:** The number of miles Lexi hikes is ____ times the number of hours.	Miles 15 | ? x 3 x 3 Hours 5 | 8

Constant Difference

The constant difference strategy involves adding or subtracting the same amount from each quantity in the given ratio or finding the difference between the quantities in the given ratio to generate what students presume (incorrectly) to be an equivalent ratio (e.g., figure 19.3a). Students who may demonstrate understanding of the scalar perspective with whole number relationships (e.g., scale up problem) may revert to a constant difference approach in non-whole number situations (e.g., scalar problem). In the example provided in figure 19.3b for the scalar problem, the student correctly scales by 2 but then adds 4 to each quantity in order to achieve the desired 20 miles. This use of a constant multiplicative factor followed by a constant additive factor potentially indicates a lack of or a very fragile understanding of the scalar perspective, and it highlights the need for students to demonstrate this understanding across multiple situations and number relationships.

Strategy Type	Assessment item problem type with associated student strategy example	
	Figure 19.3a: Scale Up Problem	Figure 19.3b: Scalar Problem
Constant Difference (incorrect)		10 hours in 20 miles 8×2+4=20 miles 3×2+4=10 hours
	Figure 19.3c: Scale Up Problem	Figure 19.3d: Scale Down Problem
Scalar Additive	4 6 8 12 12 18	miles 6 8 9 hours 6 3 1.5
	Figure 19.3e: Scale Up Problem	Figure 19.3f: Scalar Problem
Scalar Multiplicative	$4 \times 3 = 12$ $6 \times 3 = 18$	$8\overline{)20.0}$ 2.5 16 40 40 $3 \times 2.5 = 7.5$ 7.5 hours
Scalar Multiplicative: Scale Up & Down	Figure 19.3g: Scalar Problem	Figure 19.3h: Functional Problem
	mi 8 4 hrs 3 1.5 4·5=20 1.5 ×5 7.5hrs 7.5	3 6 7 8 5)15 +3=18+3= 21+3= 24 -15 0 3
	Figure 19.3i: Scalar Problem	Figure 19.3j: Functional Problem
Functional	$\frac{8}{3}=\frac{20}{a}=7.5$ 7½ hrs 0.375×20=7500 8)3.00 24 60 56	15 ×3 ? ×8 24 miles
	Figure 19.3k: Functional Problem	
Cross-Multiplication Procedure	15 4 5 8 15 24 ×8 5)20 120 10 20 20 0	

Fig. 19.3. Student strategy examples by assessment item type

Scalar Additive

Students using a scalar additive strategy focused on iterating additively, doubling, or halving the initial ratio until the desired number of the given quantity in the second ratio is reached. In figure 19.3c the student is coordinating the two quantities in the ratio as a composed unit in an additive fashion: perhaps doubling the original 4:6 ratio to generate the 8:12 ratio and then adding another unit of 4:6 to generate the 12:18 ratio. While this method generates the correct answer and is likely an important step in students' developing understanding, it is essential to recognize the student is not demonstrating clear understanding of the scalar or functional perspective in terms of the constant multiplicative relationships. Students utilizing the scalar additive strategy may also possess the ability to partition or halve the ratio in an additive fashion as presented in figure 19.3d for the scale down problem but do not demonstrate understanding of scaling by a single factor of 4 which would be indicative of the next strategy.

Scalar Multiplicative

The scalar multiplicative strategy focuses on treating the initial ratio as a composed unit that is scaled up or down by multiplying or dividing by a single scale factor. Figure 19.3e provides an example from the scale up problem of a student utilizing a scalar multiplicative strategy by multiplying each quantity in the initial 4:6 ratio by 3 to obtain the 12:18 ratio. However, based on the presented work it is unknown whether the student can continue to apply this perspective as the number relationships or situation increases in difficulty (see this potential misconception in figure 19.3b). In figure 19.3f, the student demonstrates a potentially more sophisticated understanding of the scalar multiplicative strategy by first dividing the 20 miles by 8 miles to determine the 2.5 scale factor and then applying this scale factor to the 3 hours to get 7.5 hrs.

Scalar multiplicative subcategory: Scale up and down

The scale up and down strategy involves a slightly less sophisticated application of the scalar multiplicative strategy. We saw this strategy as a potential precursor to the multiplicative scalar perspective. It involves scaling the initial ratio in two or more steps by easier—often whole number—relationships. Students employing this strategy focused on treating the initial ratio as a composed unit and using a combination of scaling up and down to reach the desired number of a given component. This strategy only emerged on the scalar and functional problem types as the number relationships became more difficult. In figure 19.3g, the student starts by halving each quantity in the original 8:3 ratio to get a 4:1.5 ratio, and then recognizes the times five relationship to scale up the 4 miles to 20 miles and the 1.5 hours to 7.5 hours. This strategy is distinct from and less efficient than the scalar multiplicative strategy used in figure 19.3f. Students using a scale up and down strategy often get to a unit rate, which is related to the functional perspective. However, it is important to keep in mind that students who can calculate the unit rate may not actually possess the functional perspective of proportional reasoning. For example, in figure 19.3h the student starts by dividing 15 by 5, which one might think is leading to a functional perspective. However, the subsequent student work would indicate the student perceived the resulting 3 as a unit rate indicating 3 miles per 1 hour and added this 3:1 ratio to the original 5:15 ratio to generate the 6:18 ratio and so on until achieving the desired 8:24 ratio. This example highlights how use of a particular procedure (e.g., dividing one quantity in the ratio by another) does not necessarily indicate understanding of the functional perspective. In particular, students who find the unit rate may still have difficulty expressing one quantity in the ratio as a constant amount of times smaller or larger than the other quantity in the ratio.

Functional

The functional strategy involves dividing one quantity in the initial ratio by the other to find the constant of proportionality and then using this constant to generate the missing value in the desired ratio. Figure 19.3i provides an example of a student using the functional perspective to generate the missing value in the equivalent ratio. It is difficult to determine from the students' work whether they are applying a procedure they have memorized (i.e., divide one number in the ratio by the other and multiply to generate the missing value) or whether they have a deep understanding of the functional perspective and can flexibly use it in various situations. On the other hand, the work generated in figure 19.3j, while definitely a simpler problem because of the ease of the number relationships, appears to indicate an initial understanding of the functional relationship as one quantity in the ratio being a certain number of times the size of the other quantity, in this case 3 times as large. This should not be interpreted too broadly in terms of students' understanding of the functional perspective, but it does provide initial evidence with easy number relationships.

Cross Multiplication

It is important to examine the cross multiplication procedure in relation to the scalar and functional perspectives. The cross multiplication algorithm is an efficient approach for

$$\frac{2x}{3} = \frac{4+x}{-3}$$

However, in proportional situations where the ratios are provided as numerical quantities, such as

$$\frac{15 \text{ miles}}{5 \text{ hours}} = \frac{x \text{ miles}}{8 \text{ hours}}$$

with a single unknown quantity in only one ratio, the cross multiplication algorithm adds unnecessary steps and formality to a situation that can often be solved relatively easily if one possesses a fluent and flexible understanding of the scalar and functional perspectives. Even with "ugly" numbers, one can algorithmically use a scalar or functional strategy with decimal multipliers, making the cross multiplication algorithm unnecessary. Thus, while we note the utility of the cross multiplication procedure with rational algebraic equations, we question its usefulness as a tool in proportional reasoning situations. For example, in figure 19.3k the student performs the cross multiplication algorithm to solve a problem that is relatively simple from a functional perspective.

The strategies displayed should be viewed as evidence of a student's potential understanding and ability to apply a particular perspective. However, when the evidence is based on only a few assessment items, we cannot assume a student who generates a correct answer using a particular strategy possesses full understanding of the scalar or the functional perspectives; there are inherent issues with describing students' thinking based on a few examples and without the opportunity for discourse with the student about the process he or she used. But we also cannot assume because students achieved the correct answer that they are "proficient" with a mathematical topic (as is the case with most assessments). For example, a student could and did correctly solve all four assessment items using a scalar additive or scale up and down strategy. However, these strategies will not work as number relationships increase in difficulty or transfer to new situations. There is a clear benefit to analyzing classroom assessments from a student cognition perspective to determine the type and level of reasoning in which students are engaging and to use this information to inform instruction.

■ Application to Proportional Reasoning

Our purpose in utilizing the NRC's (2001) assessment framework was to provide an explicit example of utilizing student thinking in the design and analysis of student assessments with proportional reasoning as our example context (see fig. 19.1 for a graphic overview). Presenting the cognition, observation, and interpretation elements of the framework provides an example of the elements in application. Within cognition, we identified the two perspectives of *scalar* and *functional* understanding of proportional relationships within the research literature. The observation element focused on operationalizing the cognition ideas through the development and articulation of four specific problem types: scale up, scale down, scalar, and functional. These problem types were designed to highlight students' cognitive processes as they engaged in proportional reasoning activities. While these specific items and problem types are still in the development process, they were useful in providing information about the type and level of students' proportional reasoning. The interpretation element involved the identification of five common student strategies: constant difference (incorrect), scalar additive, scalar multiplicative, functional, and cross multiplication. Within scalar multiplicative, a distinction was found between students who could use the scalar multiplicative relationship in a single step versus those students who scaled up and down to continue using easier—often whole number—relationships.

■ Application to the Classroom

The goal of focusing on students' cognitive processes in the design and analysis of assessment items is to inform classroom instruction. There are multiple ways in which the assessment items and the analysis of student strategies presented can be used to inform instruction. The following scenario is one example of such an analysis but is not the limit of its application.

A teacher starting a new unit on proportional reasoning may want to determine the background knowledge the students have of this topic. As an exit ticket activity, students use an index card to show work for the scale up problem: "Jane estimates she takes 4 hours to hike 6 miles. Approximately how far can she hike in 12 hours?" The teacher then sorts the student work into the following strategy categories: (*a*) constant difference, (*b*) scalar additive, (*c*) scalar multiplicative, and (*d*) other. The resulting data should inform the starting place of instruction for the unit. For example, if several students are using an incorrect additive strategy it may be appropriate to start instruction with a contextual question where students can physically manipulate classroom objects to help them visualize why their additive strategy doesn't work in a proportional situation (e.g., "Jane gets 3 paper clips for every 5 rubber bands, so how many paper clips for 15 rubber bands"). However, if the majority of students already indicate understanding of the multiplicative scalar relationship, you may want to increase the difficulty of the number relationships (e.g., with the scalar problem) to see if students can abstract their scalar multiplicative strategy to a generalizable procedure (e.g., dividing to determine a scale factor as in fig. 19.3f) or administer the functional problem to determine what level of understanding students have of that perspective. The objective is to utilize the student thinking revealed by the assessment items to inform instruction. This type of analysis can also be applied to identify students for invention or extension groupings (e.g., response to intervention situations) and to provide direction in terms of the focus of instruction for these groups.

■ Application to Other Topics

The NRC assessment framework can be applied to multiple mathematics topics beyond proportional reasoning. For example, we have used the framework described in this chapter to examine students' cognitive strategies related to iterating and partitioning fractions. We observe students by providing a number line where the placement of 0 and $2/5$ are clearly indicated and ask students to place $7/5$ and explain how they determined its location. We interpret the resulting student work to categorize their level of understanding of iterating and partitioning fractions on a number line. This information is then used to guide classroom instruction. The process of identifying an important aspect of student cognition within a mathematical topic, followed by observation and interpretation of the evidence, is a framework that embodies the philosophy of formative assessment and provides a concrete mechanism for implementing it meaningfully in the classroom.

References

Fennema, Elizabeth, Thomas P. Carpenter, Megan L. Franke, Linda Levi, Victoria Jacobs, and Susan Emson. "A Longitudinal Study of Learning to Use Children's Thinking in Mathematics Instruction." *Journal for Research in Mathematics Education* 27, no. 4 (1996): 404–34.

Lamon, Susan J. *Teaching Fractions and Ratios for Understanding*. New York: Routledge, 2005.

Lesh, Richard, Thomas Post, and Merlyn Behr. "Proportional Reasoning." In *Number Concepts and Operations in the Middle Grades*, edited by James E. Hiebert and Merlyn Behr, pp. 93–118. Reston, Va.: National Council of Teachers of Mathematics, 1988.

Lobato, Joanne, and Amy B. Ellis. *Developing Essential Understanding of Ratios, Proportions, and Proportional Reasoning for Teaching Mathematics in Grades 6–8*. Reston, Va.: National Council of Teachers of Mathematics, 2010.

National Council of Teachers of Mathematics (NCTM). *Curriculum and Evaluation Standards for School Mathematics*. Reston, Va.: NCTM, 1989.

———. *Principles and Standards for School Mathematics*. Reston, Va.: NCTM, 2000.

National Governors Association Center for Best Practices and Council of Chief State School Officers (NGA Center and CCSSO). *Common Core State Standards for Mathematics*. Washington, D.C.: NGA Center and CCSSO, 2010.

National Research Council (NRC). *Knowing What Students Know: The Science and Design of Educational Assessment*, edited by James W. Pellegrino, Naomi Chudowsky, and Robert Glaser. Washington, D.C.: National Academies Press, 2001.

Steinthorsdottir, Olof B., and Bharath Sriraman. "Icelandic 5th-Grade Girls' Developmental Trajectories in Proportional Reasoning." *Mathematics Education Research Journal* 21, no. 1 (2009): 6–30.

Tourniaire, Francoise, and Steven Pulos. "Proportional Reasoning: A Review of the Literature." *Educational Studies in Mathematics* 16, no. 2 (1985): 181–204.

CHAPTER 20

Embedding Formative Assessment in Curriculum Design: A Research-Based Approach

Maryl Gearhart, *University of California, Berkeley*
Geoffrey B. Saxe, *University of California, Berkeley*
Darrell Earnest, *University of Massachusetts, Amherst*
Lina Chopra Haldar, *University of California, Berkeley*
Anna McGee, *University of California, Berkeley*
Yasmin Sitabkhan, *RTI International, Washington, D.C.*

When formative assessment is deeply embedded in instruction, teachers regularly interpret student understanding and use evidence to support student learning (Black and Wiliam 1998; Heritage 2011; National Council of Teachers of Mathematics [NCTM] 2013; Shepard 2005; Wiliam 2011). Unfortunately, the promise of formative assessment may be unrealized if curriculum materials do not provide teachers with useful formative assessment techniques. In this chapter, we introduce a research-based curriculum that embeds formative assessment in every lesson to support teaching and learning.

The curriculum, *Learning Mathematics through Representations* (LMR), is a four-week unit created to strengthen elementary students' understandings of integers and fractions. We will highlight three features of the LMR design for embedded assessment: problem-solving *tasks* challenge students to reason about core mathematical ideas; *lesson designs* support the use of tasks for both assessment and instruction; and the *lesson sequence* supports a learning progression so assessments provide formative guidance over the course of the lessons. LMR's program of design research illustrates the key role of research in the design of embedded assessments that enable teachers to gauge student learning and progress.

■LMR's Embedded Assessment Tasks: An Illustrative Episode in a Fifth-Grade Classroom

To introduce embedded assessment tasks in *Learning Mathematics through Representations*, we invite you into a fifth-grade classroom where Ms. Schaefer (a pseudonym) is launching lesson 5 in the LMR Integers unit. Ms. Schaefer was a participant in a study of the efficacy of the LMR curriculum.

As Ms. Schaefer puts a number line problem with irregularly spaced tick marks on the document projector (see part *a* in fig. 20.1), she comments to her students, "This is an opening problem, and you're not supposed to get it right away. It's supposed to represent challenges for you, so work through it—this is where the learning gets juicy." Most students in Ms. Schaefer's class do not have experience with irregularly spaced tick marks on a number line, so it is not surprising that they solve the task in figure 20.1a in different ways. One student applies the common procedure of assigning a number pattern to tick marks—the student counts by tens backwards along the tick marks ("60, 50, 40, 30") and marks 30 in the box (see fig. 20.1b, top). Another student modifies this procedure by reasoning that the interval from 60 to 50 is an interval of ten, and the interval from 50 to the box is the same length so it must have the same value of ten; the student then marks 40 in the box (see fig. 20.1b, bottom). In the whole-class discussion that follows, the learning "gets juicy" as Ms. Schaefer engages the class in a discussion of the discrepancy between these two solutions in order to open up learning opportunities for all of her students.

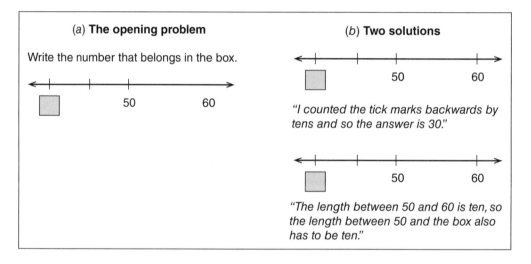

Fig. 20.1. Ms. Schaefer leads a discussion of (*a*) an opening problem and (*b*) two student solutions.

Is Ms. Schaefer's opening problem an assessment task or an instructional task? In this episode, the opening problem serves two functions: an assessment of students' understandings of relationships between numerical values and linear units, and an instructional resource for a class discussion about the mathematical principles linked to the representation of integers on the number line. The features of the number line representation in figure 20.1a are key resources for Ms. Schaefer's approach to coordinating assessment and instruction. If the lesson had opened with a number line like the one shown in figure 20.2—a number line with 0 at the leftmost tick mark and regularly spaced tick marks labeled with a familiar number pattern—a student's correct response could conceal partial understanding. A student who responds "40" to figure 20.2 is likely to have intuitions about order, mastery of skip counting by tens, and facility with the procedure of labeling tick marks with a number pattern, but this student may or may not understand that the length of an interval of ten must have the same value everywhere on this number line. The line in figure 20.2 would provide Ms. Schaefer less opportunity for assessment as well as instruction about an idea fundamental to a robust understanding of number lines. Instruction in Ms. Schaefer's classroom can "get juicy" because the unfamiliar features of the number line in figure 20.1a challenge students to reflect upon and modify their problem-solving strategies, and to reason about relationships between interval lengths and tick mark values.

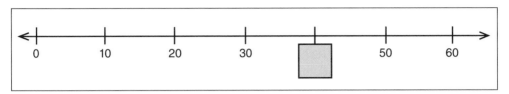

Fig. 20.2. Textbooks commonly use number lines with equidistant tick marks.

■ Research Foundation for LMR's Embedded Formative Assessment Tasks

In *Knowing What Students Know*, the National Research Council recommends designing educational assessments based on evidence from research on learning and teaching (National Research Council [NRC] 2001). As shown in figure 20.3, the LMR program of design research was organized as a suite of studies to guide the design of the curriculum, followed by an efficacy study that validated LMR's effectiveness. All studies were conducted in urban elementary schools with diverse populations. (See Saxe et al. [in press] for more on the design research that led to the curriculum unit.)

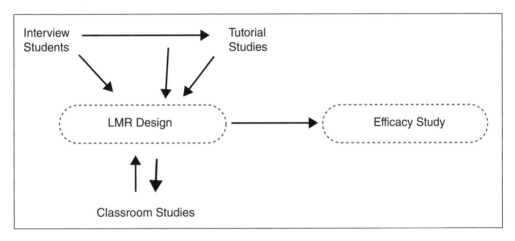

Fig. 20.3. LMR conducted a suite of studies to design and evaluate LMR lessons and embedded assessments.

In the first phase of design research, we conducted *interview studies* with students (Saxe, Shaughnessy, Gearhart, and Haldar 2013). Our purpose was twofold: to gather information on the partial understandings and strategies that students were likely to bring to a curriculum that uses the number line as the representational context for integers and fractions, and to identify useful tasks that elicit diverse strategies and reasoning. In the interview studies, we employed tasks that included more common (like fig. 20.2) and less common number line representations (like fig. 20.1a). From students' responses, we learned that fifth graders generally understand the idea of order on the number line, and they use procedures for counting tick marks (or intervals) and labeling tick marks with familiar number patterns. However, when presented with number line representations rarely used in textbooks (e.g., unevenly spaced tick marks or no 0), many students use routine procedures without considering the lengths and values of number line intervals. The interview studies provided us with a bank of number line tasks that held promise for both assessment and instruction.

In the second phase, the *tutorial study* was an investigation of strategies to support students' understandings of integers on the number line (Saxe et al. 2010). We designed a coordinated set of techniques: a progression of tasks to support students as they build understanding of the properties of number lines; Cuisenaire rods as linear measurement tools; and the gradual introduction of number line definitions and principles (e.g., order, unit, multiunit, and symmetry) to support the growth of student reasoning and problem solving. Adapted from the interview study, the tasks in the tutorial could not be readily solved with commonly taught procedures and arithmetic facts. The tasks served as both instructional resources and formative assessments that enabled the tutor to gauge student understanding and provide additional instructional support as needed. Our research documented the effectiveness of the tutorial; compared with students in the control group, tutorial students progressed from partial to more complete understandings. The task sequence in the tutorial study became the foundation for the design of the LMR lesson sequence in the third phase of design research.

In the *classroom studies* of the third phase, we collaborated with teachers to develop the curriculum and embedded assessments through an iterative process of design, implementation, investigation, and revision. The initial construction of the lesson sequence was guided by interview and tutorial findings regarding typical patterns of partial understanding and useful sequences of tasks. Teachers piloted pedagogical strategies for using the tasks as resources for both assessment and instruction. Over repeated cycles of refinement, we produced a four-week curriculum unit with embedded assessments, and we closed this phase with a full pilot that yielded promising evidence of LMR's potential.

Our research concluded with an *efficacy study* with a matched-classrooms design that involved 21 classrooms (Saxe, Diakow, and Gearhart 2013). LMR students made strong and persistent gains in their understandings of integers and fractions, and their gains exceeded those of students in comparison classrooms. The contribution of LMR's embedded formative assessments to LMR's effectiveness was corroborated by additional qualitative studies (Saxe et al., in press).

■ Three Features of LMR's Embedded Formative Assessments

LMR's embedded assessments enable teachers to gauge student understanding as students progress through the curriculum. In the sections that follow, we provide detail on three features of LMR's embedded assessment design. While our focus is on LMR, the features of LMR's assessments are useful heuristics for the design of formative assessment in any mathematics curriculum unit.

Tasks challenge students to reason about core mathematical ideas

LMR tasks challenge students to reason about core mathematical ideas because students cannot readily solve these tasks with routine procedures or arithmetic facts. In whole-class discussions, students communicate and refine their understandings of the representation of numerical values on the number line.

One of our design strategies for LMR tasks is to include either an incorrect or an uncommon number line representation and to ask students to evaluate the placement of numbers on the line. Figure 20.1a illustrates a task with an uncommon number line, and figure 20.4 illustrates additional tasks and the partial understandings that emerge in students' reasoning about these tasks. Task 4a requires students to evaluate an incorrect representation from a negative integers lesson. As with many number lines in textbooks, the tick marks on the number line in task 4a are equally spaced. However, unlike many textbook number lines, the assigned values are not coordinated with interval lengths; the value of the interval from 0 to 3, for example, is not equal to the value of the interval from 3 to 5. Task 4b challenges students to match a familiar area model for $1/4$ with one of three number lines representing three different values. All three number lines have features that are common in textbooks: the lines begin with 0 and are partitioned into equal intervals. To identify the correct answer choice, students must consider how part-whole relations are represented on number lines as distances from 0 in unit and subunit intervals. In task 4c, students must choose the correct numeric representation for a value represented on the number line. The unit interval from 0 to 1 has the common feature of equally partitioned fifths, but the second unit interval from 1 to 2 is not represented; the line represents only one subunit beyond 1 (i.e., the interval between 1 and $6/5$), and thus students must reason about relationships between unit intervals and subunit intervals to identify the correct solution.

The capacity of LMR tasks to support assessment and instructional functions depends on teachers' understanding of the ways that students are likely to reason about strategies and solutions. To support teachers, each lesson guide provides information on likely patterns of partial understanding. As illustrated in the right column of figure 20.4, lesson guides illustrate contrasting solutions, various ways that students use Cuisenaire rods as measurement tools, and typical patterns of reasoning. To support instructional uses of tasks, each LMR lesson guide also suggests techniques to support students' reasoning about task solutions—for example, contexts for student presentations, queries to elicit reasoning (e.g., "How did you solve . . . ?" "What principle did you use . . . ?"), and counter-suggestions to engage students in interpreting other students' ideas (e.g., "Another student solved the problem this way . . ."). (LMR lesson guides are available at http://www.lmr.berkeley.edu/.)

Of course, teachers also create their own techniques for using tasks to elicit and build on student reasoning. Mr. Nelson, for example, often made intentional errors when he solved a task on the whiteboard, and after defending his solution, he would invite students to comment. Here is a typical episode:

> Mr. Nelson poses the figure in figure 20.4b—a square with one quadrant shaded—and he asks students to select a number line that shows the same fraction. Mr. Nelson insists that answer (*a*) is correct, because there are 4 intervals marked on the line, and the arrow is pointing to the end of the first interval. Many students object ("Noooooo!"), and Mr. Nelson then elicits their ideas. As he integrates students' arguments, he applies the definition for denominator: *The denominator is the number of subunits between 0 and 1 (or an equivalent unit interval) and not the entire line.*

Sample Tasks and Task Descriptions	Partial Understandings	More Complete Understandings
4a. Task engages students in reasoning about the coordination of linear units and tickmark values to the left as well as the right of 0. Are the numbers placed correctly on the number line? Mark your answer in the box. yes □ no □ −7 −5 −3 0 3 5 7	Focusing on equal interval lengths or on familiar number patterns. **Examples:** *It's "yes" because the-numbers skip count 3, 5, 7 on one side, and −3, −5, −7 on the other side.* *It's "yes" because the spaces are equal.*	Coordinating interval lengths and tickmark values. **Example:** *It's "no" because the intervals have different values but they're all the same length. It's a distance of 3 from 0 to 3, but it's the same distance from 3 to 5, so the "5" should be a "6." The tickmarks should be labeled 3, 6, 9 to the right of 0, and −3, −6, and −9 to the left of 0.*
4b. Task introduces the new definition of "subunit" by engaging students in reasoning about relationships between fractions of a region and fractions as distances from 0. Some fraction of this is shaded. Which number line shows the same amount? (a) 0 1 2 (b) 0 1 2 (c) 0 1 2	Establishing denominator and numerator values based on counts of number line tickmarks or intervals, with inconsistent attention to the role of 0 or the unit interval. **Examples:** *It's "a." The square shows ¼, so I found ¼ on the line. I counted 4 tickmarks from 0, and that was my denominator "4," and then I counted 1 tickmark from 0, and that was my numerator "1."* *It's "b." The square shows ¼, so I found ¼ on the line. The 1 on the line matches the "1" in ¼, and then I counted 4 spaces between 1 and 2, and the 4 spaces matches the 4 in ¼.*	Establishing the denominator value by partitioning the 0 to 1 interval into equal segments, establishing the denominator value by counting all segments, and establishing the numerator value by counting the segments from 0 to the arrow. **Example:** *It's "c." The square shows ¼, and in c the arrow is pointing to ¼ the distance between 0 and 1. The unit interval is divided into four equal fourths, so "4" is the denominator, and the arrow is pointing to the end of the first fourth.*

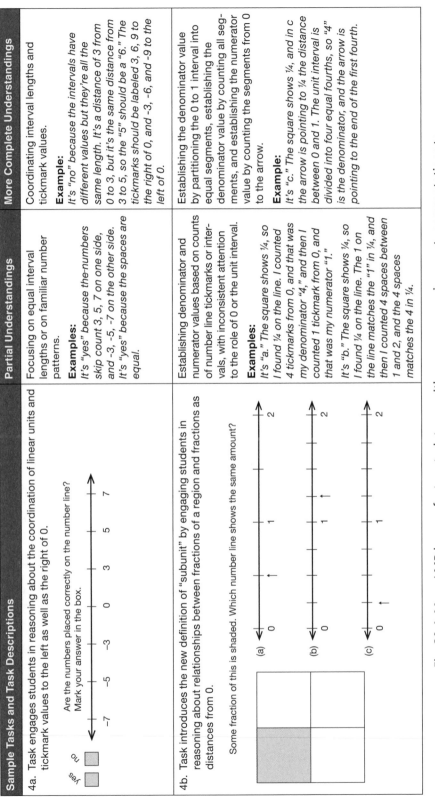

Fig. 20.4. Many LMR lessons feature task types with uncommon or incorrect representations to elicit students' partial understandings.

Sample Tasks and Task Descriptions	Partial Understandings	More Complete Understandings
4c. Task introduces fractions greater than one to help students consolidate their understandings of denominator (the number of subunits in the unit) and numerator (the number of subunits from zero). What number is the arrow pointing at? 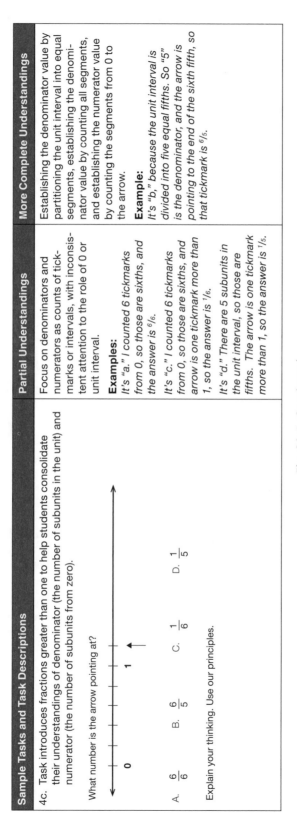 A. $\frac{6}{6}$ B. $\frac{6}{5}$ C. $\frac{1}{6}$ D. $\frac{1}{5}$ Explain your thinking. Use our principles.	Focus on denominators and numerators as counts of tickmarks or intervals, with inconsistent attention to the role of 0 or unit interval. **Examples:** *It's "a." I counted 6 tickmarks from 0, so those are sixths, and the answer is $^6/_6$.* *It's "c." I counted 6 tickmarks from 0, so those are sixths, and arrow is one tickmark more than 1, so the answer is $^1/_6$.* *It's "d." There are 5 subunits in the unit interval, so those are fifths. The arrow is one tickmark more than 1, so the answer is $^1/_5$.*	Establishing the denominator value by partitioning the unit interval into equal segments, establishing the denominator value by counting all segments, and establishing the numerator value by counting the segments from 0 to the arrow. **Example:** *It's "b," because the unit interval is divided into five equal fifths. So "5" is the denominator, and the arrow is pointing to the end of the sixth fifth, so that tickmark is $^6/_5$.*

Fig. 20.4. Continued

The lesson design supports the use of tasks for both assessment and instruction

In LMR lessons, instruction builds on assessment of student thinking. As shown in figure 20.5, LMR lessons are designed in five phases that integrate independent work, whole-class discussions, and partner work. Across these phases, tasks are similar in content and format, but over the course of the lesson phases, tasks shift in their function between assessment and instruction.

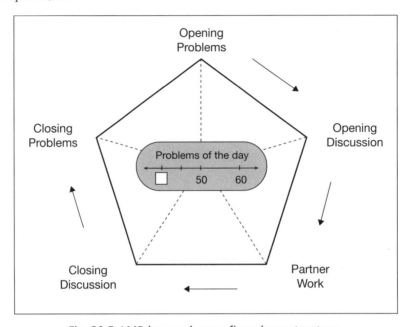

Fig. 20.5. LMR lessons have a five-phase structure.

Consider Ms. Schaefer's Integers Lesson 5, which begins with students' independent work on several *opening problems,* including the task with the irregularly partitioned number line at the center of figure 20.5. The lesson guide provides information on likely patterns of partial understanding, and Ms. Schaefer uses the opening problems as an opportunity to assess these patterns—she roves to observe student responses. Her walk around the room does not provide her an assessment of every student's understanding, but her walk does allow her to gather information on the diverse mathematical ideas that are important for the class to investigate as a community. When she initiates the *opening discussion*, she guides the class in an investigation of conflicts between task solutions, and the function of tasks shifts to instruction that provides opportunities for all students to reason and communicate about core number line principles.

Partner work is the context for Ms. Schaefer's students to extend their insights from the opening discussion as they tackle additional tasks. Ms. Schaefer supports students by asking targeted questions to assess understanding and scaffold reasoning and problem solving (Gearhart and Saxe 2014; Shepard 2005). The worksheets are sequenced in difficulty, and Ms. Schaefer assesses student understanding and then encourages higher-achieving students to work on extension problems while she works with students who need support. In the *closing discussion*, Ms. Schaefer guides students in a review of key tasks from the partner work, and she also poses the task in figure 20.6 to help students consolidate their understandings of the definitions for unit and multiunit interval.

As illustrated in figure 20.6, students represent their solutions to the task "Mark 1, 3, and 5 on a number line" in different ways. While most solutions are correct, students' number lines differ in the lengths of the multiunit intervals, the inclusion of 0, and the representation of unit intervals. The contrasts among students' correct solutions provide Ms. Schaefer the opportunity to review definitions for multiunit interval and unit interval, as well as the idea that *every number has a place on the number line, but not every number needs to be shown.*

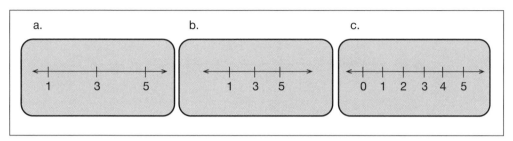

Fig. 20.6. Ms. Schaefer's students solved the closing discussion task, "Mark the numbers 1, 3, and 5 on a number line on your whiteboard," in three different ways.

At the lesson's end, the *closing problems* serve as a formative assessment. As illustrated in figure 20.7, the parallel tasks in the opening and closing problems (which differ only in numerical values) enable Ms. Schaefer to assess individual student progress at the end of the lesson to identify any students needing additional support.

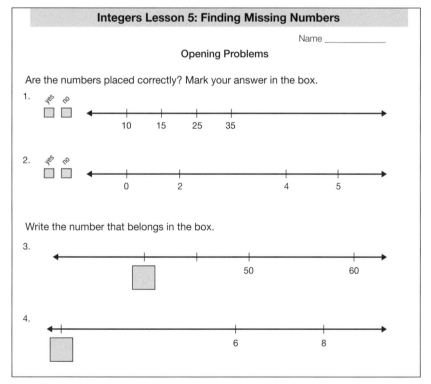

Fig. 20.7. LMR's opening and closing problems are aligned, and the closing problems serve as daily formative assessments.

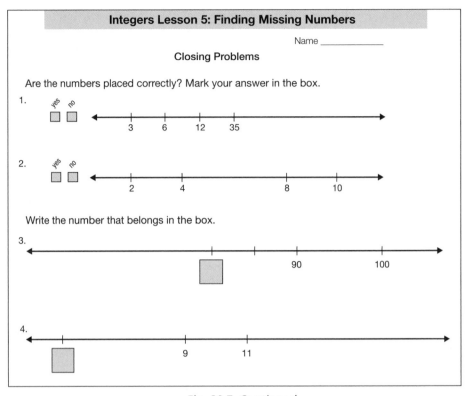

Fig. 20.7. *Continued*

The lesson sequence supports a learning progression so assessments provide formative guidance over the course of the lessons

Because the LMR lesson sequence is designed to support a progression of learning, the closing problems in any one lesson are formative assessments that help teachers anticipate the understanding that students will bring to the next lesson. LMR's foundation in learning progressions (and the use of embedded formative assessments to support those progressions) is consistent with the Common Core State Standards for Mathematics (National Governors Association Center for Best Practices and Council of Chief State School Officers [NGA Center and CCSSO] 2010) and the accompanying progressions documents (Common Core Standards Writing Team 2013).

We can use the challenging task that Ms. Schaefer presents in Integers Lesson 5 (see fig. 20.1a) to illustrate how lessons support a progression of student understanding. The lesson progression is depicted in figure 20.8. In lesson 1, Ms. Schaefer's class investigated number lines that violate order, and they agreed to establish the *order* principle, the idea that numbers increase from left to right and decrease from right to left. In lesson 2, the class investigated number lines with tick mark values that are not coordinated with interval lengths, and they agreed to establish definitions for *interval* and *unit interval* to consolidate the idea that tick mark values and linear units needed to be coordinated on number lines. Lesson 3 activities extended the ideas of order and unit interval by introducing students to *multiunit interval* and the idea that *every number has a place on the number line, but not every number needs to be shown*. Lesson 4 engaged students in constructing and reasoning about intervals of varying lengths. Number lines were marked with 0 and a series of multiunit intervals; to locate new points, students needed to extend the multiunit series and partition multiunit intervals into unit intervals.

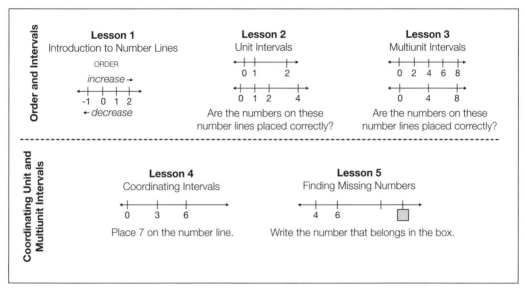

Fig. 20.8. This excerpt from the Integers sequence illustrates sample tasks and the definitions introduced in each lesson.

When Ms. Schaefer launches lesson 5, she knows from the lesson 4 closing problems that some of her students have persistent challenges reasoning about relationships between linear units and tick mark values. For example, some students solved the "Place 7" problem in lesson 4 by placing 7 at the location for 9 (treating the interval from 3 to 6 as a unit interval), and other students placed 7 just to the right of 6 (respecting order without considering the lengths of unit and multiunit intervals). As Ms. Schaefer launches each new lesson, her review of the closing problems from the prior lesson supports her efforts to keep the class on a learning progression focused on the representation of integers and fractions on the number line.

■ Reflections on Curriculum-Embedded Assessment

Research has established that formative assessment is a critical component of effective instruction, and teachers need resources to help them build their assessment expertise. Teachers can consult publications that describe assessment techniques spanning content areas and grade levels (e.g., Wiliam 2011), but teachers also need research-based assessment techniques embedded in curriculum. If teachers are to "know what students know" as students progress through particular materials (NRC 2001), curriculum developers must provide teachers with targeted assessments and research-based information on typical patterns of partial understandings. The *Learning Mathematics through Representations* curriculum illustrates one approach to embedded assessment. We suggest that teachers and curriculum developers can adapt LMR's three design elements—task design, lesson design, and lesson sequencing—to curriculum materials in other mathematical domains and at other grade levels.

LMR *tasks* incorporate either an incorrect or an uncommon number line representation to challenge students to reason about the applicability of common procedures and the relevance of core mathematical ideas. Curriculum developers and teachers can use LMR task design when writing or revising materials. For example, tasks in a geometry unit on plane shapes might feature uncommon or incorrect figures to assess students' understandings of geometric definitions (Clements 2007). Arithmetic tasks might position the equal sign in both common (e.g., 5 + 7 = {**box**}) and less common expressions (e.g., 8 + 4 = {**box**} + 5) to assess students' understandings of the equal sign (Carpenter, Franke, and Levi 2003). Tasks in an algebra unit might feature uncommon equations; after students have experience graphing the straight line equation $y = \text{m}x + b$, teachers can present $y = b + \text{m}x$, as well as $b + \text{m}x = y$, or even $c(\text{m}x + b) = y$, in order to elicit and build upon students' partial understandings of slope and y-intercept (e.g., the partial understanding that the first number is the slope).

LMR *lesson designs* support ongoing formative assessment, and teachers and curriculum developers can extend the lesson design to other curriculum materials. Parallel opening and closing problems can provide daily formative assessments of student progress. Sequenced worksheets can support differentiated instruction when teachers circulate during partner work to probe student reasoning and to identify which students are ready for more challenge and which students need support (Gearhart and Saxe 2014). Opening and closing discussions can provide teachers windows into student thinking as students make public how they are conceptualizing tasks and the solution approaches of others. Of course, these LMR lesson components are not entirely new ideas. "Warm-ups" and "do-nows" are common methods for pre-lesson assessments, and "exit slips" are common techniques for post-lesson assessment. However, LMR's approach to close alignment of tasks across the opening problems, partner work, and closing problems strengthens a teacher's capacity to gauge how students have revised their understandings over the course of the lesson.

Finally, the LMR *lesson sequence* is designed as a learning progression, and teachers and curriculum developers can utilize a similar approach to lesson sequencing. For example, when teachers collaborate with colleagues to revise materials so lessons build on each other, they can revise the closing problems so students' responses provide daily information on students' readiness for the next lesson. For students, a sound learning progression helps to ensure that the new ideas they construct in one lesson support their learning in subsequent lessons. For teachers, a sound progression provides a framework for supporting student progress over the entire sequence. Given the emphasis on learning progressions in the Common Core State Standards (Common Core Standards Writing Team 2013), we expect that teachers will have greater access in the future to curriculum designed on research-based learning progressions.

References

Black, Paul, and Dylan Wiliam. "Assessment and Classroom Learning." *Assessment in Education: Principles, Policy and Practice* 5 (1998): 7–73.

Carpenter, Thomas P., Megan L. Franke, and Linda Levi. *Thinking Mathematically: Integrating Algebra and Arithmetic in Elementary School.* Portsmouth, N.H.: Heinemann, 2003.

Clements, Douglas H. "Curriculum Research: Towards a Framework for 'Research-based Curricula.'" *Journal for Research in Mathematics Education* 38, no. 1 (2007): 35–70.

Common Core Standards Working Team. "Progressions Documents for the Common Core Math Standards" (2013). http://ime.math.arizona.edu/progressions/.

Gearhart, Maryl, and Geoffrey B. Saxe. "Differentiating Instruction in Shared Mathematical Contexts." *Teaching Children Mathematics* 20 (2014): 426–35.

Heritage, Margaret. "Formative Assessment: Enabler of Learning." *Better: Evidence-Based Education* 3, no. 3 (2011): 18–19.

National Council of Teachers of Mathematics (NCTM). "Formative Assessment: A Position of the National Council of Teachers of Mathematics" (2013). http://www.nctm.org/formative/.

National Governors Association Center for Best Practices and Council of Chief State School Officers (NGA Center and CCSSO). *Common Core State Standards for Mathematics.* Washington, D.C.: NGA Center and CCSSO, 2010.

National Research Council (NRC). *Knowing What Students Know: The Science and Design of Educational Assessment,* edited by James W. Pellegrino, Naomi Chudowsky, and Robert Glaser. Washington, D.C.: National Academies Press, 2001.

Saxe, Geoffrey B., Kenton de Kirby, Marie Le, Yasmin Sitabkhan, and Bona Kang. "Understanding Learning across Lessons in Classroom Communities: A Multi-Leveled Analytic Approach." In *Doing Qualitative Research: Methodology and Methods in Mathematics Education*, edited by Angelika Bikner-Ahsbahs, Christine Knipping, and Norma Presmeg. New York: Springer, in press.

Saxe, Geoffrey B., Ronli Diakow, and Maryl Gearhart. "Towards Curricular Coherence in Integers and Fractions: A Study of the Efficacy of a Lesson Sequence That Uses the Number Line as the Principal Representational Context." *ZDM* 45, no. 3 (2013): 343–64.

Saxe, Geoffrey B., Darrell Earnest, Yasmin Sitabkhan, Lina C. Haldar, Katherine E. Lewis, and Ying Zheng. "Supporting Generative Thinking about the Integer Number Line in Elementary Mathematics." *Cognition and Instruction* 28 (2010): 433–74.

Saxe, Geoffrey B., Meghan M. Shaughnessy, Maryl Gearhart, and Lina C. Haldar. "Coordinating Numeric and Linear Units: Elementary Students' Strategies for Locating Whole Numbers on the Number Line." *Mathematics Teaching and Learning* 15 (2013): 235–58.

Shepard, Lorrie A. "Linking Formative Assessment to Scaffolding." *Educational Leadership* 63, no. 3 (2005): 66–70.

Wiliam, Dylan. *Embedded Formative Assessment.* Bloomington, Ind.: Solution Tree Press, 2011.

CHAPTER 21

Applying CCSSM's Definition of Understanding to Assess Students' Mathematical Learning

Lillie R. Albert and Rina Kim, *Boston College, Chestnut Hill, Massachusetts*

Russell and Airasian (2012) argue that assessment indicates "a process of collecting, synthesizing, and interpreting information in order to make a decision" (pp. 10–11). Assessment should be distinguished from testing or evaluation. The major purpose of assessment is collecting information about student learning through a variety of activities intended to assist in decision making about students' progress and teachers' instructional practices. Evaluation illustrates a process of judging student performance grounded in information collected throughout assessment (Gronlund 2006). The National Council of Teachers of Mathematics (NCTM 2014) proposes that assessment should be an essential element of instruction that includes evidence of students' mathematical proficiency regarding content and teachers' use of assessment to improve their practices. In the same vein, the Common Core State Standards for Mathematics [CCSSM] (National Governors Association Center for Best Practices and Council of Chief State School Officers [NGA Center and CCSSO] 2010) recommends that assessments as a part of mathematics instruction should include connections between the mathematical practices and mathematical content. Current research suggests that assessment should play a significant role in mathematics instruction and that assessment practices should be used to improve student learning in the classroom (Collins 2011; Phelan et al. 2011).

CCSSM (NGA Center and CCSSO 2010) proposes that elementary teachers should know how to assess students' mathematical understanding. "Mathematical understanding is the ability to justify, in a way appropriate to the student's mathematical maturity, why a particular mathematical statement is true or where a mathematical rule comes from" (p. 4). We believe that this definition of mathematical understanding may be useful to teachers for thinking about student learning in mathematics. As a framework, it may assist teachers in constructing instructional activities as well as assessment tasks that represent their students' mathematical learning.

■ Purpose and Direction

The purpose of this chapter is to illustrate how a framework grounded in CCSSM's definition of understanding informs teaching practices and serves as a catalyst for helping teachers develop worthwhile assessment tasks that represent student mathematical learning. We analyzed teacher-developed items constructed by South Korean elementary teachers to assess mathematical understanding and to target learning proficiencies. Although there may not be a large difference among mathematics itself as a subject from country to country, international research provides opportunities to understand various issues about the teaching and learning of mathematics (Cai 2005). Our assertion is that examining how South Korean elementary teachers use assessment tasks to motivate students to express mathematical understanding may help us to work more effectively with U.S. teachers in creating similar tasks that encourage students to develop a deeper understanding of conceptual and procedural processes.

The ideas presented in this chapter draw on data from a much broader and more extensive work that explored South Korean elementary teachers' pedagogical content knowledge for teaching mathematics (Kim and Albert, in press). Eleven South Korean elementary teachers with more than five years of teaching experience participated in this study, serving as facilitators for a professional development course focusing on constructing classroom assessment items. The teachers/facilitators submitted the classroom assessment items they developed and participated in interviews to describe the purpose and meaning of the items. We analyzed 203 classroom assessment items, including examples of students' responses, and we classified the items into three categories according to a framework based on the definition of *mathematical understanding* presented in the CCSSM (NGA Center and CCSSO 2010) document. What follows is an outline and description of the approach applied to meet the stated purpose of this chapter.

■ Framework for Analyzing Assessment Items

The CCSSM (NGA Center and CCSSO 2010) document emphasizes that elementary teachers should know how to assess students' mathematical understanding and procedural skills. Mathematical procedural skill is the ability to solve problems by using algorithms effectively and appropriately. Mathematical understanding comprises three categories, according to the definition by CCSSM: the ability to justify, understanding of why a particular mathematical statement is true, and understanding of where a mathematical rule comes from. These three categories provided a framework for analyzing and organizing the assessment items of this study. A detailed explanation of each category follows.

Students' Ability to Justify

The explanation offered in CCSSM (NGA Center and CCSSO 2010) of what constitutes mathematical understanding assumes that students should know how to support their conclusions by communicating the process used and constructing quality justifications. Mathematical justification is the ability to provide solid reasons for one's own conclusion (Talbert 2006). A good mathematical justification, including mathematical reasoning, requires the skill to construct mathematical conjectures, develop and evaluate mathematical arguments, and select and use different types of representations (Kramarsk and Mervarech 2003).

For instance, students may justify their process for the addition of one-digit numbers with a visual fraction model. Let's assume that a student is asked to solve the problem 2 + 2. If the student only has procedural skills, the student may find the answer is 4 without providing appropriate justification. However, if this student has a mathematical understanding of the related mathematical concepts (e.g., concepts of numbers including discrete and continuous quantities) using various representations, the student could justify the process for solving this problem in different ways. For example, when students are presented with a problem illustrating addition with a discrete quantity, as shown in figure 21.1, they must understand that when combining two groups into one group they need to use addition. A further justification of this interpretation for addition is that students show appropriate use of manipulatives to model combining two distinct sets to find out how many there are in the new set.

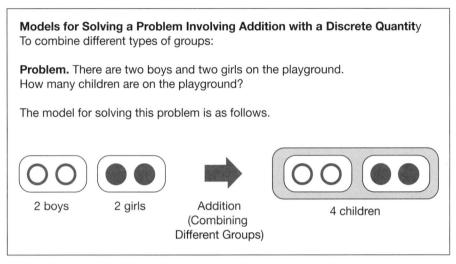

Models for Solving a Problem Involving Addition with a Discrete Quantity
To combine different types of groups:

Problem. There are two boys and two girls on the playground. How many children are on the playground?

The model for solving this problem is as follows.

2 boys   2 girls   Addition
                             (Combining
                             Different Groups)   4 children

Fig. 21.1. A student's justification for solving the equation 2 + 2 = ?

Although mathematical understanding of addition can ultimately emerge from modeling addition situations using manipulatives as a justification strategy, it is also important that students engage in activities that require them to show justifications that go beyond discrete embodiments, such as addition with a continuous quantity. For example, in order to solve the problem "There are 2 liters of water in a jar. John adds 2 liters of water to the jar. How many liters of water are in the jar?" students must understand that although there are no concrete or pictorial objects to count, they must use addition.

Using concrete and mental representations to model mathematical justifications provides critical information about how the problem was solved and perhaps conveys how the mathematics makes sense. "A particularly important ontological distinction relevant to mathematical modeling involves the nature of quantities, which can be viewed as either *discrete* or *continuous*" (DeWolf, Bassok, and Holyoak 2013, p. 389). As illustrated in fig. 21.1, the student selected to use manipulatives to represent her understanding of addition. That is, the student's ability to choose a proper mathematical model according to the related mathematics concept provides strong evidence for mathematical justification.

Students' Understanding on Why a Particular Mathematical Statement Is True

CCSSM (NGA Center and CCSSO 2010) proposes that students should interpret a statement in different situations to judge the truth of that statement, since mathematical statements can be either true or false. For example, the mathematical statement "Multiplication always increases a number" could be either true or false depending on the definition of the number. When the number is defined as a natural number, this statement holds true, as the original number always becomes larger when multiplied by another natural number. In the example $3 \times 5 = 15$, we can apply the concept of sets to solve the multiplication equation with natural numbers. This model is analogous to the one that we used for addition, since we are only adding repeatedly. It shows that $3 + 3 + 3 + 3 + 3 = 15$, or 5 groups of 3 equals 15 ($5 \times 3 = 15$). Also, in this case, multiplication by a whole positive number certainly increases a number.

However, under certain conditions, the statement will be false, given that there is a key distinction concerning the product that emerges from multiplying by a whole number and the product that emerges from multiplying by a fraction. "When we multiply by a whole number greater than 1, the product is greater than the second number being multiplied. However, when we multiply by a fraction less than 1, the product is less than the second number being multiplied" (Bennett and Nelson 2011, p. 308). When it comes to fractions, the original number decreases when it is multiplied by another fraction that is less than 1. As shown in figure 21.2, we do not use the concept of repeated addition to solve this multiplication equation with fractions. The product $2/5 \times 14/15$ means $2/5$ of $14/15$. The shaded part of the second rectangle represents $28/75$, showing the original number decreases when multiplied by a fraction because the fraction is less than 1. Thus, students need to understand that when multiplying by a fraction greater than 1, the product increases and when multiplying by a fraction less than 1, the product decreases.

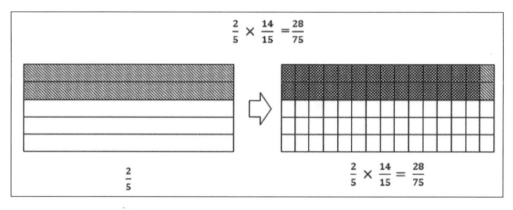

Fig. 21.2. Product of a fraction multiplied by a fraction

Students' Understanding of Where a Mathematical Rule Comes From

According to CCSSM (NGA Center and CCSSO 2010), "the student who can explain the rule understands the mathematics, and may have a better chance to succeed at a less familiar task" (p. 4). For instance, assume that that we will teach division of fractions containing different denominators as illustrated by $2/5 \div 14/15$. Students who know the mathematical rule for division of fractions may find the answer for the expression based on procedural skills: finding the reciprocal of the second fraction, multiplying the numerators to obtain the new numerator, and multiplying the denominators to obtain the new denominator, as shown in figure 21.3, example A. When students only demonstrate procedural skills, they might not understand why they need to find the reciprocal of the second fraction or the basic concept of division but could still find the answer by memorizing the process.

Example A

$$\frac{2}{5} \div \frac{14}{15} = \frac{2}{5} \times \frac{15}{14} = \frac{2 \times 15}{5 \times 14} = \frac{30}{70} = \frac{3}{7}$$

Reciprocal of the second fraction

Example B

$$\frac{2}{5} \div \frac{14}{15} = \frac{\frac{2}{5}}{\frac{14}{15}} = \frac{\frac{2}{5} \times \frac{15}{14}}{\frac{14}{15} \times \frac{15}{14}} = \frac{\frac{2}{5} \times \frac{15}{14}}{1} = \frac{2}{5} \times \frac{15}{14} = \frac{30}{70} = \frac{3}{7}$$

Fig. 21.3. Students' processes of division of fractions

On the other hand, students who have an understanding of where the mathematical rule comes from may solve the problem in a different way, as shown in figure 21.3, example B. Students who have an understanding regarding the process of the division of fractions may know why they need to multiply the reciprocal of the second fraction. When we denote the answer as above, $2/5$ is the numerator, and the second fraction $14/15$ is the denominator. The students should understand that the value of the fraction would not change when multiplying both the numerator and denominator by the same number. Students who know that the denominator may be omitted when it is equal to 1 understand that we multiply the numerators to arrive at a new numerator and multiply the denominators to arrive at a new denominator, as shown in figure 21.3. Then, students might see the *invert and multiply rule* for dividing fractions as a shortcut.

Although we considered three categories of mathematical understanding according to the definition by CCSSM (NGA Center and CCSSO 2010), we acknowledge that the three categories may not be independent of one another. Students may not understand why a particular mathematical statement is true without the ability to justify each mathematical statement. Similarly, students may not be able to justify their mathematical ideas or processes of solving mathematics problems without knowing where a mathematical rule comes from. That is, these three categories are intertwined when considering students' mathematical understanding. Thus, assessment of each category should be closely connected to the others. Moreover, we believe that this framework is relevant to students' mathematical learning and understanding. It calls for an approach to teaching, learning, and assessing that requires continual reconstruction of classroom teaching and assessment practices. The challenge for teachers is to fully realize the practical applications inherent in CCSSM.

■ Results of Analysis

This section consists of the three major categories discussed in the previous section. We present the results of the analysis of 203 teacher-developed assessment items, which are presented in table 21.1. Two of the categories, *the ability to justify* and *understanding of why a particular mathematical statement is true* are classified into two subgroups. For example, the category the ability to justify consists of the subgroups *justifying mathematical thinking through mental representations* and *justifying mental representations using mental networks*. To broaden our understanding of these specific assessment items, excerpts from interviews are provided, along with one or two representative samples of each category or subgroup. All assessment items were translated from Korean to English, and the names of all the teachers mentioned are pseudonyms.

Table 21.1
Mathematical understanding assessment items per category

Categories	Classification of Subgroups within a Category	Number of Assessment Items
Students' Ability to Justify	Justifying mathematical thinking through mental representations	35
	Justifying mental representations using mental networks by comparing similarities and differences with other mathematics concepts	31
Students' Understanding Why a Particular Mathematical Statement Is True	Making mathematical judgments about real-world situations	36
	Describing what makes a given statement true using different mathematical situations and representations	40
Students' Understanding of Where a Mathematical Rule Comes From*	_____	61
Total		203

Note: Classifications of subgroup within this category were not found.

Assessment Items on Students' Abilities to Justify

For the category of *the ability to justify*, the teachers developed items that called for students to use mental representations and mental network. We apply Skemp's (1989) idea that mathematical understanding includes the relationship made among mental representations and concepts.

Justifying and Using Mental Representations

The teachers developed assessment items to provide opportunities for students to justify their mathematical thinking through mental representations. Figure 21.4 is an illustration of how first graders used appropriate mathematical representations to justify their answer. The student used a pictorial model to represent the numbers 5 and 3 and then compared the numbers of circles, concluding that 5 is greater than 3.

Question. Compare the following two numbers. Which one is larger (greater)? Show how you solved it.

5 , 3

A Student's Answer and Justification:
I draw circles in order to represent each number.

5   ○ ○ ○ ○ ○   3   ○ ○ ○

As you can see, there are two more circles for the number 5 than the number 3. Therefore, 5 is larger than 3.

Fig. 21.4. A grade 1 student's example of using a mathematical representation

One purpose of this item was to provide students the opportunity to explain why one number is larger than another. This was the beginning instruction for inequality of whole numbers, involving discrete quantities. Mrs. Jeong explained that her students were not familiar with this type of item and worried about them having to consider several concepts at once, such as students attempting to develop an understanding of inequality of whole numbers using both discrete and continuous quantities. Although the example illustrated in figure 21.4 models discrete quantities, Mrs. Jeong's explanation focused on students' modeling of continuous quantities. She explained, "If I ask students which is a longer period of time, 5 minutes or 3 minutes, then students need to consider the concept of continuous quantities and should use a mathematical model that shows continuous quantities, such as a number line. I need to let them become familiar first with these types of assessment items over time." Mrs. Jeong's explanation implies that it is essential to provide students with mathematical experiences that involve both discrete and continuous quantities but these types of experiences should develop gradually. Also, her explanation suggests that students need experience in providing explanations that clarify their justifications. A further insight is that students may present stronger mathematical reasoning that explains how to use mental representations by connecting them to concepts and procedures they already understand (National Research Council 2001).

For the item presented in figure 21.5, the goal was not just for students to reduce (or simplify) the fraction but to assess their understanding by allowing them to manipulate a given mathematical representation. Mr. Kim's purpose was to assess students' understanding "beyond traditional paper-based assessment that requires students to find a common denominator. I want to assess students' understanding of why we need common denominators and the meaning of dividing the numerator and denominator." Therefore, Mr. Kim recognized that representations are a central element for developing critical thinking and conceptual understanding of mathematics content (Pape 2003; Steele and Johanning 2004). Mr. Kim explained further, "Although this student may not have explained the concept exactly, she at least proves that she knows the meaning of reduction. When I used the traditional assessment item, more than 80 percent of my students got the correct answer. However, after I changed the items [to draw out student justification], less than 50 percent of students could solve the problem illustrating an appropriate process."

Question. Reduce the fractions to a common denominator, and show your process of how you solved it.

A Student's Answer and Justification.
In order to reduce the fraction, I looked for a group, which has the same number of hearts. The group represents the common denominator. Thus, I made a group as follows.

I found that there are 2 groups of two hearts in the numerator, and 3 groups of two hearts in the denominator. Therefore, the answer is, $\frac{2}{3}$.

Fig. 21.5. A grade 5 student's explanation of simplifying a fraction

Justifying and Using Mental Networks

As noted previously, students might justify their mental representation by comparing similarities and differences with other mathematics concepts. Therefore, teacher-developed assessment items can be used to gather information about students' understanding of the relationship among mathematical representations. In this respect, the South Korean elementary teachers developed assessment items to assess students' abilities to justify using mental networks. The representative assessment is shown in figure 21.6.

Mrs. Choi, who developed this assessment item, noted, "The largest benefit of these types of items is to provide food for thought to students regarding the relationship among mathematics concepts. Some students believe they should memorize the definitions of mathematics concepts, thinking the concepts will never change. However, this is not true." When probed for more information, Mrs. Choi explained, "I believe students needed practice thinking differently about relationships among mathematics concepts, and this type of item can help students improve their mathematical understanding regarding the relationship among mathematics concepts."

Assessment Items on Why a Particular Mathematical Statement Is True

The teachers developed items that encouraged students to articulate explanations that supported their arguments about particular mathematical statements. The examples presented in this section show real-world situations that assess students' ability to judge why a particular mathematical statement is true and also assess if students are able to describe a mathematical situation that would make a statement true.

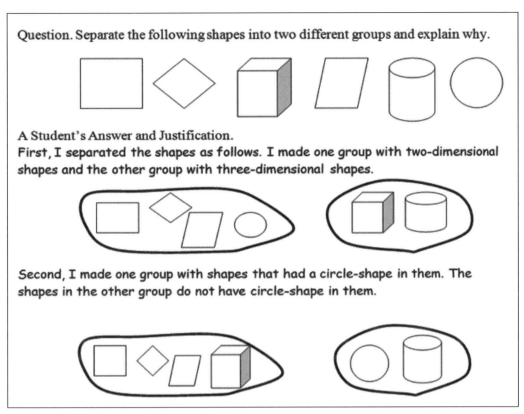

Fig. 21.6. A grade 6 student's justifying using mental networks

Real-World Situations about Why a Particular Mathematical Statement is True

Mathematical statements can be either true or false in different real-world situations because the mathematical context changes. Thus, teacher-developed assessment items provide opportunities for students to make mathematical judgments about context specific problems. The item shown in figure 21.7 considers students' ability to interpret a mathematical statement grounded in a real-world problem. Mr. Ki, who developed this item, explained his intention, stating, "Students should realize that they can use mathematics concepts selectively according to the real-life situation. This type of assessment item will help students understand that the answer might be different according to the situation." After pausing for a moment, Mr. Ki continued, stating, "When I developed this item, I used the term *mathematical error* intentionally. My students [need to] realize that there can be mathematical errors if they misinterpret a mathematical situation."

Description of What Makes a Given Statement True

Students should know how to interpret mathematical representations in diverse mathematical relationships that include providing justification of how they solved mathematics problems. The teachers argued that students should understand different mathematical situations and use appropriate representations. Mr. Lee suggested, "Usually, by asking them to develop a mathematics problem with a given representation, we can assess students' interpretation of the mathematical representation" (see fig. 21.8). Mr. Lee also stated that he saw changes in his mathematics classroom with these assessment items. "When I used traditional assessment items, students would not listen to my explanations. They believed they would be okay if they knew how to find the answer. However, when I changed the items, my students knew that they needed to listen carefully and to participate in classroom discussions actively."

Question. Read the statement below to see if it contains a mathematical error for rounding numbers (up or down). Please explain your thinking.

Statement. A farmer in Daegu sells apples by putting 10 apples into a box. The farmer prepared 5 boxes in order to sell 49 apples.

A Student' Answer and Interpretation.
I think that the statement has mathematical errors. The farmer did round up the number of apples in order to put them into a box. However, I believe that the farmer should round down, since a box of 9 apples will not be sold. Thus, the farm needs 4 boxes instead of 5 boxes.

Fig. 21.7. A grade 3 student's example of a real-world situation

---

Question. Write your own mathematics problem that can be solved using the following mathematical representation.

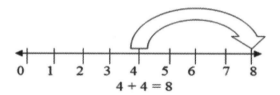

$$4 + 4 = 8$$

A Student' Answer.
There are 4 liters of water in the bucket. I add 4 liters more into the bucket. How many liters of water are in the bucket?

Fig. 21.8. A grade 3 student's example of interpretation of a mathematical representation

Students' Understanding of Where a Mathematical Rule Comes From

The teachers found that one of the best ways to assess students' understanding of where a mathematical rule comes from is to ask students how they obtained the mathematical rule. The example shown in figure 21.9 demonstrates how teachers might assess students' understanding. It shows the work of a grade 4 student. Mrs. Yang, who developed this assessment item, reasoned, "If we keep asking students to calculate the area of a parallelogram, we will probably never know whether they really understand where the formula or rule comes from. I believe that the core of mathematics is not to find the right answer to the problem, but to think logically in order to reach a better conclusion. Instead of asking what is the value *of*, ask how can we find 3.14." This teacher's reflection suggests that she came to realize that "Mathematical understanding and procedural skill are equally important, and both are assessable using mathematical tasks of sufficient richness" (NGA Center and CCSSO 2010, p. 4).

Question. Kim set up the equation in order to calculate the area of a trapezoid. Why do you think Kim put ÷ 2 in the equation?

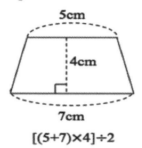

$$[(5+7)\times4]\div2$$

A Student's Answer
If I combine two of the same trapezoids, it will looks like a parallelogram.

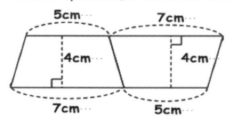

We calculate the area of the parallelogram by multiplying (7cm + 5cm) times 4cm. However, we need to divide the area by 2, since we used two of the same trapezoids. The area of the trapezoid is ½ of the area of the parallelogram.

Fig. 21.9. A Grade 4 student's example of where a mathematical rule comes from

How Did Assessing for Understanding Influence Teachers' Practices?

Designing tasks or items to assess mathematical understanding might influence the instructional practices of teachers in several ways. Teachers can use the evidence of students' mathematical understanding to improve their instructional practices or to document effective teaching (Popham 2008). "The more teachers know about students' levels of understanding, the more effective and targeted [their] instruction can be" (Oberdorf and Taylor-Cox 2012, p. 5). From the interviews of the participating teachers, it seems that they learned that the assessment tasks or items could provide worthwhile evidence of students' knowledge and understanding about a particular concept. The teachers recognized that preparing students to provide rich explanations or justifications to express their mathematical understanding of a rule, procedure, or process required engaging learners in continual practice and experience. Additionally, a key element in the development of mathematical understanding is the use of representation. "As students communicate and represent mathematics in forms other than symbolic ones, they provide the teacher with insight into their emergent understandings. Such insights can help the teacher modify instruction so that learning occurs" (Thompson and Chappell 2007, p. 195).

Although CCSSM's definition of mathematical understanding appeared to be a worthwhile framework in which to analyze assessment items generated by South Korean elementary teachers, we believe that, in general, this framework can help teachers develop and apply assessment tasks in a variety of instructional environments, considering three key expectations. First, the work does not end after students have finished the assessment task or item; rather, a practical understanding would be that the work is an ongoing process, which helps teachers identify the knowledge and understanding students bring to the learning process. Second, a core expectation is that "students' [mathematical] understanding emerges in a continual cycle, one that always highlights the ways in which students are constructing knowledge" (Albert 2002, p. 72). The third expectation is that as a result of instructional practices, teachers can broaden their understanding of how students use representations to construct mathematical understanding. Considering these expectations together illustrate why engaging students in assessment tasks that inform teaching practices is a valuable and important effort that should be studied not only by South Korean elementary teachers, but also by teachers globally, including teachers in the United States.

■ Conclusion and Implications

In this chapter, we analyzed the work of South Korean elementary teachers based on a framework grounded in CCSSM's (NGA Center and CCSSO 2010) definition of mathematical understanding, which included the ability to justify, understanding of why a particular mathematical statement is true, and understanding of where a mathematical rule comes from. We presented different types of teacher-developed items to assess students' mathematical understanding. The teachers' overarching purpose was to use the assessment items to advance their students' understanding of challenging mathematical concepts. Placing emphasis on worthwhile and meaningful assessment items may encourage students to give sufficient reasons for why a procedure, process, solution, or representation is appropriate.

As the teachers analyzed and interpreted their students' responses, they were able to make sense of students' mathematical understanding and progress. Therefore, they gained valuable insights regarding how to improve their instructional practices. Thus, an implication is that designing mathematics assessment items in which the focus is mathematical understanding *may* serve as a catalyst for improving mathematics instructional practices. "To become an integral part of the instructional process, assessment cannot be a one-shot, do-or-die experience for students. Instead, assessments must be part of an ongoing effort to help students learn" (Guskey 2003, p. 10). This view of assessment suggests that teachers can learn by studying students' mathematical understanding to transform instructional strategies or practices. Additionally, assessment of mathematics understanding, as a part of instruction, should lead student learning in the mathematics classroom. Assessment should consider the content students know and take into account the degree of their understanding, which includes their ability to connect concepts and apply their understanding of these concepts to new mathematical situations. In conclusion, the assessment tasks discussed exemplify that teachers may experience a similar path, as illustrated by the South Korean elementary teachers, when they develop and analyze assessment tasks that promote student mathematical understanding.

References

Albert, Lillie R. "Bridging the Achievement Gap in Mathematics: Sociocultural Historic Theory and Dynamic Cognitive Assessment." *Journal of Thought* 37 (2002): 65–81.

Bennett, Albert B., and L. Ted Nelson. *Mathematics for Elementary Teachers: A Conceptual Approach*. Boston: McGraw Hill, 2011.

Cai, Jinfa. "U.S. and Chinese Teachers' Constructing, Knowing, and Evaluating Representations to Teach Mathematics." *Mathematical Thinking and Learning: An International Journal* 7 (2005): 135–69.

Collins, Anne. *Using Classroom Assessment to Improve Student Learning: Math Problems Aligned with NCTM and Common Core State Standards*, Reston, Va.: National Council of Teacher of Mathematics, 2011.

DeWolf, Melisa, Miriam Bassok, and Keith. J. Holyoak. "Analogical Reasoning with Rational Numbers: Semantic Alignment Based on Discrete Versus Continuous Quantities." In *Proceedings of the 35th Annual Conference of the Cognitive Science Society,* edited by Markus Knauff, Michael Pauen, Natalie Sebanz, and Ipke Wachsmuth, pp. 388–98. Austin, Tex.: Cognitive Science Society, 2013.

Gronlund, Norman. E. *Assessment of Student Achievement.* 8th ed. Boston: Allyn and Bacon, 2006.

Guskey, Thomas R. "How Classroom Assessments Improve Learning." *Educational Leadership* 60, no. 5 (2003): 6–11.

Kim, Rina, and Lillie R. Albert. *Mathematics Teaching and Learning: South Korean Elementary Teachers' Knowledge for Teaching Mathematics,* New York: Springer, in press.

Kramarsk, Brach, and Zemira R. Mervarech. "Enhancing Mathematical Reasoning in the Classroom: The Effects of Cooperative Learning and Metacognitive Training." *American Educational Research Journal* 40 (2003): 281–301.

National Council of Teachers of Mathematics (NCTM). *Principles to Actions: Ensuring Mathematical Success for All.* Reston, Va.: NCTM, 2014.

National Governors Association Center for Best Practices and Council of Chief State School Officers (NGA Center and CCSSO). *Common Core State Standards for Mathematics.* Washington, D.C.: NGA Center and CCSSO, 2010.

National Research Council (NRC). *Adding It Up: Helping Children Learn Mathematics,* edited by Jeremy Kilpatrick, Jane Swaffold, and Bradford Findell. Washington, D.C.: National Academies Press, 2001.

Oberdorf, Christine, and Jennifer Taylor-Cox. *Using Formative Assessment Drives Common Core Mathematics, Pre–K–5.* New York: Eye on Education, 2012.

Pape, Stephen J. "Compare Word Problems: Consistency Hypothesis Revisited." *Contemporary Educational Psychology* 2, no. 8 (2003): 396–421.

Phelan, Julia, Kilchan Choi, Terry Vendlinski, Eva Baker, and Joan Herman. "Differential Improvement in Student Understanding of Mathematical Principles Following Formative Assessment Intervention." *Journal of Educational Research* 104 (2011): 330–39.

Popham, W. J. *Transformative Assessment*. Alexandria, Va.: Association for Supervision and Curriculum Development, 2008.

Russell, Michael. K., and Peter W Airasian. *Classroom Assessment, Concepts and Applications.* 7th ed. Dubuque, Iowa: McGraw Hill, 2012.

Skemp, Richard R. *Mathematics in the Primary School*. London: Routledge. 1989.

Steele, Diana F., and Debra I. Johanning. "A Schematic-Theoretic View of Problem Solving and Development of Algebraic Thinking." *Education Studies in Mathematics* 57 (2004): 65–90.

Talbert, Robert. "What Makes a Good Mathematical Justification?" *Chronicle of Higher Education,* November 25, 2006. http://chronicle.com/blognetwork/castingoutnines/2006/11/25/what-makes-a-good-mathematical-justification/.

Thompson, Denisse R., and Michaele F. Chappell. "Communication and Representation as Elements in Mathematical Literacy." *Reading & Writing Quarterly* 23 (2007): 179–96.

Assessment: A Powerful Focus for the Improvement of Mathematics Instruction

Dylan Wiliam, *University College London*

Students do not learn what we teach. It is this simple, empirically demonstrable, but rather inconvenient, fact that makes assessment such an important aspect of teaching. If our students learned what we taught, assessment would be unnecessary. We could simply document what we had taught, secure in the knowledge that what our students knew was faithfully recorded in our teaching logs. However, as every teacher knows, what our students learn as a result of any particular piece of instruction is impossible to predict with any certainty (Denvir and Brown 1986a, 1986b). Only by assessing our students can we be sure that the instruction we have planned and implemented has had the intended outcome. Without assessment, we might as well be speaking our lessons into a video camera relayed to students in another classroom. That is why assessment really is the "bridge" between teaching and learning.

As Lee Cronbach has pointed out, assessment is really nothing more than a procedure for making inferences (Cronbach 1971). We engage students in certain activities, as a result of which we elicit evidence, on the basis of which we draw conclusions. These inferences are sometimes about the students themselves, sometimes about the effectiveness of curricula, and sometimes about the adequacy of instruction offered by a district, a state, or even a country.

Shifting our attention from the assessments to the inferences that they allow us to make is important because the shift in perspective makes many issues in assessment much simpler to think about. For many years, validity was thought of as a property of a test—a test was thought to be valid to the extent that it assessed what it purported to test. This definition dates back to at least the 1930s (Garrett 1937) although it is also frequently used today (see, for example, International Reading Association and National Council of Teachers of English 2010). However, trying to make validity a property of a test quickly leads to absurdities.

For example, if we have a mathematics test that has a high reading demand, then it may be a valid test for good readers; but for students with weaker reading skills, it is impossible to know whether low scores indicate poor mathematics knowledge or poor reading skills. The same test would be more valid for some students than others. Even with the same group of students, an assessment may be valid for some purpose but not others.

Another area where shifting attention to inferences, rather than assessments, is helpful is in thinking about formative and summative assessment—a theme running throughout the chapters of this book.

As with the idea of validity, some authors have applied the formative-summative distinction to the assessments themselves—they talk about formative assessments and summative assessments in the plural. The difficulty with such a formulation is that the same assessment can be used both formatively and summatively. For example, if a teacher assigns a class a test and scores the students' responses, that will provide information about which students have learned the material being tested and which have not. If all that happens is that the scores get recorded in a grade book, then the test would presumably be functioning summatively.

It is important to note that such a process can increase student achievement. There is now a substantial body of research that shows that simply testing students regularly increases achievement (Brown, Roediger III, and McDaniel 2014). However, even though students might learn more from regular testing, it does not seem appropriate to call this process "formative" for the simple reason that the assessment does not "form" the future direction of their learning (indeed, the benefits of practice testing occur even if the test is never scored).

If, on the other hand, results are fed back to students, then that would be likely to have a greater effect on learning, and if students were told the correct answers that might have a still greater effect (two scenarios that psychologists call "knowledge of results" and "knowledge of correct results" feedback, respectively). The test scores would also indicate to the teacher which students need additional support, allowing the teacher to direct help to the students who need it most. By helping the teacher make a smarter decision about the allocation of her time, the test results would "form" the direction of the students' learning. Even better, the assessment might help the teacher provide more specific feedback to the student. If, for example, the teacher noticed that a student consistently completed multi-digit subtractions by subtracting the smaller digit from the larger, whether it was in the minuend or the subtrahend, this would give the teacher some ideas about what to say to the student. The same assessment, therefore, can serve both a summative purpose (e.g., evaluating the student's arithmetic skills) and a formative one (providing feedback to the students, and suggesting to the teacher what to do next).

So, in the same way that validity is best thought of not as a property of assessments, but of the inferences they support, then the distinction between formative and summative is best thought of as a classification of the kinds of inferences that are made on the basis of the evidence generated by the assessments. Where the inferences are related to the student's current level of achievement, or to their future performance, then the assessment is serving a summative function. Where the inferences are related to the kinds of instructional activities that are likely to maximize future learning, then the assessment is functioning formatively. We may still talk about "formative assessments" in the plural, but it is important to understand that this is just a convenient shorthand for "assessments designed to yield evidence that can be used formatively."

Of course, the same assessment evidence may support both kinds of inferences, but in general, assessments that are designed to support summative inferences (that is, inferences about current or future levels of achievement) are not particularly well-suited to supporting formative inferences (that is, inferences about instructional next steps). It is, in general, easier to say where a student is in his or her learning than what should be done next. It might be assumed that assessment designed primarily to serve a formative function would require, as a prerequisite, a detailed specification of the current level of achievement, but this does not necessarily hold. It is entirely possible that the assessment might identify a range of possible current states of achievement that nevertheless indicate a single best course of future action—we might not know where the student is, but we know what he or she needs to do next.

■ Defining Formative Assessment

Different authors have proposed different definitions of formative assessment over the years. Michael Scriven, who first proposed the formative-summative distinction, intended that it be applied only to the evaluation of curriculum (Scriven 1967). It was Benjamin Bloom who extended the idea to student assessment (Bloom 1969). Some have argued that the term "formative assessment" has lost its meaning and argue for "assessment for learning" as a better phrase (Broadfoot et al. 1999), while others have argued that this just moves the definitional burden somewhere else and also clouds the essence of the distinction (Bennett 2011).

In particular, different authors disagree about how much time can elapse between evidence collection and its impact on instruction, whether it is necessary for the students from whom the evidence was collected to be direct beneficiaries of the process, whether students have to be actively engaged in the process, and whether the evidence actually has to impact instruction (see Wiliam and Leahy [2015] for an extended discussion). While these issues are certainly important in terms of determining how effective formative assessment is likely to be, there would seem to be little to gain by adopting restrictive definitions of formative assessment that include some people's views on formative assessment and exclude those of others.

In order to move the debate onto more productive ground, it seems more sensible to define formative assessment in as broad and inclusive a way as possible, and then to focus on what, precisely, gets formed by the formative assessment process. In an attempt to do this, Black and Wiliam (2009) defined assessment as being formative—

> to the extent that evidence about student achievement is elicited, interpreted, and used by teachers, learners, or their peers, to make decisions about the next steps in instruction that are likely to be better, or better founded, than the decisions they would have taken in the absence of the evidence that was elicited. (p. 9)

One important feature of this definition is that the focus is on decisions rather than data. Over recent years, increasing attention has been given to the idea of "data-driven decision making"; but as Carney and colleagues point out in chapter 19 of this volume, it is important to plan questions with a range of potential actions in mind—a process that could be described as "decision-driven data collection." More precisely, it would be even better described as "decision-driven evidence collection" because, as Wainer (2011) points out, "Evidence is data related to a claim" (p. 148). Without some potential claim or inference, data is just data; it becomes evidence when it acquires a specific meaning. That is why just collecting instructional data in the hope that it might come in useful at some point is unlikely to lead to effective action. The data has to be collected with a view to how it will be interpreted and used.

■ Formative Assessment in This Volume

There are a number of consequences of Black and Wiliam's definition of formative assessment that are relevant to the chapters in this volume. One is that formative assessment is independent of any choice about what it is that students should be learning, or how. Formative assessment does require that one is clear about what it is that students are to learn, but it does not impose a particular view of the mathematics curriculum, nor does it entail any particular view of what happens when learning takes place.

For example, chapter 2 by Bay-Williams and Kling explores the power of formative assessment for the learning of number facts, while chapter 18 by Scherrer focuses on formative assessment within a situated perspective on learning. As Sfard (1998) has pointed out, we are likely to make far more progress in understanding the learning of mathematics if we accept the value of both of these perspectives. For those who focus on mathematical knowledge as being "inside the head," we need to explain why transfer from one context to another is so difficult. For those who emphasize learning mathematics as increasing participation in communities of practice (Lave and Wenger 1991) there is the challenge of explaining what Eugene Wigner called "the unreasonable effectiveness of mathematics" (Wigner 1960)—the idea that "mathematical concepts turn up in entirely unexpected connections . . . [and] often permit an unexpectedly close and accurate description of the phenomena in these connections" (p. 2).

A second consequence of this definition is that no particular timescale is specified for the assessment to function formatively. Many of the chapters discuss relatively short-cycle formative assessments such as classroom observation of students doing mathematics (Young-Loveridge and Bicknell [chapter 6]; Fennell, Kobett, and Wray [chapter 5]), but as chapter 17 by Rankin shows, analyses over longer timescales can also be useful in improving instruction and student achievement.

A third consequence of the definition is that formative assessment is defined in a completely generic way. The advantage of such an approach is that it can provide a clear focus for all the teachers in a school to work in a coherent way on their practice, rather than having the social studies teachers pursuing one initiative and the mathematics teacher another. It also provides consistency for students from lesson to lesson, so that they see the same processes being used in different subjects. However, despite what some (e.g., Bennett 2011; Coffey et al. 2011) have claimed, this does not mean that formative assessment does not have important domain-specific aspects. Indeed, shortly after the article "Inside the Black Box" (Black and Wiliam 1998) was published, separate publications drawing out the implications of the research for mathematics teachers were produced (Wiliam 1999a, 1999b, 2000). What makes a good question in math will be very different from what makes a good question in social studies, and chapter 1 by Silver and Smith clearly illustrates the value of allying the pedagogical practices of formative assessment with cognitively demanding mathematics tasks.

Many of the chapters in this volume address issues related to the five strategies of formative assessment proposed by Leahy and colleagues (2005). These strategies are discussed in detail by Fennell, Kobett, and Wray (chapter 5) and by Marynowski (chapter 15). Chapter 13 by Rigelman as well as chapter 8 by Elrod and Strayer highlight an important issue with regard to the strategy of "clarifying, sharing and understanding learning intentions and success criteria," namely, the issue of whether learning intentions and associated success criteria should focus on the *processes* students should use in completing the assigned task or on the qualities of the final *product*.

Providing guidance on processes that will lead to success can provide support to students, but such support also tends to make it less likely that students find creative solutions of their own. The chapter by Elrod and Strayer also highlights a particular issue with scoring rubrics; as Michael Polanyi has pointed out, they often do not have the same meanings to novices that they do to experts (Polanyi 1958). It is often more helpful to regard rubrics as encapsulations of the shared understandings that exist when students are enculturated into the communities of practice of which their teachers are already members.

To this end, Bleiler and colleagues (chapter 9) highlight the power of involving students in the construction of assessment rubrics—what is sometimes called a process of "co-construction." When students are engaged in the process of developing the success criteria, whether in the form of a rubric or some other format, the problem identified by Polanyi is substantially avoided because the students' understanding is anchored in the work that gave rise to the rubric, rather than the rubric itself. Effective summative assessment requires teachers to form a "community of practice" (Lave and Wenger 1991) with regard to achievement (so that they would give the same grade to a particular piece of work). Effective formative assessment requires enculturating the students into the same community of practice so that they come to understand the standards against which their work will be assessed. As Royce Sadler (1989) once said:

> The indispensable conditions for improvement are that the student comes to hold a concept of quality roughly similar to that held by the teacher, is able to monitor continuously the quality of what is being produced during the act of production itself, and has a repertoire of alternative moves or strategies from which to draw at any given point. In other words, students have to be able to judge the quality of what they are producing and be able to regulate what they are doing during the doing of it. (p. 121)

■ Choosing Tasks and Establishing Progressions

As a number of the chapters in this volume make clear, choosing the tasks that will be used to find out what students have learned is far from straightforward. Many studies have shown that, too often, teachers choose tasks that assess only surface features (see, for example, Black et al. 2010). Of course, as noted above, this is not in itself a bad thing. If the curriculum consisted only of surface features of mathematics, with students being asked to undertake mathematical procedures but not explain them, then this would be internally consistent. However, such an approach is not consistent with any curriculum that would lead students toward mastery of the Common Core State Standards. This is why teachers need support, and this is why the "unpacking" of what it means to understand mathematically presented by Albert and Kim (chapter 21), as well as the framework provided in chapter 11 by Hunsader, Thompson, and Zorin, are so helpful in supporting teachers to envision what might be possible in terms of student outcomes and the assessment of those outcomes. The same issues are raised by Sears and colleagues in chapter 7. They show that the assessment examples included in geometry textbooks, no matter how faithfully they are implemented in the classroom, are simply incapable of generating evidence that support inferences about important and valued aspects of mathematical performance.

A related issue with regard to task selection is identified by Slavit and Nelson (chapter 4) and by Rigelman (chapter 13), and that is whether the tasks we select can be relied upon to generate the evidence that we seek as teachers. In other words, can we be sure that "If they know it, they show it"—what I have termed elsewhere as the "disclosure" of an assessment (Wiliam 1992). As Rigelman makes clear, this is a particular issue in open-ended mathematical tasks. If we devolve to the students the responsibility for negotiating their own way through the task, they may find a way of completing the task quite successfully in their own terms, without using the mathematics the teacher intended. There is no simple resolution of this tension, but as Rigelman points out, if the students understand the criteria of mathematical quality that have been adopted, then they are more likely to be able to ensure that their work shows what mathematics they are capable of.

Two chapters—chapter 20 by Gearhart and colleagues and chapter 3 by Kim and Lehrer—show how formative assessment can be enhanced by the adoption of learning progressions. In a traditional model of assessment, students are told whether they achieved a particular outcome or not. When assessment is conducted relative to a learning progression, students learn where they are on the progression. Even if the assessment itself does not indicate the next steps in learning, the fact that the student's current achievement is located at some point along a learning progression provides a clear indication of "where next?"

■ Changing Practice

Of course, ultimately, all of the above issues will be moot unless teachers embrace these ideas and change their classroom practice—an issue that several of the chapters in this volume address. One issue is resistance by teachers. When teachers hear about the power of classroom formative assessment to engage students and improve instruction, a common response is, "I'd love to teach in this way, but I have to raise my test scores." There is a widespread belief that teaching well is somehow incompatible with raising test scores. However, as chapter 16 by Walcott and colleagues demonstrates at the very least, the use of constructed-response—rather than multiple-choice—questions is associated with higher student scores on the National Assessment of Educational Progress (NAEP). It doesn't look like teachers have to choose.

Even when teachers want to change practice, there is now clear evidence that they cannot do so quickly. One of the important findings of early work on supporting teachers in their development of classroom formative assessment was that it was difficult, if not impossible, to change what teachers were doing in classrooms without also changing what students where doing (Black et al. 2003). As Dempsey and colleagues make clear in chapter 14, teachers often initially focus on their own role in the process, but typically they quickly come to see that changes are also needed in the role of students too. Specifically in terms of the last two strategies of formative assessment identified by Leahy et al. (2005) it is important to activate students as learning resources for one another and to activate students as owners of their own learning.

One of the reasons why, at least in the United States, so much effort has been invested in the long-cycle and medium-cycle formative assessment is that, in general, it is much harder to change what teachers do when students are present than it is to change what teachers do when students are not present, because changing what teachers do in classrooms is essentially a process of habit change (Heath and Heath 2010). However, as Lee and colleagues show in chapter 12, practicing responses with other teachers provides teachers with the confidence to try out some of these practices. A particularly important observation in this chapter is the need for a shift from a "theory to practice" view of teacher professional development to one of "practice to theory." Teaching is a physical, embodied task, and too often we ignore the fact that much of the knowledge teachers bring to the task of teaching is tacit rather than explicit. As a number of writers have observed over the years, in many issues it is often easier to get people to act their way into a new way of thinking than it is to get them to think their way into a new way of acting. That said, it is also sometimes important to create drivers of change, and getting teachers to think about their practice can be especially helpful here; the pencil-and-paper assessments of "mathematical habits of mind" described by Sword and colleagues in chapter 10 are an important contribution.

Rather, therefore, than debating whether we should be using a theory to practice model or a practice-to-theory model for teacher professional development, it might be more appropriate to think of the process as a theory to practice to theory to practice to theory to practice model, in a never-ending cycle. Ultimately, there may always be a "knowing-doing" gap, as Dempsey and colleagues (chapter 14) describe in their Assessment Work Sample Method. Unless teachers experience some disconnect between what is and what might be, the incentives for change are reduced. What this volume shows is that assessment can provide a powerful focus to generate theoretical insights into, and practical ideas for the improvement of, mathematics teachers' practice.

References

Bennett, Randy Elliot. "Formative Assessment: A Critical Review." *Assessment in Education: Principles Policy and Practice* 18, no. 1 (2011): 5–25.

Black, Paul, Chris Harrison, Jeremy Hodgen, Bethan Marshall, and Natasha Serret. "Validity in Teachers' Summative Assessments." *Assessment in Education: Principles, Policy and Practice* 17, no. 2 (2010): 215–32.

Black, Paul, Chris Harrison, Clare Lee, Bethan Marshall, and Dylan Wiliam. *Assessment for Learning: Putting It into Practice*. Buckingham, U.K.: Open University Press, 2003.

Black, Paul, and Dylan Wiliam. "Inside the Black Box: Raising Standards through Classroom Assessment." *Phi Delta Kappan* 80, no. 2 (1998): 139–48.

————. "Developing the Theory of Formative Assessment." *Educational Assessment, Evaluation and Accountability* 21, no. 1 (2009): 5–31.

Bloom, Benjamin S. "Some Theoretical Issues Relating to Educational Evaluation." In *Educational Evaluation: New Roles, New Means: The 68th Yearbook of the National Society for the Study of Education (Part II)*, edited by R. W. Tyler. Vol. 68, no. 2, pp. 26–50. Chicago: University of Chicago Press, 1969.

Broadfoot, Patricia M., Richard Daugherty, John Gardner, Caroline V. Gipps, Wynne Harlen, Mary James, and Gordon Stobart. *Assessment for Learning: Beyond the Black Box*. Cambridge, U.K.: University of Cambridge School of Education, 1999.

Brown, Peter C., Henry L. Roediger III, and Mark A. McDaniel. *Make It Stick: The Science of Successful Learning*. Cambridge, Mass.: Belknap Press, 2014.

Coffey, Janet E., David Hammer, Daniel M. Levin, and Terrance Grant. "The Missing Disciplinary Substance of Formative Assessment." *Journal of Research in Science Teaching* 48 (2011): 1109–36.

Cronbach, Lee J. "Test Validation." In *Educational Measurement* (2nd ed.), edited by Robert L. Thorndike, pp. 443–507. Washington, D.C.: American Council on Education, 1971.

Denvir, B., and M. L. Brown. "Understanding of Number Concepts in Low-Attaining 7–9 Year Olds: Part 1. Development of Descriptive Framework and Diagnostic Instrument." *Educational Studies in Mathematics* 17, no. 1 (1986a): 15–36.

————. "Understanding of Number Concepts in Low-Attaining 7–9 Year Olds: part II. The Teaching Studies." *Educational Studies in Mathematics* 17, no. 2 (1986b): 143–64.

Garrett, Henry E. *Statistics in Psychology and Education*. New York: Longmans, Green, 1937.

Heath, Chip, and Dan Heath. *Switch: How to Change Things When Change Is Hard*. New York: Broadway Books, 2010.

International Reading Association, and National Council of Teachers of English. *Standards for the Assessment of Reading and Writing*. Rev. ed. Newark, Del.: International Reading Association/National Council of Teachers of English, 2010.

Lave, Jean, and Étienne Wenger. *Situated Learning: Legitimate Peripheral Participation*. Cambridge, U.K.: Cambridge University Press, 1991.

Leahy, Siobhan, Christine Lyon, Marnie Thompson, and Dylan Wiliam. "Classroom Assessment: Minute-by-Minute and Day-by-Day." *Educational Leadership* 63, no. 3 (2005): 18–24.

Polanyi, Michael. *Personal Knowledge*. London: Routledge & Kegan Paul, 1958.

Sadler, D. Royce. "Formative Assessment and the Design of Instructional Systems." *Instructional Science* 18 (1989): 119–44.

Scriven, Michael. "The Methodology of Evaluation." In *Perspectives of Curriculum Evaluation* (vol. 1), edited by Ralph W. Tyler, Robert M. Gagné, and Michael Scriven, pp. 39–83. Chicago: Rand McNally, 1967.

Sfard, Anna. "On Two Metaphors for Learning and on the Dangers of Choosing Just One." *Educational Researcher* 27, no. 2 (1998): 4–13.

Wainer, Howard. *Uneducated Guesses: Using Evidence to Uncover Misguided Education Policies*. Princeton, N.J.: Princeton University Press, 2011.

Wigner, Eugene F. "The Unreasonable Effectiveness of Mathematics in the Natural Sciences." *Communications in Pure and Applied Mathematics* 13, no. 1 (1960): 1–14. doi:10.1002/cpa.3160130102

Wiliam, Dylan. "Some Technical Issues in Assessment: A User's Guide." *British Journal for Curriculum and Assessment* 2, no. 3 (1992): 11–20.

_____. "Formative Assessment in Mathematics: Part 1: Rich Questioning." *Equals: Mathematics and Special Educational Needs* 5, no. 2 (1999a): 15–18.

_____. "Formative Assessment in Mathematics: Part 2: Feedback." *Equals: Mathematics and Special Educational Needs* 5, no. 3 (1999b): 8–11.

_____. "Formative Assessment in Mathematics: Part 3: The Learner's Role." *Equals: Mathematics and Special Educational Needs* 6, no. 1 (2000): 19–22.

Wiliam, Dylan, and Siobhan Leahy. *Embedded Formative Assessment Handbook*. West Palm Beach, Fl.: Learning Sciences International, 2015.